Carrier Oils
For Aromatherapy
And Massage

4th Edition

Len Price
with Shirley Price

Riverhead Publishing, Stratford-upon-Avon, Warwickshire, England

CARRIER OILS FOR AROMATHERAPY AND MASSAGE
Leonard Price
With Shirley Price

This edition first published 2008

© 1990, 1996 Len Price
© 1999 Riverhead Publishing, Stratford-upon-Avon

First Edition 1990
Second Edition 1996
Third Edition 1999 (Completely revised and enlarged)
Third Edition, Second Impression 2004
Third Edition, Third Impression 2006
Fourth Edition 2008 (Completely updated, supplemented, enlarged and newly presented)
Fourth Edition, Second Impression 2010

British Library Cataloguing–in–Publication Data.
A catalogue record for this book is available from the British Library.

ISBN 1 874353 02 6

Set in New Baskerville ITC, 9½ on 12
Printed in Oxford, England

Cover Design and Artwork: Matt Price
Illustrations: Len Price

MMX

Contents

Chapter 3: Fixed oils and skin permeation

Section 2A – Fixed oils

Section 2B – Macerated oils

Section 3 – Appendices, Bibliography and sources, Glossary, Index

Tables

Figures

Plant Illustrations

About the authors

Len Price has a great interest in plant oils and has devoted his working life for the past 35 years to the study of their properties, safety aspects and relevant research in this field. He is co-author, with Shirley Price, of the well-respected book "Aromatherapy for Health Professionals' and was the sole author of previous editions of 'Carrier Oils for Aromatherapy'. As well as being a qualified aromatherapist and a Fellow of the International Society of Professional Aromatherapists, which he helped to found, Len Price together with his wife Shirley, was instrumental in the development of aromatology (Aromatic Medicine) as a specific branch of aromatherapy and together they ran a world renowned aromatherapy training and products organisation for twenty five years.

Shirley Price is one of the world leaders in aromatherapy who has authored seven books on aromatherapy which regularly feature in the best selling lists and has taught aromatherapy for almost forty years. As a former cookery teacher and lecturer, Shirley has put together several recipes for this book using the most popular oils.

Authors' note

Every effort has been made to ensure that any potential hazard of any plant or plant product mentioned has been indicated; all plant products must be used with care. All plants and their oils, like many everyday things, may be harmful if used improperly, eg if they are taken internally when prescribed for external use, if they are used in excess or for too long a time. Allergic reactions and unpredictable sensitivities may occur. The authors do not recommend the use of oils as a replacement for a doctor's diagnosis and subsequent medication although they may be used to complement allopathic treatments. The authors do not advocate, endorse or guarantee the curative effects of any of the substances listed in this book. The decision whether to use in any way any of the oils mentioned must be at the discretion of the individual.

Foreword

Once again, Len and Shirley Price demonstrate that they remain at the forefront of aromatherapy education and their unrelenting passion for all that is aromatherapeutically related is evident in this book. Together with their excellent publication *Understanding Hydrolats* (published by Churchill Livingstone, an ideal companion text) this book on carrier oils provides the learner, as well as the experienced practitioner, with indispensable detail which is highly relevant to their practice of aromatherapy and massage. Importantly, it also takes them one step further along the road of evidence based practice without losing touch with the 'art' of the therapy.

When Riverhead first published the edition of *Carrier Oils for Aromatherapy and Massage* in 1999, a welcome spotlight was turned onto the humble carrier oils which many therapists take for granted, using them simply as vehicles for massage, or for dilution and application of essential oils. Until then, the dearth of solid information on the therapeutic contributions of fixed oils (culinary benefits apart) meant that most therapists restricted their carrier oil choice to the classic bases (sweet almond, grapeseed...) introduced to them during their initial training. This book has since challenged therapists to select their bases more carefully in order to enhance their therapeutic interventions and has encouraged them to widen their therapeutic arsenal based on a greater knowledge and understanding of these active bases.

Despite the superior volume of carrier oil applied to the skin in aromatherapy and massage, until this book first appeared, few therapists were aware of the relevance of obtaining quality bases and even fewer paid heed to careful storage and issues of safe use. Thanks to the spotlight this book provided, the humble carriers were at last acknowledged as active – and therefore reactive – products which require as much attention in terms of selection, handling, storage and use as essential oils. No other publication concerning carrier oils has since come close in terms of accuracy of information or usefulness to the therapist... Until today! Now we have a revised and enlarged edition that not only explores an even wider palette of fixed and infused oils, but also tickles the palate with a number of culinary tips and health–giving recipes.

This latest edition is nothing less than we have come to expect from these tireless world leaders of aromatherapy: up–to–date, evidence–based, highly relevant and therapeutically useful information presented in an accessible style and format. This is no mean feat; Len and Shirley have mastered the delicate balance of presenting technical and scientific detail in a way that is accessible, motivating and easily understood. It gives us great pleasure to welcome this new edition of the book and we wish it the success that it deserves.

Bob and Rhiannon Harris
Essential Oil Resource Consultants, La Martre, France

Preface

The information in this book has been gathered over a period of time from a large number of sources. It is not intended to be definitive, but a stepping stone along the way, since in the reawakening field of aromatherapy there is a vast amount of research and discovery before us, which will surely enhance the practice of aromatherapy. To quote Montaigne:

Quelqu'un pourrait dire de moi que j'ai seulement fait ici un amas de fleurs étrangères, n'y ayant fourni du mien que le filet à les lier.
Michel Eyquem de Montaigne 1588 Essais III, xii

[It could be said of me that in this book I have only made up a bunch of other men's flowers, providing of my own only the string that ties them together.]

Health benefits have always been derived from the use of plant products from the time of cave dwellers right up to the coming of scientific medicine towards the end of the 19th century with its synthetic products and sometimes 'miracle' cures (antibiotics, sulphonamides, etc). It is true that herb products were involved in this new medicine, but scientists made the mistake of thinking that only one part contained all the therapeutic activity of the whole plant, thinking that the effect of the other constituents was negligible, thus ignoring the effects of synergy and the quenching power (i.e. negating undesirable effects) of the whole. This situation is even more complex as there are many plant compounds that have not yet been identified, much less synthesized.

On the rise of this new medicine, all plant based folk medicine went into rapid decline and was practised only by a relatively few 'cranky' people; this continued until the side effects of the new synthetic medicines started to become apparent. Since this realisation, there has been a return to a more balanced approach to health matters and what was once viewed as an 'alternative' to allopathic medicine is now regarded as being 'complementary'. There is a place for both approaches, classical and holistic and there has been a gradually accelerating increase in the use of plant material for the improvement of health over the last 3-4 decades. The action of plants is generally more gentle and they can be used long term avoiding side effects – when used sensibly and with knowledge.

Despite the fact that there are many unidentified compounds in plants, there is now proven effectiveness for the use of plants for health and it is possible to use them on a daily basis as part of a lifestyle where necessary, for instance, for the relief of such chronic conditions as rheumatism, recurring cramp, indigestion and so on. Plants are grown in a controlled fashion specifically for therapeutic use and the end product is subjected to careful checking.

In this book it is hoped to show the preventative and beneficial health effects of fixed plant oils. Fats and oils are important in our lives, as evidenced by the fact that each year eighty million tonnes of fats and oils are used, mostly derived from plants. They are utilised by the food, cosmetics and pharmaceutical industries and it would be difficult for us to live without the benefits they bring to us, including the minerals, vitamins and energy giving calories, the many and varied uses such as lighting, heating, beauty products, anointing, lubricating, in the home (e.g. for polish, hinges, cooking), etc. and of course therapeutically for massage and diet.

Generally speaking, when choosing an oil blend for use in aromatherapy application and massage generally, not enough consideration is given to the qualities and properties of the individual fixed oils used as carrier oils: if the true worth of some of the carrier oils were more understood and appreciated it could only be beneficial to the treatment given. Many fixed oils have intrinsic desirable therapeutic qualities and in some treatments as much attention should be paid to the choice of the carrier oil as to any essential oils which may be added to it. The quality of the carrier oil also should be carefully considered - it is after all usually more than 90% of the mix applied to the client when massage is the method of aromatherapy used. There is little point in selecting high quality essential oils for a massage if the bulk of the mix, i.e. the carrier oil, has been produced to a standard which is inappropriate for therapeutic use in any hands-on discipline. Oils produced specifically for therapeutic use should be used, wherever possible those obtained by simple cold expression from plant material, organic whenever possible, and in good condition.

Refined oils suitable for cooking and frying have their role, but they are best not used in therapeutic treatment: mineral oils, generally speaking, should not be used especially when adding essential oils as permeation of the skin is hindered.

Today industry has succeeded in giving us oils which possess calories but are devoid of nutrition and without therapeutic properties, thanks to modern refining processes (see Chapter 1).

Plants have the job, vital to the continued existence of mankind, of converting the light energy radiating from the sun into an energy form which we humans can use; hence plants from which we obtain the fixed oils should have been exposed to as much good quality sunlight as possible. Oils from a sunny area possess a vibrant energy and intrinsic synergy which those coming from a cloudy area do not (the words 'vital force' are deliberately not chosen because of inappropriate connotation).

Fixed oils, possessing as they do lubricating, emollient and dietetic qualities, provide a meeting place for aromatherapy and nutrition, and at times it is difficult to separate the one from the other. Any study or inquiry into carrier oils inevitably arouses interest in all aspects of the usefulness of these all-round health giving oils, with their vitamins, minerals and attributes beneficial to the general health; taken internally the oils are health giving and a few recipes employing some of the most popular oils are given in this book. It is hoped that the following pages will help in both the study of aromatherapy and of massage generally and give guidance in choosing carrier oils which are the most appropriate, effective and of a suitable quality.

Although there is quite a large body of research on the nutritional aspects of plant oils, very little work has been done on their use in massage and aromatherapy applications, so although references are quoted whenever appropriate and possible, much of the information in this book is anecdotal, and some readers may view this as a drawback. It is to be hoped that, on reading this book, the reader will be motivated to find out more about these wonderful oils and perhaps to take them more seriously than hitherto.

> Knowledge exists to be imparted.
> **Ralph Waldo Emerson**

The author would be very grateful to receive any personal experience that any reader may have regarding the properties and effects of fixed oils mentioned in this book (or indeed of any other oil) which it is thought might be helpful and which could be added to this text to improve it and thus make available additional information to all aromatherapists and massage therapists.

Sharing knowledge is like sharing friendship, when more is given, more is received.

Len Price 2008

List of oils mentioned in this book

(Macerated oils are marked †)

Common name	Scientific name
Almond sweet	*Prunus amygdalis* var. *dulcis*
Aloe vera†	*Aloe vera*
Apricot	*Prunus armeniaca, P. americana*
Argan	*Argania spinosa*
Arnica†	*Arnica montana*
Avocado	*Persea gratissima*
Babassu	*Orbignya phalerata*
Borage	*Borago officinalis*
Calendula†	*Calendula officinalis*
Camelina	*Camelina sativa*
Camellia	*Camellia sinensis*
Carrot†	*Daucus carota*
Castor	*Ricinus communis*
Centella†	*Centella asiatica, Hydrocotyle asiatica*
Chamomile†	*Matricaria recutita*
Cherry stone	*Prunus avium, P. cerasus*
Cocoa butter	*Theobroma cacao*
Coconut	*Cocos nucifera*
Cohune	*Attalea cohune, Orbygnia cohune*
Corn	*Zea mays*
Cottonseed	*Gossypium barbadense*
Cumin	*Cuminum cyminum*
Evening primrose	*Oenothera biennis, O. lamarkania*
Grapeseed	*Vitis vinifera*
Hazelnut	*Corylus avellana*
Hemp seed	*Cannabis sativa*
Jojoba	*Simmondsia chinensis, Buxus chinensis*
Kukui nut	*Aleurites moluccans*
Lime blossom, linden†	*Tilia europoea, T. cordata*
Linseed	*Linum usitatissimum*
Macadamia	*Macadamia ternifolia, M. integrifolia*
Mango seed	*Mangifera indica*
Meadowfoam	*Limnanthes alba*
Monoi†	*Gardenia tahitensis*

Mustard seed	*Sinapis alba*
Olive	*Olea europoea*
Palm kernel	*Elaeis guineensis*
Passionflower[†]	*Passiflora incarnata*
Peach kernel	*Prunus persica*
Peanut	*Arachis hypogea*
Pecan	*Carya illinoinensis*
Perilla seed	*Perilla frutescens var.*
Pistachio	*Pistacio vera*
Poppy seed	*Papaver somniferum*
Pumpkin seed	*Curcurbita pepo*
Rapeseed	*Brassica napus, B. campestris*
Rice bran	*Oryza sativa*
Rose hip	*Rosa mosquetta, R. rubiginosa, R. canina*
Safflower	*Carthamus tinctorius*
Sea buckthorn[†]	*Hippophae rhamnoides*
Sesame	*Sesamum indicum*
Shea butter	*Vitellaria paradoxa*
Sisymbrium	*Sisymbrium irio*
Soya	*Glycine max*
St. John's wort[†]	*Hypericum perforatum*
Sunflower	*Helianthus annuus*
Tamanu	*Calophyllum inophyllum*
Walnut	*Juglans regia*
Watermelon seed	*Citrullus vulgaris*
Wheatgerm	*Triticum vulgare, T. durum, T. aestivum*

Section 1 –
Chemistry

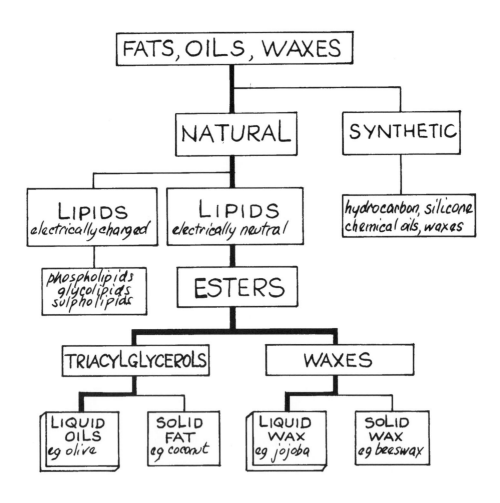

Table 1.1 Lipids

1 The nature of fixed and macerated plant oils

Introduction

Fats and oils are part of us; they feature in our food, our structure; they are vital to our life and we start consuming them in mother's milk; they provide reserves of energy during the active years and in old age fats are very necessary. What is not well understood by the majority of people is that there are many different fats and oils, each with its own make up and each having a role to play that is sometimes unique. We have to choose the appropriate kind of oil or fat for the situation in which we find ourselves, and for nutrition the differences between the various types of fats and oils produced in nature are becoming better understood.

When it comes to massage, however, there is not enough appreciation by therapists of the properties and uses of many of the vegetable oils available to them. Everyone is aware that oils are used extensively in skin care preparations to improve the condition of the skin, nails and hair and it is hoped that this book, with all its shortcomings, will extend the knowledge and uses of vegetable oils, thus helping to bring greater health benefits to all who use them. To use plant oils properly and to best advantage, it is necessary to study and understand their varied constituents; their composition will influence the choice of oil to achieve a particular end. There is a therapeutic cross reference table in the final section of the book to act as a guide to the use of oils, but each oil, together with its composition and properties, is listed alphabetically in the second section and it is here that the reader will find pertinent detailed advice.

Definitions and terminology

Fixed oils and essential oils – There are distinct differences between fixed and volatile plant oils. The plant oils used as carriers in aromatherapy and massage are referred to as 'fixed' oils because they do not evaporate. Plant essential oils do evaporate because they are volatile.

- Fixed oils leave a permanent oily mark on paper because of their lubricating quality and non–volatile nature.
- Essential oils do not leave an oily mark on paper, although any colour present will leave a stain.
- Fixed oils are not soluble in alcohol.
- Essential oils generally are soluble in alcohol.

In general, fixed oils are miscible with ether, chloroform and petroleum spirit. All essential oils dissolve easily and completely in fixed oils in all proportions: unscrupulous suppliers sometimes make use of this fact by using fixed oils to dilute essential oils in order to deceive unwary buyers.

The chemical difference between fixed oils and essential oils results in contrasting general characteristics.

Characteristic	Fixed oil	Essential oil
Volatility	low	high
Viscosity	high	low
Aroma	weak	strong
Soluble in ethanol	no	yes
Emollient	yes	no
Extraction	solvent, expressed	distilled, expressed
Edible	yes	in small quantity (supervised)

Table 1.2 Comparison of fixed and essential oil characteristics

It can sometimes be difficult to discriminate between a 100% genuine essential oil and an essential oil dissolved in a carrier oil. A simple test (not definitive) is to put one drop on to the back of your hand, whereupon one of the following will happen:

- if it is a pure essential oil (distilled or expressed) it will disappear into the skin quite quickly.
- if it is an absolute or a resin it may feel very slightly oily or sticky (and will also be coloured). NB Genuine sandalwood essential oil, being viscous, can also feel slightly oily.
- if the essential oil is incorporated in a carrier oil it will lubricate the back of your hand.

Lipids – Chemically speaking, fixed oils are classed as lipids. This is a diverse family of compounds found naturally in plants and animals, and the term encompasses not only oils but also fats. Although their structures are similar, at normal room temperatures (15°C) fats are solid and oils are liquid (see Table 1.1). The definition of a lipid is quite broad in that it covers any plant or animal molecules which are not soluble in water but soluble in organic solvents: all such molecules are classed as lipids. Lipids are important for our good health, being concerned in cell structure, vitamins, bile action and are a reserve of energy.

Fatty acids – are organic chain compounds composed of carbon, hydrogen and oxygen atoms. When the carbons in the chain are linked by a single bond then the acid is called a saturated fatty acid, shortened to SFA. When the carbons are linked by one double bond it is a monounsaturated fatty acid (MUFA) and when two carbons or more are linked by double bonds then it is known as a polyunsaturated fatty acid (PUFA) (see also Ch. 2).

Triacylglycerols – Fats and oils are formed when a special type of alcohol called glycerol reacts with a fatty acid. In vegetable oils the fatty acids usually have a long hydrocarbon chain (typically containing 16 or 18 carbon atoms) attached to the carboxyl group (–COOH), the acid part.

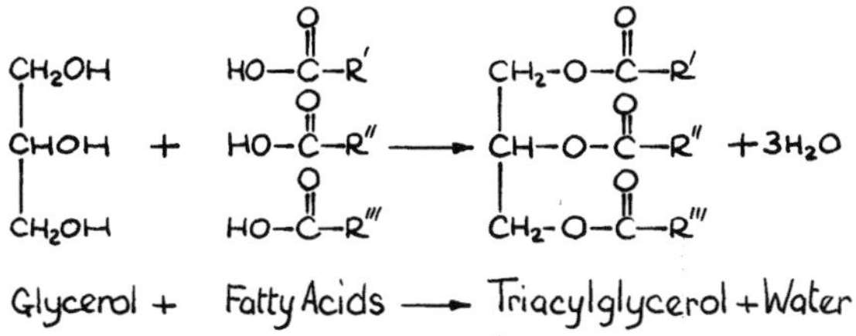

Fig. 1.1 Glycerol/fatty acids/triacylglycerol – make up of a triacylglycerol

The resulting compounds are triacylglycerols, formerly known as triglycerides, and a variety of these are possible. Triacylglycerols feature in our diet, and we digest them by utilising a lipase enzyme to reverse the above reaction. In the above chemical formulae R′, R″ and R‴ represent chains of carbon atoms. Simple triacylglycerols are those in which R′, R″ and R‴ are the same, i.e. three molecules of the same fatty acid have reacted with one molecule of glycerol. Complex triacylglycerols are those in which R′, R″ and R‴ are different. Perhaps not surprisingly, naturally occurring triacylglycerols are all complex. It can be seen that because in a molecule of fat there is only one molecule of glycerol bound together with three molecules of fatty acids, most of the weight of a fat molecule is made up of fatty acids.

Compound	Formula	Molecular Weight
Glycerol	C_3H_8O	92
Stearic acid	$C_{18}H_{36}O_2$	284
Arachidonic acid	$C_{20}H_{32}O_2$	304

Saponification

These fixed oils which are made up of fatty acids combined with glycerol (more commonly known as glycerine) are insoluble in water, but when separated from the glycerol the fatty acids will mix with water. This can happen either when the oil is treated with a solvent (e.g. benzene) or during digestion when in contact with an alkali (e.g. pancreatic juice containing the enzyme lipase).

The process of separation is known as saponification and this ability constitutes a basic difference between vegetable oils which can be saponified and mineral oils (e.g. liquid paraffin) which cannot be saponified and therefore cannot be assimilated. Note that most natural fats contain some substances which cannot be separated, such as the fat soluble vitamins A, D, E and K.

Thus saponification is the way in which fatty acids are made available for us to use in our bodies:

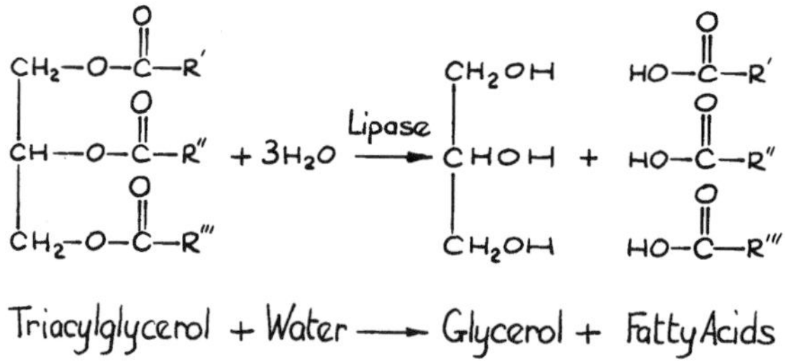

$$CH_2-O-\overset{\overset{\displaystyle O}{\|}}{C}-R' \\ CH-O-\overset{\overset{\displaystyle O}{\|}}{C}-R''\ +3H_2O\ \xrightarrow{\text{Lipase}}\ CH_2OH \\ CH_2-O-\overset{\overset{\displaystyle O}{\|}}{C}-R''' \quad CH_2OH \quad HO-\overset{\overset{\displaystyle O}{\|}}{C}-R' \\ HO-\overset{\overset{\displaystyle O}{\|}}{C}-R'' \\ HO-\overset{\overset{\displaystyle O}{\|}}{C}-R'''$$

Triacylglycerol + Water $\longrightarrow$ Glycerol + Fatty Acids

Fig. 1.2 Triacylglycerol/fatty acids/glycerol

Mineral Oils – Mineral oils are hydrocarbons of high molecular weight, and therefore a different class of compound from the triacylglycerols and lipids of vegetable origin. Mineral oils are not broken down by the body's digestive system and because of this have no nutritional value.

Mineral oils are also oily and greasy, but they are not used in massage because they have a tendency to clog the pores. However, because of these pore sealing qualities they are used on babies' bottoms, to help prevent the intrusion of urine, thus reducing the risk of nappy rash.

Vegetable oils – Vegetable oils constitute the bulk of the mix used to perform an aromatherapy massage. Their function is to 'carry' or act as a vehicle for administering the essential oils to the body, hence the term 'carrier oil'. They also act as a lubricant, making it possible to carry out massage movements. All carrier oils are emollient, to a greater or lesser degree.

Basic vegetable oils – Sweet almond, apricot kernel, grapeseed, peach kernel and sunflower are among the most common carrier oils, and can be used with or without essential oils for straightforward body massage. They are generally pale in colour, not too thick and have very little smell, unless the seeds or nuts have been roasted first to produce flavourful cooking oils.

Special vegetable oils – Certain vegetable oils tend to be more viscous and heavier than basic ones, and can be rather expensive. These include avocado, olive, sesame, rose hip and wheatgerm. The really rich oils such as avocado and wheatgerm are seldom, if ever used, on their own. It is more usual to add 10–25% of these two to 75–90% of a basic carrier oil.

Organic vegetable oils – Strictly speaking, organic oils can only be produced from organically grown plant material using approved processes, and it is not easy to find reliable sources of such oils. In practice the word organic may be applied either to the raw material or to the production process. For example, an oil may be derived from organically grown seeds by a non–organic process or, as can often happen (because it is not always easy to find organically grown seeds), non–organic seeds may be converted into oil by organic production methods. The rules for organic processing generally exclude the use of chemicals, and a truly organic fixed oil is obtained only from plants which are both organically grown and organically processed.

As the rules for organic growing and production of vegetable oils vary from country to country (and in some cases are non–existent), it can be a difficult task to source a particular quality.

Macerated oils – Macerated oils have additional properties to all the vegetable oils described above because of the way they are produced. Particular parts of certain plants are chopped up and added to a selected carrier oil (usually sunflower or olive) and the mix is agitated gently for some time before placing in strong sunlight for several days. All of the oil–soluble compounds present in the plant material (including the essential oil chemicals) are transferred to the carrier oil, which consequently contains extra therapeutic properties. The macerated mixture is then filtered carefully to remove all the added plant material. (See below).

Production of fixed plant oils

The production of commercial oils may start with crude imported oil but the best quality oil is derived directly from the nuts and seeds. The oil content of the various seeds pressed for their oil varies widely, for example soybeans have a content of 20%, while rapeseed, palm kernel and peanuts contain about 50%, but sunflower has up to 55%: the content of oil in the plant material has an obvious influence on the end price. As with essential oils, many factors have an important influence on the quality of the finished product:
 • obtaining the highest quality raw material is vital
 • time of harvesting
 • conditions of storage
 • method of extraction
 • means of transportation.

7

Often it is preferable to store the raw materials rather than the finished or part–finished oil, as the seeds contain their own natural antioxidants and have tough outer coatings for further protection against oxidation. If there should be any undesirable products formed during storage these would normally be passed into the oil cake by–product, leaving the oil free of any such materials.

Clearly, oils derived from the kernels of fruits, eg almonds and peaches, are more protected from drifting chemical sprays and pollution than are the more exposed seeds such as corn and sunflower.

Cold Pressed Oils – Cold pressed vegetable oils are the best and are generally superior to those found in supermarkets. In the 'cold' pressing process, excessive heat is avoided in order to minimise changes to the natural characteristics of the oil.

Traditionally, there are two methods of cold pressing. In one, the raw material (seeds, nuts or kernels) is simply pressed with a hydraulic press and the oil is squeezed out. This process is only used for soft oily seeds and plant material such as olive, sesame and sunflower.

Harder seeds, such as safflower, require more force and a large, powerful screw device known as an expeller is used to crush the plant material, which may be passed through the expeller more than once. The process generates a certain amount of heat and in France a legal temperature limit of 60°C is applied to oils that are classed as cold pressed. There is not an equivalent limit in the United Kingdom. Some specialist suppliers may be able to offer oils that have been expressed at temperatures below 45°C but these will command a premium price as usually less oil is obtained.

The crushed shells, etc are removed from the oil by a succession of filters, the last of which is made of paper. The oil obtained is usually clear (avocado is an exception as it is usually cloudy – unless refined - especially in cold conditions) and has its taste and nutritional properties intact. The vegetable pulp that remains still contains a reasonable amount of oil and is either used for animal feed or sent to another factory for further processing. Here it will be subjected to a high temperature, high pressure process, or it may be treated with steam and solvents. The oils obtained from such additional processing are not ideal for aromatherapy or massage (see refined oils below).

Refined oils

Highly refined oils are products which have been tailored to meet the particular requirements of large scale users such as the pharmaceutical industry, cooking oil manufacturers, food processors and cosmetics companies. The process is useful commercially as much more oil is obtained this way than by cold pressing (see Fig. 1.3).

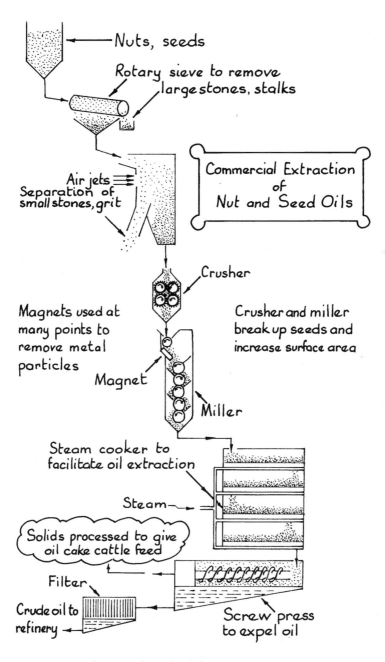

Fig. 1.3a Commercial extraction of nut and seed oils

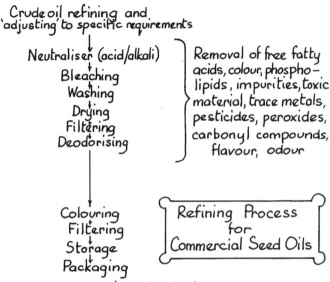

Crude oil refining and 'adjusting' to specific requirements

Neutraliser (acid/alkali)
Bleaching
Washing
Drying
Filtering
Deodorising

} Removal of free fatty acids, colour, phospho-lipids, impurities, toxic material, trace metals, pesticides, peroxides, carbonyl compounds, flavour, odour

Colouring
Filtering
Storage
Packaging

Refining Process for Commercial Seed Oils

Nitrogen is used throughout the process to displace oxygen to prevent the formation of peroxides and carbonyl compounds. This is to improve stability and to protect unsaturated fatty acids which are prone to oxidative deterioration.

Fig 1.3b Refining process for commercial seed oils

As indicated above, processing frequently involves the use of high temperatures and chemicals, which means that many of the natural properties of the oil are lost. The whole character of the oil is altered, which is why its use in aromatherapy is not desirable. This is the type usually found on supermarket shelves.

Refining may include:

- removal of colour by bleaching. Because the colour of the unrefined oil may vary from batch to batch, bleaching gives a uniform colour. This may then be enhanced by the addition of a 'natural' pigment such as xanthophyll (a derivative of chlorophyll) or β–carotene to produce a finished product with a standard colour.
- removing gums, which may be formed in the presence of water due to impurities in suspension. Hot water is added and then by the use of a

10

centrifugal separator the gum particles are thrown to the bottom of the container, leaving the clarified oil on top.

- removal of taste and smell so that the end product is bland and tasteless. During processing some of the natural chemicals can break down to yield aldehydes and ketones, materials with a strong taste and smell, and these are removed by the use of superheated steam (temperatures around 200°C).
- addition of synthetic antioxidants to extend the shelf life.
- addition of vitamins and minerals to replace those destroyed during the refining process.
- removal of organic solvents. The yield of oil from the 'cake' of crushed and cooked nuts, etc can be increased by the use of solvents such as hexane and petroleum spirit, and these have to be stripped off. The refining removes most of the solvent residues, but some 1–2 parts per million (ppm) still remain.
- removal of any free fatty acids which can be bitter to the taste and corrosive. A figure known as the Acid Value gives an indication as to the level of free fatty acids in an oil, and when the Acid Value is greater than 5.0 the oil can give a burning sensation in the back of the throat. Oils high in free fatty acids can also react with metal containers, forming products which will result in decreased shelf life. The acids can be removed by the use of a solution of caustic soda to convert the fatty acid into an insoluble soap. This soap can be removed after it has settled to the bottom of the neutralising tank. The oil is then washed and dried to remove the last traces of soap.
- removal of natural waxes, as these materials lead to cloudiness, especially if the oils are stored at low temperatures (e.g. 4°C).

Despite going through some or all of the above processes the resulting oil can still legally be labelled as 'pure' and even 'natural'. For example, here is a piece from a technical paper describing the processing of a vegetable oil:

'...seeds harvested in 1985 and 1986 were crushed in October 1986 by direct solvent extraction using the extruder for seed pretreatment. The resulting crude oil was phosphoric acid pretreated, alkali refined, vacuum bleached with activated clay and carbon, and deodorised, yielding oil with 0.7 loviband colour, and bland flavour and odour.'

A pure oil maybe – but not the best for aromatherapy and massage!

Hydrogenation of oils

Whilst it is true that some margarines are manufactured from unsaturated vegetable oils, clearly some form of transformation is needed to change the liquid oil into the solid margarine. This modification involves bringing the polyunsaturated oils into contact with hydrogen in order to turn them into more saturated fats which are then solid. The purpose of this is to increase the keeping quality of the material and give it a longer shelf life, and to harden it so that it will spread satisfactorily, unlike liquid vegetable oils which are obviously unsuitable for spreading purposes,

Hardening liquid oils involves its conversion into a solid or semi solid fat by a chemical method called hydrogenation. Since this process was introduced in the early twentieth century there has been a rapid increase in the production of vegetable oils and eating habits have changed considerably; previously animal fats featured largely in the diet but this has decreased considerably due to the availability of hardened vegetable and fish oils.

Hydrogenation is the heating of a liquid oil in the presence of metal catalysts and hydrogen - this hardens the oils into margarine and shortening. (Ascherio & Willett 1997); it is the addition of hydrogen to the double bonds of the unsaturated fatty acids combined with the glycerol in an oil and during hydrogenation one molecule of hydrogen is absorbed by each double bond.

The hydrogen process requires the presence of a catalyst; finely divided nickel is used industrially. During this process the oil is exposed to semi toxic and toxic metals (such as nickel and aluminium) The oil is stirred and hydrogen gas is pumped in; it is then heated to start the reaction, and as the reaction is exothermic further heating is not necessary. After hydrogenation the oil is cooled and filtered to remove the nickel which can be re-used.

The most commonly occurring unsaturated fatty acids found in combination with glycerol in vegetable oils, namely oleic, linoleic and linolenic acids, contain one, two and three double bonds respectively. As they all contain eighteen carbon atoms, complete hydrogenation would convert them all into stearic acid (Fox & Cameron 1975 p.100). Stearic acid has a much higher melting point (70°C) than any of the other three, consequently the hydrogenated oil is harder than the original.

However, hydrogenation is a selective process, some triglycerides becoming saturated more rapidly than others so the reaction can be controlled and the amount of saturation regulated so that the product does not become too hard. The most unsaturated triglycerides are partially hydrogenated before the less unsaturated ones react. This means that in terms of the common fatty acids combined in the triacylglycerides more linolenic acid is converted into linoleic in a given time than linoleic into oleic. The relative rates of reaction of oleic, linoleic and linolenic are in the ratio 1:20:40 (Fox & Cameron 1975 p.102). This fact enables the hydrogenation to be controlled, and food oils may be only partially saturated with hydrogen.

This is important from a nutritional point of view, because some unsaturated acids are needed but cannot be produced by the body. These essential unsaturated acids must, therefore, be supplied in the diet. Also complete hydrogenation would make fats too hard and lacking in plasticity for use in food preparation.

The hydrogenated fats produced (sometimes bleached and deodorized with the use of chemical products) are now widely used in foods, having been considered to be more healthy than saturated, cholesterol containing animal fat. Hydrogenated hard fats and non–hydrogenated liquid oils may be blended to form soft margarines. Soya oil is often lightly hydrogenated to help prevent the development of a bad taste and smell with time, which can happen even if kept in a refrigerator.

Trans fatty acids

In carrying out the hydrogenation process the nature of the oil changes - either partially or completely as double bonds are destroyed - from unsaturated to saturated and importantly trans fatty acids (see App. E) are introduced into the food supply.

Plant fatty acids containing double bonds have a cis configuration, meaning that the hydrogen atoms adjacent to double bonds are on the same side of the longitudinal carbon axis. In trans fatty acids, the hydrogen atoms

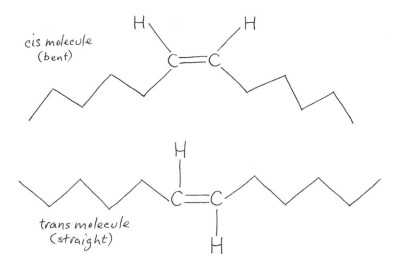

Fig. 1.4 Cis and Trans molecules

adjacent to the double bonds occur on alternate sides of the main axis. The trans configuration is produced when polyunsaturated plant oils are subjected to the process of partial hydrogenation in order to achieve chemical stability.

Thus the structural form of the unsaturated fats is altered, and trans configurations obtained which are not found in nature. It has been suggested that in the long term these may block the formation of prostaglandins in the body. Current scientific evidence suggests that the body employs trans fats as it would the saturated variety and cannot make use of their altered double bonds; in the body they can behave in a way similar to saturated fats – namely, raising blood cholesterol levels (Emmerson & Ewin 1996, Ascherio & Willett 1997). Even though, on average, only 2% of our energy intake comes from trans fats, whereas about 16% comes from saturated fats (HMSO 1990) it was recommended in 1991 that the then current average intake of trans fats should not be exceeded (HMSO 1991).

It may, therefore, possibly be better therefore to eat small amounts of naturally saturated fat, such as butter, rather than an artificial saturated product such as most margarines.

Extraction of plant oils and healing properties

Some plants do not contain a sufficient quantity of oil to obtain it (economically) by expression. Therefore another method must be used to acquire the plant properties that are desired for therapeutic use. Some processes employing elevated temperatures may inactivate some temperature sensitive bioactive nutrients (and this may include the distillation process, which is used to extract the volatile molecules from the plant material (essential oils).

Some of the methods possible are mentioned here.

Firstly, maceration is a the preferred method of extraction of plant properties and this is achieved by immersion in warm lipids (see below for more detail). Other methods have their faults.

Secondly, expression, but this is not possible practically if the plant contains insufficient of the properties needed to make the use of a press efficient.

Thirdly, solvent extraction is a method using an organic solvent and this is frequently the case for the manufacture of food additives and flavours, but is to be avoided for therapeutic use. Generally organic solvents for skin care products are to be avoided.

Fourthly, carbon dioxide (CO_2) extraction does not result in the same chemical make up of herbal extracts is as that of oil extracts; modern clinical trials conducted to demonstrate biological activity, therapeutic efficiency and safety of oil extracts have not been repeated with CO_2 extracts.

At present knowledge acquired over the centuries by practical experience of the healing effects apply only to traditional oil extracts

Maceration

The verb to macerate exists in the English language generally and can be used in different senses as shown by the following definitions,

- to make soft by soaking or steeping in a liquid.
- to separate into constituents by soaking.
- to cause to become lean, usually by starvation; emaciate

The specific maceration process for achieving certain special therapeutic massage oils, which is quite different from the usual pressing process, is where substances are extracted from plant material by steeping or soaking in a solvent. For this purpose the solvent must be a good quality fixed oil, such as olive, soya, almond, sunflower, etc and this allows the extraction of lipophilic compounds from the plant substance.

The plant material e.g. flowers, leaves, etc is often comminuted (chopped up), thus breaking plant cell walls and allowing easier release of the lipophilic molecules, which include any essential oil compounds and some larger molecules which would not appear in a distilled product. The material is then placed in the base vegetable oil, put in a warm place (traditionally in a sunny place) and frequently stirred for up to three weeks. A small amount of preservative must be added to the base oil to prevent it turning rancid; 5% of wheatgerm oil is sometimes used for this purpose. The resulting vegetable oil, known technically as a macerate, now containing the lipophilic plant compounds including colouring and any essential oil, is then strained off or filtered and stored in containers.

The components extracted from the plant material are the oil soluble elements, including not only the volatile molecules but also the colour and other elements of the plant. Thus a macerated oil is virtually a ready blended massage oil consisting of a suitable base oil containing the therapeutic components of the chosen plant.

The maceration method is used to produce several oils suitable for therapeutic massage e.g. *Hypericum perforatum* (St. John's wort), *Calendula officinalis* (marigold), *Tilia* sp flos (lime blossom) etc. In the case of St. John's wort only the buds and flowers are used and these are steeped in a good quality vegetable oil; this was traditionally olive oil, but today other oils may be used. The maceration process is allowed to go on for many days, up to three weeks, with occasional agitation to facilitate the transfer of the lipid soluble active constituents of the plant into the oil. This produces in effect a ready mixed massage oil which may be enhanced for even better therapeutic

15

effect by the addition of essential oils where thought appropriate. It must be emphasised that maceration is the only way that the essential oils from e.g. *Calendula officinalis* (marigold, the flowers only are used) and other plants are made available for use by the therapist.

Maceration is basically a similar method to hot enfleurage (see below) but using a vegetable oil instead of animal fat is a simpler and less inexpensive method of extraction, allowing massage oils to be made at home by the therapist: this method can easily be carried out at home for rose, lavender, thyme, sage and other aromatic herbs from the garden; a pinch of preservative is necessary. It is possible to make special macerations in sunflower oil for specific purposes, as some therapists do, by making a special selection of herbs for the maceration.

There are two usual methods for preparing a macerated oil at home.

One method uses sunlight for heat (not always practical in the UK)

Place finely chopped fresh herb in a jar, fill with oil and cover with muslin to keep out insects, then leave for 2 weeks in direct sunlight shaking the jar twice daily (bring indoors at night if necessary to retain the warmth. Strain and repeat the above with fresh plant material but using the same oil.

A second method uses the heat from boiling water in the kitchen, which is much quicker.

Put finely chopped herb in a heat proof bowl and cover with vegetable oil. Place the bowl over a pan of boiling water and heat for one hour (a bain-marie may be used). Remove from the heat and strain, repeating the procedure using the same oil but fresh herb.

The final step for both methods is to strain or filter and pour into a light proof container, affixing a label showing date, oil used, herb, etc. Each method will allow a shelf life for the oil obtained of 12 months under suitable storage conditions (see below).

One change of plant material is usually sufficient to achieve a good result for herbs from the Lamiaceae family, but plants from other families where the essential oil is not so accessible or perhaps not so plentiful may benefit from a second change of plant material in the same oil.

Maceration is a technique which is also used as part of the process for winning essential oils;

Betula lenta – the bark is subjected to warm water maceration causing hydrolysis of the glycoside gaultherin thus release of methyl salicylate followed by steam distillation of the warm, water macerated bark.

Prunus amygdalis bitter almond oil – water maceration followed by steam distillation of the expressed and partly deoleated kernels.

Other uses for maceration

Regarding sage, the US 1848 Dispensatory (like Culpeper) says that an infusion of sage with honey and vinegar is useful as a gargle for inflammation of the throat, and relaxation of the uvula. The Dispensatory goes on to say that when used as a pleasant drink in febrile complaints, or to allay nausea, the maceration should continue but a very short time, so that all the bitterness of the leaves may not be extracted. A gargle with rose vinegar may be derived from the ten day maceration of 100g of dried, well chopped petals in a good wine vinegar (lukewarm gargling with a teaspoonful to a glass of water).

The city of Grasse produces a brochure mentioning maceration which the French call *enfleurage a chaud*, a process through which the scent of plants is absorbed by hot fat at about 80°F. Known since the distant past, maceration by fat was first used in Grasse. Very pure fat of about three parts of pork to one part of beef is mixed with the flowers, which are then macerated at a temperature close to the melting point of the fat. The flowers are slowly stirred throughout the operation to ensure maximum absorption, and are replaced several times until the fat is saturated with perfume. The rejected flowers still hold some perfumed fat, and this is removed by pressure; all fat is then treated, resulting in the very expensive absolute oil. This method is used with roses, violets and jonquils but in perfumery, maceration of this kind has now been superseded by the process of extraction with volatile solvents.

Storage

The triacylglycerols that make up fixed oils can undergo attack by oxygen and moisture in the atmosphere and fatty acids present will also react with oxygen in the presence of light or elevated temperatures. This means that the correct storage of carrier oils is most important.

Bulk quantities should be kept in stainless steel containers, under an inert gas and at a suitably low temperature. Therapists also should keep their oils cool and preferably in the dark. As is the case with essential oils, the head space above the oil in a container (or bottle) should be minimised. Thus, oil which may take some time to use is best decanted off into a number of smaller bottles (with minimal air space), which can then be used singly as needed.

Natural – synthetic

Before the 20th century the natural oils, used in make up and cosmetic preparations generally, soon succumbed to oxygen and became quite unpleasant to the nose. To counteract the 'off' smell, pleasant smelling materials were added to mask the bad odour. This situation changed when the petrochemical industry started to produce paraffin hydrocarbon oils, such as

17

mineral oil, petrolatum and paraffin wax. These possessed oxidative stability and soon replaced the triacylglycerides because they do not go rancid and have a long shelf life. They are not 'green' but this not of great concern at the time.

Contemporaneously improved emulsifier technology using synthetic ingredients enabled the production of stable emulsions of water and oil giving a wide range of long shelf life creams.

Today users of cosmetic products are asking for a return to natural ingredients which, on the whole, do not possess oxidative stability while at the same time demanding high tech products, thus creating a problem for the cosmetic industry.

As with cosmetics, a similar pattern can be seen with fats in foods. At one time everyone ate lard, butter, dripping but with the advent of hydrogenated foods (and advertising) most people were persuaded to change their eating habit e.g. from natural butter to margarine. Now emerging facts about the adverse health effects of the trans fats created during the hydrogenation process are bringing about a swing back to the natural product – although perhaps used more sparingly.

Conclusion

The quality of carrier oils is equally as important as the quality of essential oils, and inferior product is, unfortunately, generally easy to come by. Aromatherapists need to use the least refined, nearest–to–nature material available, and this is more likely to be obtained from a knowledgeable specialist supplier. It is well worth while taking the time and the trouble to establish a relationship with a company or companies you feel you can trust, and who are ethical and honest in their approach.

2 The chemistry of fixed oils

Triacylglycerols

The chemical nature of fixed oils has already been discussed and the key materials have been identified as glycerol and a selection of fatty acids. When glycerol combines with three acids (whether the acids are all the same or all different) a particular sort of ester known as a triacylglycerol (=triglyceride) is formed.

As glycerol is the common component in almost all of the vegetable oils, the differences that exist between the carrier oils can be attributed to the nature of the fatty acids. The three alcohol groups in glycerol may combine with the same acid or three different acids and as there are many fatty acids there are many different vegetable oils.

Fatty acids

The organic acids that contribute to the triacylglycerols were first identified in animal fats, which led to their name, but we now know that these materials are found in vegetable oils as well. There are many different fatty acids, which can combine with glycerol to form triacylglycerols; these tend to be identified by the number of carbon atoms they contain.

Although the carbon chains vary in length, the atoms are arranged in a regular, ordered way, with the organic acid group attached to one end. The atoms which signify an organic acid group are: one carbon atom, two oxygen atoms and one hydrogen atom – often written as COOH and sometimes referred to as a carboxyl group. For example:

$H.COOH$	Methanoic acid (formic acid)
CH_3COOH	Ethanoic acid (acetic acid)
CH_3CH_2COOH	Propanoic acid
$CH_3CH_2CH_2COOH$	Butanoic acid
$CH_3CH_2CH_2CH_2COOH$	Pentanoic acid
$CH_3CH_2CH_2CH_2CH_2COOH$	Hexanoic acid
and so on, with each successive acid increasing in length by one CH_2 unit	

Table 2.1 Short chain fatty acids

The names of the acids used above are the up–to–date versions; you may recognise formic acid and acetic acid, which are the older names for the first two on the list.

19

Organic acids are not so corrosive and aggressive as mineral acids.

The fatty acids which form the triacylglycerols found in vegetable oils have much longer chains of carbon atoms than those in Table 2.1 and so are bigger and heavier molecules. A shorthand method has been devised to enable the formulae for these compounds to be written down easily. All that is necessary is to count the number of carbon atoms present, thus pentanoic acid becomes a C_5 acid and hexanoic acid a C_6 acid. The fatty acids of interest to us are generally in the range of C_{12} to C_{24}.

Clearly, with such long chain fatty acids reacting with glycerol, the resulting triacylglycerols are very large molecules. So large in fact that they cannot easily penetrate the skin, unlike the comparatively smaller molecules that make up essential oils.

Humans are not capable of detecting the odour of any molecule bigger than C_{20}.

Reference is often made to the fatty acid content of vegetable oils. It is important to recognise that these fatty acids are not simply dissolved in the oils (i.e. present in an uncombined state and therefore able to take part in reactions). They are acids, which have already reacted with the glycerol to form the appropriate triacylglycerol, and so are present as 'bonded' units.

The commonest fatty acid unit found bonded in carrier oils is derived from octadecanoic acid with 18 carbon atoms and a formula of:

$$CH_3CH_2CH_2CH_2CH_2CH_2CH_2CH_2CH_2CH_2CH_2CH_2CH_2CH_2CH_2CH_2CH_2COOH$$

How much easier to use the shorthand form of C_{18} for this acid!

Octadecanoic acid used to be known as stearic acid, and because of this name many people thought that it came only from animal sources, but this is not necessarily the case. Vegetable stearic acid is widely available, and although use of the modern name could help to dispel any misinterpretation, the common name is the most frequently used.

Saturated and unsaturated fatty acids

Everyone nowadays has heard of saturated, monounsaturated and polyunsaturated fats, but what does it all mean?

There are three groups of fatty acids: saturated, monounsaturated and polyunsaturated and oils are made up of a mixture of these three group; however, one is always predominant and determines its classification. For example, olive oil is classed as monounsaturated because, while it contains 13.5% of saturated fatty acids and 8.4% polyunsaturated fatty acids, the monounsaturated fatty acids are in the majority at 73.7%.

Saturated fatty acids – Carbon atoms can form single bonds as well as double bonds with each other:

$$C-C \; single \; bond \qquad\qquad C=C \; double \; bond$$

Compounds that contain carbons linked only by single bonds are said to be saturated whereas those with one or more double bonds between carbon atoms are unsaturated, as the carbon atoms involved are not bonded to the maximum possible number of other atoms. Fatty acids that contain one double bond are said to be monounsaturated whereas those with more than one double bond are polyunsaturated.

If the presence or absence of double bonds is taken into consideration the shorthand form for the fatty acids can be modified to give (common names used):

Stearic acid	C18:0	(saturated; contains no double bond)
Oleic acid	C18:1	(monounsaturated; contains only one double bond)
Linoleic acid	C18:2	(polyunsaturated; contains two double bonds)
Linolenic acid	C18:3	(polyunsaturated; contains three double bonds)

Table 2.2 Saturated and unsaturated fatty acids

– indicating that stearic acid is a fatty acid which has 18 carbons in the chain and does not contain any double bonds, whereas oleic acid, which also has 18 carbons in the chain, contains one double bond.

The so called 'hard' fats are mostly made up of triacylglycerols containing saturated carbon chains such as those based on palmitic and stearic acids. The most saturated of all the vegetable based products is coconut oil, which contains triacylglycerols based on caproic acid, a material that is also found in butter. Many vegetable and nut oils are high in saturated fats apart from coconut oil e.g. palm, avocado, peanut…

Shorthand	Common name	Modern name
C12:0	lauric	dodecanoic
C14:0	myristic	tetradecanoic
C16:0	palmitic	hexadecanoic
C18:0	stearic	octadecanoic
C20:0	arachidic	eicosanoic
C22:0	behenic	docosanoic
C24:0	lignoceric	tetracosanoic

Table 2.3 Common saturated fatty acids

Unsaturated Fatty Acids – Oils that are liquid at room temperature are based on triacylglycerols containing high proportions of unsaturated fatty acid units such as those found in palmitoleic and oleic acids.

Shorthand	Common name	Modern name
C16:1	palmitoleic	9–hexadecenoic*
C18:1	oleic	9–octadecenoic*
C18:2	linoleic	9, 12–octadecenoic*
C18:3	linolenic	9, 12, 15 octadecatrienoic*
C20:4	arachidonic	5, 8, 11, 14 eicosatetraenoic*
C20:5	timnodonic	5, 8, 11, 14, 17 eicosapentaenoic*

*The numbers indicate the position of the double bond in the chain.

Table 2.4 Common unsaturated fatty acids

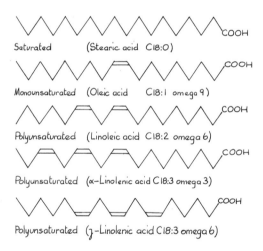

Fig. 2.1 Saturated and unsaturated fatty acids – graphical notation

Vegetable oils can contain a high proportion (>80%) of unsaturated fatty acid units, which is why they are important for our health. Fatty acid composition varies: in animals there are less than 1% of fatty acids with 5 or 6 double bonds, whereas plants have 5–6% and fish have 15–30%. Plant fatty acids are usually unsaturated (i.e. containing one or more double bonds) and are liquid at room temperature, with the exception of palm fatty acid which is a saturated 16 carbon chain and is solid. Double bonds are not as strong as single bonds and introduce an element of weakness into a compound. Once opened up they can absorb other molecules for transportation elsewhere in the body and can also facilitate the natural digestive breakdown of the triacylglycerols.

Human breast milk is designed to be easily digested. Analysis has shown that not only does it contain high levels of both vitamin E and triacylglycerols based on oleic acid, but it is also broken down via an alkaline reaction. Cow's milk, on the other hand, contains a larger proportion of saturated fatty acid units and 80% less vitamin E than human milk. Cow's milk is less easily digested as the process is carried out by an acid reaction

Essential fatty acids

Our bodies do not manufacture some fatty acids which are necessary for continued good health, so we must ingest them as a part of our diet (WHO 1990). These are given the term 'essential' because they are so important, and there are two of them: linoleic acid and α–linolenic acid.

The essential fatty acids resemble, and complement, naturally occurring prostaglandins in the body which regulate blood pressure, increase blood flow to the organs and help reduce blood clots.

Gamma–linolenic acid (GLA) is a precursor of Prostaglandin E1 (PGE1), a hormone–like substance, and so the use of oils rich in bonded GLA is advantageous to people whose bodies do not produce sufficient of this material. A deficiency in these acids results in ill health and poor vision. (See Fig. 2.2)

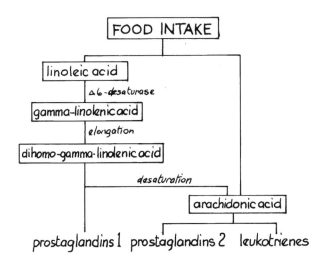

Fig. 2.2 Prostaglandin production in the body

23

Linoleic acid (LA) and alpha–linolenic acid (ALA) are essential fatty acids. Linoleic acid, an omega 6 fatty acid, is biologically inactive in the body until it is catalysed to form other omega 6 acids – gamma–linolenic acid (GLA), dihomo-gamma-linoleic acid (DHGLA) and arachidonic acid. Alpha-linolenic acid, an omega 3 fatty acid, is used by the body to form other omega 3 fatty acids – eicosapentaenoic acid, docosahexaenoic acid. Prostaglandins are complex fatty acids that act as messenger substances (they are sometimes referred to as local hormones) between cells and have many functions participating in growth, cell structure, blood clotting, inflammatory process, immune system and metabolism.

A diet rich in linoleic acid is beneficial for people with rheumatologic conditions and cardio vascular problems because it increases the production of prostaglandins 1.

Combined fatty acids found in vegetable oils – Many of the carrier oils used in aromatherapy are based on important fatty acids found in combination with glycerol:

alpha–linolenic acid	olive, rose hip, sunflower, wheatgerm
gamma–linolenic acid	evening primrose, borage
linoleic acid	evening primrose, grapeseed, sunflower, safflower
linolenic acid	avocado, evening primrose, grapeseed, olive, rose hip,
	sesame, safflower, sunflower, wheatgerm
myristic acid	grapeseed, jojoba
oleic acid	grapeseed, olive, rose hip, safflower, sunflower
palmitic acid	grapeseed, safflower, olive, sunflower
stearic acid	grapeseed, safflower, sunflower

Table 2.5 Common fatty acids found in vegetable oils

Essential fatty acid deficiency – Essential fatty acid (EFA) deficiency because of poor diet is rare in developed countries. One effect of EFA deficiency is a high rate of loss of moisture resulting in a dry skin condition which can be corrected by topical application of oils rich in EFAs (Prottey *et al* 1975, Prottey *et al* 1976, Hartop & Prottey 1976). However, fatty acid metabolism can also be impaired by complaints such as psoriasis and atopic eczema, resulting in dry skin conditions; again, topical application of products containing EFAs is of benefit (Coupland 1992, Brod *et al* 1988). Essential fatty acid deficiency is being increasingly recognised as a complication of long term fat–free parenteral nutrition (Fleming et al 1976). Remember that in oils said to be 'rich in essential fatty acids' those fatty acids are present as their triacylglycerols. (See also App. D)

Omega classification

Many fatty acids are now being given an Omega classification, e.g. Omega–3 or Omega–6. All this does is to provide a means of identifying the whereabouts of one of the double bonds in an unsaturated fatty acid. The position of the double bond is indicated relative to the carbon atom that is farthest away from the COOH (acid) group. This carbon is said to be in the omega position:

$$CH_3CH_2CH_2CH_2CH_2CH_2CH=CHCH_2CH_2CH_2CH_2CH_2CH_2CH_2COOH$$

1   2   3   4   5   6   7   8   9   10   11   12   13   14   15   16   carbon n^o

omega   alpha

Fig. 2.3a Omega classification (e.g. palmitoleic acid, an omega–7 fatty acid)

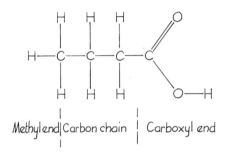

Methyl end | Carbon chain | Carboxyl end

Fig. 2.3b Example: A Fatty Acid (C4:0)

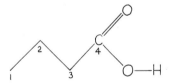

Fig. 2.3c Graphical representation of the same fatty acid molecule

In the above example, as the COOH group is on the right, the carbon atoms have been numbered from the extreme left, counting that carbon atom as number 1. So, Omega–7 means the double bond lies between the 7th and 8th carbon atom counting from the left. This shorthand method does not tell you how many double bonds there are in an unsaturated fatty acid, merely where, from the left, the first one lies; there may be more, but this system does not reveal that.

The lists of saturated and unsaturated fatty acids can be shown as:

Former name	Modern name	Symbol
lauric	dodecanoic	C12:0
myristic	tetradecanoic	C14:0
palmitic	hexadecanoic	C16:0
stearic	octadecanoic	C18:0
arachidic	eicosanoic	C20:0
behenic	docosanoic	C22:0
lignoceric	tetracosanoic	C24:0
palmitoleic***	9–hexadecenoic	C16:1 omega–7
oleic	9–octadecanoic	C18:1 omega–9
gadoleic	11–eicosanoic	C20:1 omega–9
erucic**	13–docosenoic	C22:1 omega–9
cetoleic	11–docosenoic	C22:1 omega–11
linoleic*	9,12–octadecadienoic	C18:2 omega–6
alpha–linolenic*	9,12,15–octadecatrienoic	C18:3 omega–3
gamma–linolenic	6,9,12–octadecatrienoic	C18:3 omega–6
calendic acid	8E,10E,12Z–octadecatrienoic acid	C18:3 omega–6
eicosadienoic acid	11,14–eicosadienoic acid	20:2 omega–6
dihomo–gamma–linolenic	8,11,14–eicosatrienoic	C20:3 omega–6
arachidonic	5,8,11,14–eicosatetraenoic	C20:4 omega–6
timnodonic	5,8,11,14,17–eicosapentaenoic	C20:5 omega–3
docosadienoic acid	13,16–docosadienoic acid	22:2 omega–6
adrenic acid	7,10,13,16–docosatetraenoic acid	22:4 omega–6
docosapentaenoic acid	4,7,10,13,16–docosapentaenoic acid	22:5 omega–6
clupanodonic	4,7,10,13,16,19–docosahexaenoic	C22:6 omega–3

*** Palmitoleic acid behaves like a saturated and not a monounsaturated fatty acid in its effect on LDL cholesterol. **erucic acid is considered to be carcinogenic. *linolenic acid exists in two isomeric forms; alpha (α) and gamma (γ).

Table 2.6 Fatty acid names

Antibacterial effects of carrier oils

An early antimicrobial study of natural oils showed that sweet almond oil, when added to cultures of bacteria, reduced the number of viable bacteria by 98.9% (Hill & Macht 1922). In another test the bactericidal activity of various natural oils on *Staphylococcus aureus* was studied and the time required to reduce the number of viable organisms to zero was measured, sweet almond oil taking 3–4 days, indicating much lower activity than the other oils tested (Bello 1942).

Ingestion of oils

The beneficial effects of vegetable carrier oils on the skin are normally the main consideration for aromatherapists. However, many bodily systems can be helped by the ingestion of certain vegetable oils, because all the associated nutrient properties of the plant are relevant to cold pressed oils. This is not necessarily the case with refined oils.

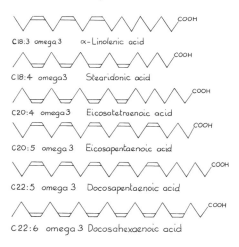

Fig 2.4 Elongation and desaturation of the omega–3 class of fatty acids

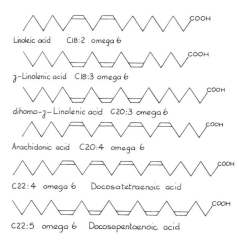

Fig. 2.5 Elongation and desaturation of the omega–6 class of fatty acids

To take full advantage of the vitamin and mineral content of the oils they must be ingested because the molecules are generally considered to be too big to penetrate the skin (the topic of skin absorption and carrier oils is considered further in the next section). The oils can be taken in salad dressings or by the spoonful at doses recommended by a suitably qualified person. Of particular importance, in terms of diet, are the triacylglycerols which are based on the essential unsaturated fatty acids, e.g. linoleic and linolenic acids. A deficiency in these acids can result in ill health and poor vision. Other important factors concerning nutrition are mentioned briefly below.

Rancidity of oils

Oils and fats can spoil by becoming rancid and this unfortunate occurrence can be brought about by light, atmospheric oxygen or moisture. When rancid the oil is chemically changed causing unpleasant changes in taste and smell.

Moisture: when this is present, hydrolytic reactions can occur causing the release of free short or medium chain fatty acids producing a soapy residue.

Air: there is less chance of rancidity occurring if storage containers are completely filled; the possible increase in volume of the oil with temperature must be taken into account (especially for large containers) but airspace must be kept to a minimum.

Oxidation processes can be stimulated by light, heat or metallic elements which allows the formation of saturated or unsaturated aldehydes or ketones. There are two important factors affecting the oxidative stability of natural vegetable oils and these are the content of antioxidants and the molecular structure. Autoxidation is the driving mechanism which brings about rancidity. Autoxidation is a self propelling catalytic reaction which forms free radicals that in turn catalyze and promote further oxidation reactions. This chain reaction occurs in three stages; it is initiated by the abstraction of a proton from a carbon atom of a fatty molecule to form a free radical; this free radical then reacts with another fatty molecule (again abstracting a proton from a carbon atom) to form a hydroperoxide plus another free radical and this process continues until two free radicals react together to terminate the autoxidation reaction. This chain of events (and influence by enzymes – lipases or lipoxygenases (Iberg 2004 p.165)) can bring about the formation of hydroperoxides (and their decomposition products), free fatty acids, aldehydes and ketones, which cause the oil to have a bad smell and make it inedible. Aromatherapists delay rancidity by adding to the blend about 5% of wheatgerm oil, which contains the antioxidant vitamin E.

Side note on the skin: In addition to reducing shelf life by causing rancidity, free radicals have been strongly implicated in premature aging and cancerous changes in the skin. One effect is strong cross–linkage of collagen and an increase in soluble collagen to cause thin, inflexible, wrinkled skin. Free radical breakdown of hyaluronic acid diminishes the skin's water retaining capacity. Free radicals can attack the vulnerable phospholipids of the cell membranes, thereby gaining access to DNA, possibly increasing the risk of cancer mutations.

Cholesterol and lecithin

Fat is an essential part of the human diet because it is the richest source of energy available; it also delays the progress of other food through the stomach and so has a satiety value. However, the kind of fat we consume is very important to health. Traditionally humans are accustomed to eating animal fats but these can sometimes do more harm than good, depending the type and quantity consumed.

All natural fats contain cholesterol and lecithin, which work together, and both are produced also within the body to perform functions vital to health.

Cholesterol is:
- a sterol, made up from fatty acids and alcohol – found in animal fat
- a combination of fatty acids and alcohol
- involved in the production of bile, several hormones and vitamin D
- essential for the healthy functioning of nerve tissue

Lecithin is:
- a compound of phosphorus, fatty acids and glycerol
- has two of the B Complex vitamins, choline and inositol, to aid in emulsifying fats, keeping them in solution and distributing them throughout the system
- a component of bile
- stored in the gall bladder and works together with cholesterol for vital body functions
- found in the tissues of the brain, liver, kidneys, heart and in the protective covering of the nerves
- aids in the emulsification and therefore the absorption of fats and makes fats fluid and transportable
- prevents cholesterol from solidifying and being deposited either as gall–stones or on artery walls
- contains choline and inositol, which aid the metabolisation of fat and favour good (HDL) cholesterol and not the bad (LDL)
- found in avocado, sesame and soya oils

Cholesterol is not all bad for us, as many people seem to think, in fact it is vital to the well being of our bodies as it needed for the healthy development of the adrenal and sex hormones, bile–salts and vitamin D.

Our bodies manufacture cholesterol in the liver as well as extracting it from foods and can also regulate the amount produced. However, problems can arise if the intake of cholesterol is too great for the body to cope with, when it may then build up in the arteries to give rise to a condition known as atherosclerosis, where the cholesterol sticks to the inner walls of the artery causing the passageway to narrow, or even to block in extreme cases.

Cholesterol can only do its job as long as it remains fluid, so when there is an imbalance of cholesterol and lecithin there is a threat to health. This imbalance may occur
- if the body's supply of lecithin is depleted due to nervous strain
- eating processed fats from which the lecithin has been lost
- old age: elderly people need polyunsaturated vegetable oils for the lecithin they contain because in old age the transportation of fat in the system is considerably slower than in young people. It may not be removed from the blood for up to twenty hours, with the result that it has more opportunity to lodge where it may be harmful

This situation may be remedied by eating foods containing the most unsaturated oils. These include corn, safflower, sesame, soya bean, sunflower seed, and fish oils, all of which have been found to lower the cholesterol level (Jeans 1973). It should also be noted that using a margarine spread liberally may be worse than using butter sparingly, as during production these spreads become saturated (see Hydrogenation). Margarine was first prepared by Hippolytus Mège–Mouriès in 1869 and factory production started at Kleve in 1888 (Iburg 2004 p.142)

Fats which raise the level of cholesterol are all animal fats (excluding those from fish, whales and seals) and products made from them such as suet, lard, dripping and dairy products; also palm oil and coconut oil, which contains more than 70% of saturated fatty acids.

Cholesterol does not dissolve in the blood serum and is circulated attached to lipoproteins (fat/protein molecules). It is thought that there are good and bad lipoproteins: low density lipoproteins (LDL) are generally regarded as the bad ones because they deposit cholesterol; high density lipoproteins (HDL) are thought to be beneficial in clearing cholesterol from the artery walls, whence it is excreted via the liver. Oils high in bound–in monounsaturated fatty acids (e.g. olive oil) appear to favour a high HDL/LDL ratio.

Houdret (2007) writes that normally the level of total cholesterol in the body should be less than 2g per litre, with 0.35g per litre minimum of HDL and a maximum of 1.5g per litre LDL. He also mentions that an excess of triglycerides in the blood may cause health problems and their level in the blood must be less than 1.5g per litre. Other authorities give figures varying between 3–5.5g per litre.

The cholesterol content per 100 g of some foods:

Egg yolk	*500mg*
Egg white	*0mg*
Butter	*25mg*
Milk (whole)	*10mg*
Milk (skimmed)	*3mg*
Cheese	*100mg*

The issue is complicated, and there are no concrete answers. Trials have thrown up conflicting results, some stating that there is little to be gained by increasing the amount of unsaturated fats in the diet with respect to atherosclerosis and coronary disease, and others saying that replacing saturated animal fats with unsaturated vegetable oils leads to better health and a longer life.

The weight of evidence would seem to be saying that we would all stand a greater chance of good health if we were to reduce overall fat intake, to abstain from animal fats and stick to plant based mono– and polyunsaturated oils. However, Erasmus (1986) thinks it probable that neither meat eaters nor vegetarians need to fear high cholesterol levels or cardio vascular disease, providing they take their food from unrefined sources, i.e. avoiding refined, denatured sugars, starches, fats and oils. Concerning weight reduction and calorie intake, any kind of fat from any source contains approximately nine calories per gram; fat is fat is fat (carbohydrates provide about 4 calories per gram).

What about milk?

That nature intended us to use unsaturated fats is clearly demonstrated by mothers' milk, which is alkaline in reaction and easy to digest, rich in oleic fatty acid and also contains a significant amount of vitamin E.

Cows' milk has a higher content of saturated fatty acids, a much lower vitamin E content (less than a fifth that of human milk) and has an acid reaction.

It is interesting to note that many cases of infant eczema and asthma among babies fed on modified cows' milk have responded favourably to the addition of unsaturated vegetable oils to their diet. The reason that some human skins react to cow's milk – and other cow products – is that in certain people, the enzyme which digests the protein in milk is absent. In trying to rid itself of the undigested protein, the skin tries to throw it out, producing the inflamed, dry skin known as eczema. However, when cow's milk and cow's cheese are removed altogether from the diet (substituting soya, sunflower or goat's milk) the eczema clears up in 95% of cases. This has been proved by the authors, who, after trying essential oils several times, included the exclusion of milk and its products from the diet, with much speedier success.

Cooking

When unsaturated oils are used in cooking it should be remembered that the increasing temperature gives a greater rate of degradation by oxidation. This means that these oils are fine for salad dressings, as there is no heat involved, but when frying or when smoking hot oil is required (i.e. when using a wok) the resulting high level of oxidation saturates the oil and makes both the oil and the fumes toxic.

Oils and fats having a high smoke point and which are more resistant to high temperatures include (Erasmus 1993):
- butter
- coconut and other tropical oils
- olive oil
- safflower oil – high oleic content
- sesame seed oil
- sunflower oil – high oleic content

Dietary oils could also be classified as a function of their heat resistance. In fact, in France, there are two categories of dietary oils: oils containing more than 2% α–linolenic acid, whose label must bear the wording 'vegetable salad oil' and those containing not more than 2% γ–linolenic acid, whose label must bear the wording 'vegetable salad and cooking oil'. This distinction (French Décret of December 2, 1973) was introduced to address the toxicity attributed to degradation products formed upon heating oils. In fact, according to the relevant professional organizations, it appears that, contrary to currently accepted ideas, the quantity of products formed is practically the same regardless of the polyunsaturated fatty acid content (Bruneton 1995). The most important point is probably the manner in which the oil is used, with common sense and good housekeeping – moderate cooking temperature and frequent renewal of the frying oil.

Removing vegetable oil stains

Twenty years ago it was difficult if not impossible to remove completely oil stains from clothing. However modern soap powders are capable of dealing adequately with oily stains on towels, covers and overalls but it is still best if they are dealt with at once, before drying of the oil to a varnish takes place. Soaking overnight in soap powder and water before washing will usually lift out the stain.

Summary

Fixed oils result from a chemical reaction between glycerol and long chain fatty acids which may be saturated, monounsaturated or polyunsaturated. Triacylglycerols formed from unsaturated fatty acids predominate in vegetable oils.

3 Fixed oils and skin permeation

Introduction

The skin was always considered to be completely impermeable (Fleischer 1877) up until the beginning of the 20th century when it was generally accepted that, although relatively impermeable to water, the skin did accept lipid soluble substances including vegetable oils and fats. Saalfeld (1911 p.171) wrote that natural fats are insoluble in water; they serve as protectives to the skin against external injuries, and partially penetrate it, in virtue of which it swells, acquires a gloss, and is protected against dryness. He also noted that it may be difficult to introduce a medicament into a greasy scalp, unless it can be got to incorporate itself or mix with the greasy secretion. Hence an ointment or oil containing the drug will penetrate in such circumstances more readily than anything else (Saalfeld 1911 p.178).

Today, although there is not a great deal of information available, we are a little better informed and now the skin is regarded as a semi permeable barrier to many materials. Natural sebum permeates the space between cells, which themselves have a lipid bilayer thus enabling small lipidic molecules to pass the stratum corneum by finding their way around and through the cells.

Factors in skin permeation by fixed oils

Fatty acid saturation

One literature review found more than 275 chemical compounds cited as skin penetration enhancers (Osborne & Henke) and included in this list are some unsaturated fatty acids.

The degree of saturation of the vegetable oil is an influencing factor on the rate of skin permeation; it appears that the greater the unsaturation of an oil, the better the penetration rate. Almost half a century ago, the percutaneous absorption of some vegetable oils was studied in adult albino rats; in this test sweet almond oil was found to have a relatively low percutaneous absorption; it was concluded that increased amounts of short chain and polyunsaturated fatty acids in oils enhances their percutaneous absorption (Valette & Sobrin 1963).

Linoleic acid, alpha–linolenic acid and arachidonic acids all enhance skin permeation more than monounsaturated fatty acids. The enhancement effects of fatty acids on penetration through the stratum corneum are structure related, associated with the existence of a balance between the permeability of pure fatty acids across the stratum corneum and the interaction between the acids and skin lipids (Tanajo *et al* 1997).

Oleic acid has been found to increase the epidermal permeability through a mechanism involving the stratum corneum lipid membrane. It is incorporated into skin lipid, disrupts the molecular packing and alters the level of hydration and so allows drug penetration more quickly (Jiang Shao Jun *et al* 1998).

Cod liver oil – the enhancing effect of marine products can generally be associated with their content of free unsaturated fatty acids (Loftsson *et al* 1997).

Viscosity

There are other influencing factors, for example viscosity of the penetrant; viscosity is the 'stickiness' or otherwise affecting the rate of flow of a substance (water has a low viscosity and treacle has a high viscosity). Viscosity plays a part with some carrier oils, some being relatively viscous (e.g. almond oil and olive oil which is mainly monounsaturated) and which are absorbed only very slowly; it is known that high viscosity fats such as lard and wool fat retard or prevent percutaneous absorption (Macht 1938). Other oils which are less viscous (e.g. grapeseed) are relatively quickly absorbed as tests involving the abdominal skin of the rat have shown. Linseed oil crosses the skin more quickly than expected from its viscosity (Scheuplein & Ross 1970) however, avocado oil also has the reputation of being easily absorbed into the skin and of aiding the penetration of substances dissolved in it, despite its relatively high viscosity.

Temperature

This is also a consideration as any oil becomes less viscous with a rise in temperature: so it can be expected that warming the oil and the hands prior to massage, then applying to a warm body would aid penetration.

Molecular size

Zatz (1993) speaking of molecular size says that considering that the horny layer is a compact membrane and that diffusing molecules must follow a tortuous path through it, it might seem obvious that the diffusion coefficient would be inversely proportional to molecular weight and size; in other words, the bigger the molecule the less the likelihood of it passing the skin barrier.

Essential oils are completely soluble in all proportions in vegetable oils, and so it must follow that the rate of absorption of an essential oil is governed to some extent by the characteristics of the vegetable oil employed as the carrier. The fixed oil also influences the amount of essential oil absorbed through the skin because the volatility of the essential oil is decreased and so it remains on the body longer, giving greater opportunity for absorption.

Skin conditions

Atopic dermatitis has been shown to respond positively to dermal application (Lovell 1981, Wright & Burton 1982, Kerscher & Korting 1992) –

but this is disputed by Sharpe & Farr (1990) – and other skin conditions, such as psoriasis, may also benefit (Ferrando 1986). There is some evidence that oils rich in bonded essential fatty acids do bring benefits where the skin is dry. The stratum corneum in normal skin is rich in saturated and polyunsaturated fatty acids and a deficiency in these essential fatty acids can result in dryness because of the increase in trans–epidermal water loss. The level of GLA in the epidermis is low because of a lack of the enzymes necessary to convert LA to GLA and in dry skin the level of LA is low. It has been observed that topical application of borage and evening primrose oils increases the level of GLA in the stratum corneum up to 2% for fourteen days following application of the oil (Hoffmann–La Roche 1989) so helping dry skin problems.

Parenteral nutrition

Consideration given to the use of cutaneously applied vegetable oils as a way of overcoming essential fatty acid deficiency in some people who have had surgery which prevents the normal digestive process, provides some sort of evidence regarding the penetration of the skin by fixed oils, or at least some of their components. Press, Hartop and Prottey (1974) used sunflower seed oil with three patients who had developed essential fatty acid deficiency after major intestinal resections. The deficiency was corrected by the application of 2–3mg of the oil per kg of body weight per day for twelve weeks. Friedman *et al* (1976) reported the correction of essential fatty acid deficiency in two infants who were given 1400mg per kg per day of topically applied sunflower oil.

The above work does seem to suggest that in order for the essential fatty acids to be made available the triacylglycerol molecules have to undergo a chemical process known as hydrolysis, and this can only take place within the body; thus all or part of the oil must necessarily have passed the skin for this to happen. However, other investigators have reported that essential fatty acid deficiency cannot be influenced by cutaneously applied vegetable oils (Hunt et al 1978, McCarthy et al 1983, O'Neill, Caldwell & Meng 1976). Miller et al (1987) examined the use of safflower oil on five patients, and deduced that topical application may improve plasma fatty acid profiles but adequacy of tissue stores remained unanswered. They noted that only the deficiency in one of the fatty acids was being addressed (linoleic acid), as safflower oil does not contain appreciable amounts of linolenic acid. They were cautious about extending the results of the study, and felt that because some of their subjects displayed abnormal results in liver function tests, such tests should be carefully monitored in all patients given cutaneous safflower oil.

Several batches of commercial Ibuprofen gel and paraffin ointments with Ibuprofen were prepared with sesame oil, sunflower oil, and oleic acid in different concentrations. When tested on hairless rat skin the drug release was raised in line with increase in oil concentration in the product (Dinda & Vijay Ratna 2006).

Permeation enhancement

Methods and compositions to aid skin permeation are provided by US Patent 5229130 which increase the permeability for transdermally administered pharmacologically active agents. The compositions are formulated using vegetable oils as skin permeation enhancers; one preferred composition contains coconut and soybean oils. Drug delivery systems for administering drugs percutaneously in combination with the vegetable oil–based enhancer compositions are also provided.

Jojoba: there is some evidence that jojoba wax, despite consisting mainly of saturated fatty acids, can permeate the skin. Jojoba merits a special mention because it is not composed of triacylglycerides but is a wax composed of esters and is therefore different from the fixed oils with respect to its actions on the skin. It appears to moisturise and soften the skin by the dual action of forming a lipid layer which is partially occlusive and by the diffusion of jojoba into the intercellular spaces of the stratum corneum. Percutaneous absorption studies at the University of Michigan demonstrated that jojoba is quickly absorbed into the skin, apparently via the pores and hair follicles); from there jojoba diffuses into the corneal layer of the skin. In support of this, photographs exist showing the oil in a 'pool' at the base of a hair and moving through the follicle wall into the corneal layer (Anon 1985).

Summary of factors affecting skin permeation

Pharmacodynamic studies concerning lipids and the skin have shown the oil characteristics summarised below to support a higher rate of permeation of the *stratum corneum*:

- low viscosity oils rather than high viscosity oils
- the greater the iodine value (i.e. more unsaturated) of an oil the higher the rate of permeation
- the lower saponification value the higher the rate of permeation
- the shorter the carbon chain length the higher the rate of permeation
- the lower the lecithin content of an oil, the greater the rate of penetration
- it is thought that jojoba with straight chain and branched esters penetrates better than do triacylglyceride oils
- blends of one or more vegetable oils as skin permeation enhancers have been mentioned, one preferred composition containing both coconut oil and soybean oil

References – Section One

Anon 1985 *Jojoba: new crop for arid lands, new raw material for industry.* US National Research Council. National Academy Press, Washington.

Ascherio A, Willett W C 1997 Health effects of trans fatty acids. *American Journal of Clinical Nutrition* 66:1006S–1010S.

Bello D 1942 Experimental researches on the microbicidal power of some animal oils (cod liver oil, tunny liver oil) and vegetable oils (crude olive oil, sweet almond oil) on Staphylococcus aureus. *Rivista Italiana Igiene* 2(7): 455–469

Brod J, Traitler H, Studer A, De Lacharriere O 1988 *International Journal Cosmetic Science* 10: 149

Bruneton J 1995 *Pharmacognosy, phytochemistry, medicinal plants.* Intercept, Andover p.135

Coupland K 1992 Natural lipids – valuable raw materials in cosmetics. In: Fridd P (ed.) 1992, 1996 *Natural ingredients in cosmetics.* Micelle, Weymouth p.68

Dinda SC, Vijay Ratna J 2006 *Enhancement of skin permeation of Ibuprofen from ointments and gels by sesame oil, sunflower oil and oleic acid.* 68(3):313–316

Emmerson M, Ewin J 1996 *A Feast of Oils.* Thorsons, London: 123.

Erasmus U 1986 *Fats and oils.* Alive Books, Burnaby: 65.

Erasmus U 1993 *Fats that heal, fats that kill.* Alive Books, Burnaby: 113.

Ferrando J 1986 Clinical trial of topical preparation containing urea, sunflower oil, evening primrose oil, wheatgerm oil and sodium pyruvate, in several hyperkeratotic skin conditions. *Med Cutan Lat Am.* 14(2): 133–137.

Fleischer 1877 Untersuchungen uber das Reabsorptionsvermögen der Menschlichen Haut. *Erlangen Habilitatsionsschrift* p.81

Fleming C R, Smith L M, Hodges R E 1976 Essential fatty acid deficiency in adults receiving total parenteral nutrition. *American Journal Clinical Nutrition* 29:976–983

Fox B A, Cameron A G 1975 Food science: a chemical approach. English Universities Press, London

Friedman Z *et al* 1976 Correction of essential fatty acid deficiency in new born infants by cutaneous application of sunflower seed oil. *Paediatrics*, 58: 650–654.

Hartop P J, Prottey C 1976 *British Journal Dermatology* 95:255

Hill J H, Macht D I 1922 A note on the antiseptic properties of olive oil. Proceedings of the Society of *Experimental Biol. Med* 20: 170–171

HMSO 1990 *The dietary and nutritional survey of British adults.* HMSO.

HMSO 1991 *Dietary reference values for food energy and nutrients for the United Kingdom.* HMSO.

Hoffmann La– Roche 1989 Information Leaflet HHN–5379A/589.

Houdret J C 2007 Danger cholesterol! *Cuisiner comme un chef.* no 2 (April) p.23

Hunt C E *et al* 1978 Essential fatty acid deficiency in neonates: inability to reverse deficiency by topical application of EFA–rich oil. *Journal Pediatrics* 92: 604–607.

Iberg A 2004 *Dumont's lexicon of oil and vinegar.* Rebo, Lisse

Jeans H 1973 *Natural oils from nuts and seeds.* Thorsons, Wellingborough

Jiang Shao Jun, Kim Young Koo, Lee Seung Hun 1998 The ultrastructural changes of stratum corneum lipids after application of oleic acid in propylene glycol. *Annals of Dermatology.* 10(3): 153–158.

Kerscher M J, Korting H C 1992 Treatment of atopic eczema with evening primrose oil: rationale and clinical results. *Clinical Investigation* 70 (2): 167–171

Loftsson T, Gunnarsdottir T, Magnusdottir L M, Frioriksdottir H, Guomundsdottir T K, Olafsson J H, Haraldsson G G, Guomundsson G, Hjaltason B 1997 Effect of various marine lipids on transdermal drug delivery – *in vitro* evaluation. *Bollettino Chimico Farmaceutico.* 136(10): 640–5

Lovell C R et al 1981 treatment of atopic eczema with evening primrose oil. The Lancet 1(8214):278

Macht 1938 The absorption of drugs and poisons through the skin and mucous membranes. *Journal American Medical Association* 110(6): 409–414

McCarthy M *et al* 1983 Topical corn oil in the management of essential fatty acid deficiency. *Critical Care in Medicine* 5: 373–375.

Miller D G *et al* 1987 Cutaneous application of safflower oil in preventing essential fatty acid deficiency in patients on home parenteral nutrition. *American Journal of Clinical Nutrition* 46: 419–423.

O'Neill J A *et al* 1976 Essential fatty acid deficiency in surgical patients. *Annals of Surgery* 185: 535–541

Osborne D W, Henke J J *Skin penetration enhancers cited in the technical literature.* Research and Development, ViroTex Corporation, TX 77381, USA

Press M *et al* 1974 Correction of essential fatty acid deficiency in man by the cutaneous application of sunflower–seed oil. *The Lancet* 6 April: 597–599.

Prottey C, Hartop P J, Press M 1975 Correction of the cutaneous manifestations of essential fatty acid deficiency in man by application of sunflower seed oil to the skin. *Journal of Investigative Dermatology* 64:228–234

Prottey C, Hartop P J, Black J G, McCormack J I 1976 *British Journal Dermatology* 94:13

Saalfeld E 1911 *Lectures on cosmetic treatments.* Rebman Ltd., London

Scheuplein, Ross 1970 Effects of surfactants and solvents on the permeability of the epidermis. *Journal Society of Cosmetic Chemists* 21: 853–873

Sharp G R, Farr P M 1990 *Lancet* 335:1283

Tanojo H. Bouwstra J A, Junginger H E, Bodde H E 1997 *In vitro* human skin barrier modulation by fatty acids: skin permeation and thermal analysis studies. *Pharmaceutical Research.* 14(1):42–9

United States Patent 5229130 http://www.freepatentsonline.com/5229130.html

Valette G, Sobrin E 1963 Percutaneous absorption of various animal and vegetable oils. *Pharmaceutica Acta Helvetica* 38(10): 710–716

WHO 1990 *Diet, nutrition and the prevention of chronic diseases.* WHO.

Wright S, Burton J L 1982 Effects of evening primrose oil (Efamol) on atopic eczema. *Lancet* 20 November 1120–1122

Zatz J L 1993 Scratching the surface: rationale and approaches to skin permeation. In: Zatz J L (ed) *Skin permeation: fundamentals and application.* Allured, Wheaton p.28

Bibliography (maceration)

American Heritage Dictionary of the English Language. 1992 Houghton Mifflin

Guenther E 1948 *The essential oils. vol 1* Van Nostrand, New York p.213

Section 2A –
Fixed oils

Almond oil (sweet)

Scientific name

Prunus dulcis (Mill), *P. amygdalis* var. *dulcis*,
P. dulcis var. *dulcis*, *Amygdalis communis*, *P. amygdalis* var. *sativa*
Family: Rosaceae

Etymology

The word *amygdalis* is from the Greek – *amugdale* and Latin – *amygdala* names for the plant. Almonds were known to the Romans as nuces graecae (Greek nuts). *Dulcis* is from the Latin and means sweet, *sativa* has the meaning cultivated and *prunus* is the Latin name for plum tree.

The plant and its environment

The almond tree is indigenous to the Middle East, and is now cultivated in the supportive warm climates of the Mediterranean countries and California. It is an ancient tree, which has been cultivated for thousands of years.

Almonds were prized by the Greeks, who introduced them to southern Europe. The trees were grown in Italy for hundreds of years before they spread to France in the 8th century and on to Britain some 800 years later. The tree is small, reaching only 3–7m (10–23ft) in height and bears white or pink blossom in the springtime, which appears at about the same time as the leaves begin to show. The fruits have a light–green, furry outer skin and have the appearance of a small, green apricot.

The oil

Sweet almond oil is one of the most used carrier oils; it is pale yellow in colour, slightly viscous and very oily. In pharmacy, almond oil means strictly the oil of *Prunus amygdalis*, although the oils of peach kernel (*Prunus persica*), apricot kernel (*P. armeniaca*) and hazelnut (*Corylus avellana*) are chemically similar. Indeed, it is a difficult matter to discriminate between these, both chemically and physically (the cost is different). An advantage that these oils have over some others is that they have less of a tendency to become rancid.

Method of extraction

The best quality oil sweet almond oil is obtained by cold pressing the kernels, which contain up to 50% oil, and then clarifying by filtration. Thus sweet almond oil can be sold as physically expressed giving a yield of 35% (when its price is similar to apricot and peach oils) but it is more often available as a refined, chemically extracted product with a yield of 50% at a lower price. After cold pressing, the kernels still contain enough oil to warrant extraction by the use of solvents and most of the almond oil available has been solvent extracted, and is the oil used in the cosmetics industry. Unfortunately, its lower price also makes the refined oil attractive to many aromatherapists, even though the cold pressed oil is superior for therapeutic purposes.

Principal constituents

Type	Based on	Content – %
Saturated fatty acid units:		
C14:0	myristic acid	trace
C16:0	palmitic acid	6.0 (3–9)
C18:0	stearic acid	1.6 (0.5–3.0)
C22:0	behenic acid	0.1 (<0.2)
Typical saturated fatty acid unit content		8.2
Monounsaturated fatty acid units:		
C16:1	palmitoleic acid	0.5 (<2.0)
C18:1	oleic acid	70.7 (60–80)
C20:1	eicosenoic acid	0.1 (<0.5)
C22:1	erucic acid	(<0.1)
Typical monounsaturated fatty acid unit content	66.5	
Polyunsaturated fatty acid units:		
pC18:2	linoleic acid	27.7 (17–30)
C18:3	α–linolenic acid	0.2 (<0.4)
Typical polyunsaturated fatty acid unit content		28

Physical properties

Odour	unrefined oil has a delicate, sweet smell and the taste has a hint of marzipan
Acid value	1.5 max
Specific gravity	0.912–0.916
Energy value Kcal/100ml	890
Iodine Value	98 (95–109)
Colour (Lovibond 5¼" cell)	20Y/2.2R (>40Y/4R)
Peroxide Value	0.9 (<5)
Unsaponifiable matter	0.3% (<1.0)
Saponification Value	190 (190–200)
Density 20°C	0.914 (0.910–0.920)

Vitamins

Vitamins A, B1, B2, B6 and E (45mg/100ml)

Folklore and traditional plant uses

Almonds were very popular in Elizabethan England soon after they were introduced into the country and were much used in cookery, which often also included almond water. Sweet almond seed or seed oil has been used as a folk remedy for bladder, breast, mouth, spleen and uterine cancers, among others (Leung & Foster 1996 p.24). Grieve (1998) says that the expressed oil is useful in bronchial diseases, tickling coughs, hoarseness, nephritic pains, etc.

Gerard (1512–1612) writes that 'the oil newly pressed out of Sweet Almonds is a mitigator of pain and all manner of aches, therefore it is good for pleurisy and colic. The oil of almonds makes smooth the hands and face of delicate persons, and cleanseth the skin from all spots and pimples'.

Therapeutic properties – internal use

Almond oil is used in laxative preparations and is said to be effective in reducing blood cholesterol levels (Leung & Foster 1996 p.23). It is also used in oily injections (Evans 1996).

Therapeutic properties – external use

- an excellent emollient (Leung & Foster 1996), alleviating and nourishing dry skin
- helps to soothe inflammation (Stier 1990)
- beneficial in relieving the itching caused by eczema, psoriasis, dermatitis and all cases of dry scaly skin
- has been used to ease irritation on baby's bottoms
- soothes sunburn; almond and hazelnut have an antierythematous action to reduce inflammation and peeling (Iberg 2004 p.196)
- has been used in gentle frictions to soften babies' cradle cap

Cosmetic use

Sweet almond oil finds use as an emollient (National Formulary Board 1975) in many pharmaceutical and cosmetic products.

Culinary use

Almonds, both whole and ground, are widely used in cakes, chocolates, marzipan and many savoury dishes.

Cautions

1   Said to be non–irritating and non–sensitising, and considered safe for cosmetic use (Fischer 1983, Leung & Foster 1996) although a few people are allergic to cosmetics containing almond oil, suffering stuffy nose and skin rash (Winter 1984). Products containing up to 25% sweet almond are practically non–irritating to rabbit skin and only minimally irritating to rabbit eyes. In sub–chronic studies sweet almond oil at 100% concentration was only slightly irritating to rabbit skin (Fisher 1983).

2   Kedvessy (1940) reported that sweet almond oil tends to become rancid more quickly than other fixed oils; marked changes in peroxide and acid values occurred when sweet almond oil was stored at room temperature (20°C–28°C) for ten weeks; the addition of antioxidants greatly increases the stability and shelf life (Hizon & Huyck 1956).

3   There exists an essential oil of bitter almond (*Prunus amygdalis* var. *amara*, *Prunus dulcis* var. *amara*) but this is not used in aromatherapy because of its toxicity. Prior to distillation the nuts are crushed and macerated in water, which leads to the formation of 2–4% hydrocyanic acid (prussic acid), due to the decomposition of amygdalin.

4   It is possible to obtain rectified bitter almond essential oil (referred to as FFPA – free from prussic acid) in competition with synthetic benzaldehyde and this is commonly used as a flavouring agent, chiefly in the agricultural food industry (Bruneton 1995).

5   It is difficult today to procure true sweet almond oil, that is one that has not been adulterated with sunflower, hazelnut or other common oils; it is essential to have a guarantee from your supplier (Goëb 2005).

Additional notes

1   Pharmacological studies reveal that sweet almond oil is absorbed slowly through intact skin (Fisher 1983).

2   Both almond and olive oils can be used for massage; fresh oils containing more essential fatty acids being the best (Erasmus 1986).

3   Goëb (2005) recommends a relaxing massage oil consisting of 40 drops lavender, 40 drops geranium (or 20 drops geranium + 20 drops ylang ylang) in 30ml sweet almond oil.

4   Sweet almond oil has calming properties and, mixed with the appropriate essential oils, can be applied to the skin to give antispasmodic and calming effects (Goëb 1998).

5   Alleged to protect the skin against moisture loss (Iberg 2004 p.196).

6   The nuts contain vitamins E, B2, the minerals magnesium, calcium, zinc, iron and a total fat content of 56–64/100g of which 34/100g MUFA.

References:

Bruneton J 1995 Pharmacognosy, phytochemistry, medicinal plants. Intercept, Andover p.125

Erasmus U 1986 Fats and oils. Alive, Vancouver p.234

Evans W C 1996 Trease and Evans' pharmacognosy. Saunders, London p.184

Fisher K T 1983 Final report on the safety assessment of sweet almond oil and almond meal. Journal American College Toxicology 2(5): 85.

Gerard J 1597 Great Herbal

Goëb Ph 2005 Connaître l'essentiel sur les huiles essentielles. MDB Editions

Goëb Ph 1998 Connaître l'essentiel sur les huiles essentielles. IAPM, Tamil Nadu p.41

Grieve M 1998 A modern herbal. Tiger Books, London p.23

Hill J H, Macht D I 1922 A note on the antiseptic properties of olive oil. Proceedings of the Society of Experimental Biol. Med. 20:170–171

Hizon R P, Huyck C L 1956 The stability of almond and corn oils for use in parenteral solutions. Journal of the American Pharmaceutical Association 45:145–150

Iberg A 2004 Dumont's lexicon of oil & vinegar. Rebo, Lisse

Kedvessy G 1940 Ber. Ungar. Pharm. Ges. 16:114

Leung A Y, Foster S 1996 Encyclopedia of common natural ingredients used in food, drugs and cosmetics. Wiley, New York pp 22–23

National Formulary Board 1975 The national formulary. 14th edition. American Pharmaceutical Association, Washington DC

Stier B 1990 Secrets des huiles de première pression à froid. Quebec p.50

Winter R 1984 A consumer's dictionary of cosmetic ingredients. Crown, New York p.49

47

Apricot kernel oil

Scientific name
    Prunus armeniaca L.
    Family: Rosaceae

Etymology
    From the Latin *prunus* meaning plum tree and *armeniaca* denoting 'of Armenia'.

The plant and its environment
    The tree is native to China whence it was transported to the Middle East, following which the Romans established many apricot orchards in southern Europe. Eventually, in 1720, the apricot tree reached the USA, where it continues to flourish. Apricots are grown commercially in the south of France.
    The apricot tree is deciduous, growing up to about 9m (30ft) high. Around February to March white flowers tinged with red appear, followed soon after by the leaves, which also have red tips when young; this feature gives the tree an attractive appearance and distinguishes it from the peach tree.

The oil
    Apricot oil is almost identical to sweet almond oil, but slightly more expensive (probably because less is produced). It is worth noting that in the production of apricot kernel oil other nuts such as almond, cherry etc are sometimes added before the actual extraction process begins.
    Persic oil is the fixed oil obtained from the kernels of various species of Prunus – apricots (*P. armeniaca*), peaches (*P. persica*), cherries (*P. cerasus*) and plums (*P. domestica*) – by cold expression. The French Pharmacopoeia has a monograph for refined persic oil obtained by 'refining and deodorizing' the crude oil.

Method of extraction
    The best quality oil for aromatherapy is obtained by cold pressing the kernels.

Principal constituents

Type	Based on	Content – %
Saturated fatty acid units:		
C14:0	myristic acid	trace
C16:0	palmitic acid	3.0–7.0
C18:0	stearic acid	0.5–1.5
C20:0	arachidic acid	<0.5
C22:0	behenic acid	trace
C24:0	lignoceric acid	trace
Typical saturated fatty acid unit content		6.5
Monounsaturated fatty acid units:		
C16:1	palmitoleic acid	0.5–1.0
C18:1	oleic acid	56–68
C20:1	eicosenoic acid	<0.5
Typical monounsaturated fatty acid unit content		65.5
Polyunsaturated fatty acid units:		
C18:2	linoleic acid	25–33
C18:3	α–linolenic acid	<0.8
Typical polyunsaturated fatty acid unit content		28

Physical properties

Odour	fairly strong, marzipan–like
Acid value	<0.2
Iodine value	104–112
Colour (Lovibond 5¼")	<40 yellow, <4 red
Specific gravity	0.912–0.917
Peroxide Value	<4
Refractive Index (25C)	1.468–1.476
Saponification Value	185–200
Energy value	890Kcal/100ml

Folklore and traditional plant uses

The crushed fruit has been used as a facial mask to soften the skin. Rosaceae seeds, apricot, peach, plum contain quantities of amygdalin and are therefore occasionally responsible for intoxication (Bruneton 1995). In traditional Chinese medicine apricot kernels are used as an antitussive and antiasthmatic and in treating tumours (Leung & Foster 1996).

Therapeutic properties – internal use

Apricot kernel oil has similar uses to those of sweet almond oil i.e. it is

49

said to be effective in reducing blood cholesterol levels and is also used in laxative preparations.

Therapeutic properties – external use
- excellent for skin protection, being both emollient and nourishing
- readily absorbed because of its texture
- beneficial in relieving the itching caused by eczema
- suitable for sensitive, dry and ageing skins

Cosmetic use

The oil can be used in brilliantine (Winter 1999 p.67). The finely milled shells are sometimes used in a facial scrub to cleanse away dead skin cells. Apricot kernel oil has traditionally been incorporated into cosmetic products for its softening action on the skin and is used in soaps and cold creams (Grieve 1998).

Cautions

1   No reported toxic effects (Winter 1999 p.67).
2   Apricot kernel ingestion is the commonest form of cyanide poisoning (Chandler 1984a, Chandler 1984b). For this reason, apricot kernels are rarely added to apricot jam unless in small quantities. Contact dermatitis from apricot kernels has been reported (Göransonn 1981).

Additional note

The crushed fruit is used as a facial mask to soften the skin.

References

Bruneton J 1995 Pharmacognosy, phytochemistry, medicinal plants. Intercept, Andover p.171
Chandler RF *et al* 1984a Laetrile in perspective. Canadian Pharmaceutical Journal 117: 517–520
Chandler RF *et al* 1984b Controversial laetrile. Pharmaceutical Journal 232: 330–332
Göransonn K 1981 Contact urticaria to apricot stone. Contact Dermatitis 7: 282.
Grieve M 1998 A modern herbal. Tiger Books, London p.51
Leung A Y, Foster S 1996 Encyclopedia of common natural ingredients. John Wiley & Sons, New York p.24
Winter R 1999 A consumer's dictionary of cosmetic ingredients. 5th edn: Three Rivers Press, New York

Argan oil

Scientific name

Argania spinosa, *A. sideroxylon*
Family: Sapotaceae

Etymology

Sideroxylon means ironwood, hence
the common name for this tree being
Morocco ironwood: *spinosa* means full of spines.
Another common name for argan oil is spinosa oil.

History

The Plant and its Environment: In the rugged highlands south of Essaouira, vast open forests of argan are found. This tree, which is unique to south western Morocco, has a hard fruit that produces a prized cooking oil. The argan tree is thorny, reaching a height of 8–10m and lives from 150 to 200 years. It is very hardy, surviving heat, drought and poor soil; its roots grow deep in search of water, helping to bind the soil, thus preventing erosion and stopping the advance of the desert. The argan tree is little known outside Morocco, but is to be found there in the South Western regions.

The fruit has a green, fleshy exterior like an olive, but is larger and rounder. Inside, there is a nut with an extremely hard shell, which in turn contains one, two or three almond–shaped kernels. The trunk of the argan is often twisted and gnarled, allowing goats to clamber along its branches and feed on the leaves and fruit. When goats eat the fruit, the fleshy part is digested but the nut remains. Later, the nuts are collected by farmers to produce oil.

The oil

Argan oil is quite fluid and is slightly darker than olive oil with a reddish tinge and it has a hint of hazelnut flavour.

Method of extraction:

The production of argan oil by traditional method is lengthy and laborious. Each nut must be cracked open to remove the kernels, and to produce one litre of oil may take 20 hours work. The nuts are roasted and then ground and the result mixed with water; the oil is then extracted manually from the paste.

Recently mechanical presses have been introduced to extract the oil, considerably reducing the time needed. Once the kernels are roasted, the mechanical press takes care of the grinding and extraction. More oil is extracted and since water is no longer added, the oil has a longer shelf life. The most consuming time of the process, cracking the nuts, is still carried out by hand. No solvent or heat is used for extraction, yielding a cold pressed oil.

Principal constituents:

The composition of argan oil is similar to that of peanut oil: mainly monounsaturated fat with omega–6 fatty acids but no omega–3.

Type	Based on	Content – %
Saturated fatty acids:		
C16:0	palmitic	12
C18:0	stearic	6
Typical saturated fatty acid content		16–20
Monounsaturated fatty acid:		
C18:1	oleic	45
Typical monounsaturated fatty acid content		45–50
Polyunsaturated fatty acid:		
C18:2	linoleic	35–38
C18:3	α–linolenic	<0.5
Typical polyunsaturated fatty acid content		32–40

Physical properties

Saponification value	170–200
Peroxide value	<6
Acid value	1.1
Iodine value	96–97
Specific gravity (20°C)	
Colour	slightly darker than olive oil, with a reddish tinge
Odour	bland characteristic odour
Shelf life	12 to 18 months

Vitamin and mineral content

The oil contains a significant amount of vitamin E.

Therapeutic properties

Argan oil is rich in polyunsaturated fatty acids but fortunately also contains a large amount of vitamin E which is a powerful antioxidant and quenches free radicals. Argan oil does not contain any alpha–linolenic acid but its high content of oleic acid makes this oil particularly interesting in the regulation of blood cholesterol. Some studies indicate that 30ml per day of this oil over a period of one month could lower cholesterol levels.

Cosmetic uses

This oil is also used for its cosmetic properties. It is a useful skin and hair care product because of its antiaging and restructuring properties due to the antioxidant and high vitamin E content. Moroccans use it to nourish the skin and protect the hair; it is used in the manufacture of soaps, creams and shampoos. The oil, rich in essential fatty acids, is used for massage, facials and as an ingredient in antiaging cream and aftershave lotion for men. Argan oil can be used in place of a night cream, a few drops being sufficient for the whole face, thus it is economic in use despite being an expensive oil. It is incorporated into antiageing creams because it possesses regenerative and firming qualities to the skin due to its content of essential fatty acids; it also preserves the elasticity of the skin (Anon 2006 p.14).

Culinary uses

It is used in cooking, but sparingly because it is expensive. A few drops stirred into couscous just before serving give a rich, nutty aroma. It can also be used in salad dressings.

The residue from the kernels after oil extraction is a thick chocolate–coloured paste from which amlou, a mix of almonds, honey and argan oil is made. It is delicious on toasts and it is claimed to be aphrodisiac. It is served as a dip for bread at breakfast time in Berber households. Its flavour is similar to that of peanut butter.

In Morocco the oil is used in salads and in tagines, to flavour semolina and on grilled peppers. Chefs employ it in marinades and it is used on artichokes and on exotic fruit salads. Argan oil is particularly good when used in association with fresh coriander.

Folklore and traditional plant remedies

For centuries, Berber women have produced argan oil for use in food and traditional Moroccan medicine. It is claimed to have various medicinal properties, such as lowering cholesterol levels, stimulating the circulation and strengthening the body's natural defences.

Cautions

There are no known contra indications.

The authenticity of this oil should be verified: the oil commands a high price and sellers often fall into the temptation to dilute it with cheaper oils. Some bottles simply contain olive oil, coloured with paprika or other substances.

Argan oil should be packed in small preferably opaque bottles and kept in a cool place; once opened it is better to keep the oil refrigerated and consume it quickly.

Additional notes

1   The argan tree (Morocco ironwood) plays a vital role in maintaining the ecological balance and the economic situation of the population.
2   In 1999, UNESCO added the argan tree to the World Heritage List.
3   There are about 21 million trees which play a vital role in the food chain and the environment, though their numbers are declining; in less than a century, more than a third of the argan forest has disappeared.

References

Anon 2006 L'argan. Maxi 9–15 October p.14

Avocado oil

Scientific name
Persea gratissima Caertn., *P. americana* Mill
Family: Lauraceae

Etymology
Persea is the Greek
name of a tender evergreen
tree and *gratissima* is Latin
for very pleasing or agreeable. *Americana*
is indicative of its origin. The word
avocado itself comes from the Aztec
language.

The plant and its environment
The avocado tree originates from the tropical
and sub–tropical areas of the Americas where it was
discovered by the Spaniards in the 15th century and
subsequently introduced into Europe. It now flourishes in
Spain, Israel and many other Mediterranean countries.

Avocados have been cultivated for more than 7000 years and now the
major areas of production are California, Florida, Cuba, Argentina, Brazil,
South America and Australia, although it was little known outside South
America until the 20th century.

The oil
Avocado oil has excellent keeping qualities but should not be kept in the
fridge, as some useful constituents would be precipitated. It is quite common
for the oil to be slightly cloudy if in cold conditions and there may even be a
deposit present, but it regains its normal clarity at normal room temperature.
These two traits can be considered a good sign insofar as they indicate that the
oil has not been through an extensive refining process. Avocado tends to
become congealed when cold – indeed the oil solidifies at 0°C but liquefies
again at room temperature. The unrefined oil is deep green in colour.

Method of extraction
The oil is expressed from dried avocado pears which have been damaged
and therefore would be unfit for marketing as fresh fruit.

The fruit is peeled and the stone removed before the fleshy portion is sliced and dehydrated in an oxygen free environment at a temperature of about 130°C. Water is removed in this way in order to avoid the formation of an unusable emulsion. The dried slices are then ground before being cold pressed and filtered to produce the oil.

The extraction process can be quite tricky and true cold pressed avocado oil is not common, as the cosmetics industry is the biggest user and prefers the refined oil. This latter is a pale yellow colour, which is favoured by the cosmetics industry so that creams and lotions are not unduly coloured. For aromatherapy use the unrefined, green, cold pressed oil is preferred as it is therapeutically more effective.

Principal constituents (Virgin oil)

Type	Based on	Content – %
Saturated fatty acid units:		
C16:0	palmitic acid	10–29
C18:0	stearic acid	<3.0
C20:0	arachidic acid	<1
C22:0	behenic acid	<0.5
Typical saturated fatty acid unit content		19
Monounsaturated fatty acid units:		
C16:1	palmitoleic acid	6–12
C18:1	oleic acid	42–66
C20:1	eicosanoic acid	<0.5
Typical monounsaturated fatty acid unit content		68
Polyunsaturated fatty acid units:		
C18:2	linoleic acid	8–16
C18:3	α–linolenic acid	<5.0
Typical polyunsaturated fatty acid unit content		13

Physical properties

Odour	similar to the ripe fruit in its native country
Acid value	0.2 max
Specific gravity	0.91–0.92
Energy value Kcal/100ml	895

Physical properties for the refined oil

Iodine value (calc)	75–95
Free fatty acid (% as oleic)	<0.5
Colour (lovibond $5\frac{1}{4}$" cell)	<60.0 yellow, <6.0 red

Refractive index at 20°c	1.455–1.475
Saponification value	180–190
Peroxide value	<3.0

Vitamins

Vitamins A, B1, B2 and D.

Minerals

Potassium, phosphorus, magnesium, sulphur, calcium, sodium, copper.

Folklore and traditional plant uses.

At one time avocado oil was believed to be an aphrodisiac. The pulp has been used as a hair pomade to stimulate hair growth, to hasten suppuration and also as an emmenagogue (Leung & Foster 1996). As well as eating it, the Aztecs used it for face masks against wrinkles.

Therapeutic properties – internal use

The avocado is almost a complete food and is easily digested. It is of help with gastric problems, constipation, urinary infection and the treatment of liver and gallbladder conditions.

Therapeutic properties – external use

- a superb emollient
- has a reputation for having a higher degree of penetration into the epidermis than most carrier oils
- valuable in massage and muscle preparations
- said to have skin healing properties (Leung & Foster 1996)
- has been used in Raynaud's disease (Stier 1990)
- moisturising, softening, anti–wrinkle (prevents premature ageing)
- especially recommended for dry skins
- for general skin inflammation

A non–saponifiable fraction in the oil is sometimes isolated, and this is good for maintaining suppleness of the skin in post–menopausal women.

Cosmetic use

Avocado oil is rich in lecithin and is widely used in cosmetic preparations, including lipsticks. A mask of crushed avocado pulp left on the face for twenty minutes both cleanses and moisturises the skin. Used in equal quantities with sesame and olive oils it affords some protection from the sun.

Culinary use

Avocado flesh is a very useful food on account of its vitamin and mineral content. Proteins are also present together with 20% fat, so the fruit is not slimming! It is used extensively in salads and starters and when emulsified it is particularly digestible. The pulp is a good source of vitamin D, higher than in butter and eggs (Joslyn & Stepka 1949) and potassium (Leung & Foster 1996).

Cautions

The colourless bleached oil which is more generally available (strangely enough, at a slightly higher price!) is not the best for therapeutic use; some of the active ingredients of avocado oil are often isolated for use in cosmetics.

Avocado oil used in shampoo, and tested on the skin and eyes of both animals and people showed some irritation, but there was no evidence of sensitisation (Winter 1999 p.73).

Poisoning of cattle, horses, goats, rabbits, canaries and fish by avocado (leaves, fruit, bark, seeds) has been reported (Lewis & Elvin–Lewis 1977).

The CIR Expert Panel states that this oil is a safe ingredient in present practice and concentration.

References

Joslyn M A, Stepka W 1949 Food research 14:459
Lewis W H, Elvin–Lewis M P H 1977 Medical botany. Plants affecting man's health.
     Wiley–Interscience, New York
Leung A Y, Foster S 1996 Encyclopedia of common natural ingredients. John Wiley & Sons,
     New York p.54–55
Stier B 1990 Secrets des huiles de première pression à froid. Self published, Quebec p.54
Winter R 1999 A consumer's dictionary of cosmetic ingredients. 5th edn: Three Rivers Press, New York

Babassu palm oil

Scientific name

Orbignya phalerata
Family: Palmaceae
Synonyms: *Orbignya oleifera*, *O. martiana*, *O. barbosiana*, *O. speciosa*.

Etymology

The common names are babaçu or babassu (from the Tupi–Guarani: *ba* = fruit; *açu* = large) in Brazil; *cusi* in Bolivia.

History

Babassu kernel oil first became an important commodity during the first World War because other supplies of vegetable oil were scarce. It was then chiefly used as an edible oil but after the war exports fell and by the mid 1960s it was zero. On occasions since then babassu oil has been exported briefly when there was a shortage of coconut oil.

The plant and its environment

The babassu palm tree is native to the coastal areas of north eastern Brazil and other regions of South America and grows to a height of about 20m.

The nuts grow high up and so babassu fruit is generally harvested after it has fallen from the bunch. The fallen fruits are gathered and split to remove the kernel. Kernel extraction has traditionally been carried out by women and children, but this is not easy as fruits vary in size considerably and the number of kernels within also varies. Consequently, machine extraction yields mostly damaged kernels that must be processed immediately to avoid rancidity.

The oil

Babassu is a non–drying oil and the physical and chemical properties very similar to coconut oil.

It is a light yellow clear oil used in food and cleansing products. This oil has properties similar to coconut oil and is increasingly being used as a replacement for coconut oil, but it is expensive.

Extraction:

Babassu oil is cold pressed from the kernel, containing about 70% lipids, and is ultra–refined without chemicals.

59

Principal constituents:

The oil has a high content of lauric and myristic acids and is considered similar to coconut oil

Type	Based on	Content – %
Saturated fatty acids:		
C12:0	lauric	44–50
C14:0	myristic	15–20
C16:0	palmitic	6–11
C18:0	stearic	3–6
C20:0	arachidic	<1
Typical saturated fatty acid content		85
Monounsaturated fatty acid:		
C18:1	oleic	10–18
Typical monounsaturated fatty acid content		15

Physical properties

Acid value (mg KOH/g oil)	2–8
Refractive index at 40EC	1.449–1.451
Iodine value (wijs)	10–18
Saponification value	244–245
Unsaponifiable matter	0.8% max
Melting point (°C)	22–26

Therapeutic properties

The melting point is quite close to that of skin temperature and giving a cooling effect when applied to the skin. Its high lipid profile (up to 70% lipids) gives it emollient properties making it good for massage.

Cosmetic uses

Babassu is emollient, being beneficial for both dry and oily skins, moisturizing the skin without an oily sheen: it leaves the skin soft, with a protective coating and can be used in bath, massage, and skin care, usually combined with essential oils.

Folklore and traditional plant remedies

Medicine is obtained by pressing from the rachis an antiseptic, styptic juice, which is used to treat wounds and bleeding;

Tar from burning babassu husks is rubbed on gums to alleviate toothache; mesocarp flour as a 'panacea' used to treat gastric ulcers, colitis, varicose veins, cellulitis, rheumatism, hernias, allergies, asthma, obesity, alcoholism and leukaemia.

Cautions

External use only.

Additional notes

1   All parts of the plant are used for many purposes:

2   Fruit – products such as medicines , beauty aids, and beverages.

3   Leaves – thatch for houses and are woven into mats for house walls.

4   Fibres – baskets, mats, fans, sieves, twine, torches, whisks, bird cages, hunting blinds, animal traps

5   Petioles – laths for window frames and support of clay–packed walls, rails for fencing, crop support, raised planters

6   Stems – timber, construction of bridges, foundations, benches

7   Whole fruit – burned to smoke rubber; used to attract game, principally large rodents

8   Kernels – consumed raw as snack nuts; made into "milk" to use as a beverage or for stewing meat and fish; pressed to extract oil used for cooking, lighting, soap; residues used as animal feed, fish and shrimp bait and as substitute or filler for coffee; beetle larvae extracted from kernels used as human food or to grease bows so as to increase resiliency

9   Mesocarp – flour used as substitute for manioc or to make chocolate–like beverage

10   Husks (endocarp) – used to make charcoal, which is a principal source of fuel for cooking, smoke also acts as insect repellent; for handicrafts

11   Exports only occur when coconut oil is scarce or its price is higher than babassu oil.

Sources

Anderson, M.D. (1991). "Book review: 'Agroecology, Researching the Ecological Basis for Sustainable Agriculture' edited by SR Gliessman; 'Agroecology' edited by CR Carroll, JH Vandermeer and PM Rosset; and 'Agricultural Ecology' by J Tivy." American Journal of Alternative Agriculture 6: 40–42

Borage oil

Scientific name
Borago officinalis L.
Family: Boraginaceae

Etymology
Borage is sometimes called beebread because bees like this plant. In the past most descriptions of borage have referred to its ability to bring happiness to people; on account of this Pliny named the plant euphrosinum. The word Borago is possibly from the Latin burra, meaning a hairy garment, and referring to the leaves.

The plant and its environment
The herb is thought to have its origins in Syria in the Middle East and is now widely grown. Its hairy stem, alternate hairy greyish green leaves and pinky blue, pretty star shaped flowers easily distinguish this annual (occasionally biennial) attractive plant. It grows to a height of 60cm (2ft).

The oil
Borage oil is cold pressed from the seeds.

In the early 1980's gamma linolenic acid (GLA), an essential fatty acid, was identified as a triacylglycerol component in borage oil, which had been obtained from the dark brown seeds by simple cold expression. With levels of 16–23%, borage oil is the richest source of GLA currently available (evening primrose oil contains much less, about 9%). However, waste black currant pulp has since been found to contain 14% GLA and is a much cheaper alternative.

It must be remembered that GLA is very fragile and can be rapidly destroyed by light, heat, humidity and the oxygen in the air. For this reason the oil should be stored in a cool, dark place.

Because it is less expensive, borage oil has been used as an adulterant in evening primrose oil in order to increase the GLA content.

Method of extraction
The oil is cold pressed exclusively from ripe borage seeds using a compressing screw thread.

Principal constituents

Type	Based on	Content – %
Saturated fatty acid units:		
C16:0	palmitic acid	9–13
C18:0	stearic acid	3–5
C20:0	arachidic acid	0–1
Typical saturated fatty acid unit content		15
Monounsaturated fatty acid units:		
C16:1	palmitoleic acid	0–0.6
C18:1	oleic acid	12–20
C20:1	eicosenoic acid	2–6
C22:1	erucic acid	1–3.5
C24:1	nervonic acid	0.5–2.5
Typical monounsaturated fatty acid unit content		22
Polyunsaturated fatty acid units:		
C18:2	linoleic acid	34–42
C18:3	α–linolenic acid	0–0.4
C18:3	gamma linolenic acid	19–29
Typical polyunsaturated fatty acid unit content		60

Physical properties

Odour	virtually none but pleasant
Acid value	1.0 max
Iodine value	140–155
Colour	golden yellow
Taste	pleasant
Peroxide value	<3

Folklore and traditional plant uses

The flowers or the flowering tops of borage have been used in teas (tisanes) for diuretic, sudorific and emollient purposes (Leung & Foster 1996). Traditionally, it was believed that the leaves and seeds of borage could help promote the milk supply in nursing mothers. Externally it has been employed as a poultice for inflammatory swellings (Grieve 1998).

There are records of its use as an antiinflammatory in the Middle Ages and also at this period it was used as a medicine to ensure good quality of blood (Goëb 1998 p.42), but of all the virtues mentioned for this plant by the ancients the most consistently reported was its ability to cheer the melancholic, to brighten the pessimist, and generally to make men merry and bring comfort. During the renaissance it was recommended to care for bouts of depression and to support the heart (Goëb 1998 p.42)

of known virtue to revive the hypochondriac and cheer the hard student.
John Evelyn 17th century

Therapeutic properties – internal use

A good source of GLA, borage oil is available in capsules, when a typical dose is two to four per day over a period of two months. From a preventative point of view it is advisable to take two courses per year

After the age of 60 it is recommended that a person should take a capsule of borage oil every day, as normal synthesis of GLA may be diminished (Leung & Foster 1996)

It is said to be good for the elderly skin, preventing dryness and premature aging, making the skin more supple (Europhyto–Institut).

For convalescents and children the capsules can be opened and mixed with food (compare with evening primrose oil).

Borage oil can be used with evening primrose oil to reduce cholesterol deposits (Bartram 1995).

The seed oil has been awarded a DIN in Canada as a GLA dietary supplement for essential fatty acid deficiency (Awang 1990)

It has been used to prevent wrinkles, to counteract unsightly stretch marks and to strengthen nails (Europhyto–Institut).

Therapeutic properties – external use

- the bonded fatty acid components of borage oil are said to defer wrinkling (Bartram 1995) so it may be feasible to add a capsule of oil to a facial treatment oil or lotion (concentration of 4–8%)
- non–irritant so may be used on the skin in cases of eczema and psoriasis
- can be used for regeneration of the skin; Goëb (1998 p.42) advises using borage oil not on its own but in a 5–10% mix in either macadamia or sweet almond oil

Cosmetic use

The high GLA content (much higher than evening primrose) recommends its use for re–establishing and maintaining normal skin function. Borage extract is used in skin care products; for skin lacking suppleness and having wrinkles apply some drops on the face morning and evening (Goëb 1998 p.42)

Culinary use

The fresh flowers make a delightful topping to a salad and can be dried for use as a tea. Fresh borage flowers can also be added to cold drinks for those long summer evenings. Some people liken the flavour to that of cucumber, and the candied flowers are used as cake decorations. The roots are used to flavour wine and the young leaves may be pickled, and also added to salads.

Cautions

1   As far as is known, borage oil has no contraindications. It is reported as being non–toxic and non–irritating to the eyes and skin (Roche 1990).

2   Borage leaf use is suspended in Germany due to the pyrrolizidine alkaloid content (Monograph 1991) which, if ingested, can lead to liver damage.

3   Borage oil is fragile and must be kept away from heat, light and oxygen to maintain its valuable properties.

Additional notes

1   On account of its high content of GLA it is advised to take half a teaspoon of this oil each day, alternating with evening primrose oil as a general revitaliser (Goëb 1998 p.42)

2   A herbal extract is used in a 'tea' for sore eyes.

References

Awang D 1990 Canadian Pharmaceutical Journal. March :121
Bartram T 1995 Encyclopedia of herbal medicine. Grace, Christchurch p.65
Monograph 1991 Borago. Bundesanzeiger. 12 July. no. 127
Europhyto–Institut undated La phytothérapie: la santé par les plantes. Editions Alpen, Monaco p.25
Goëb Ph 1998 Connaître l'essentiel sur les huiles essentielles. IAPM, Tamil Nadu p.42
Grieve M 1998 A modern herbal. Tiger books, London p.120
Leung A Y, Foster S 1996 Encyclopedia of common natural ingredients. John Wiley & Sons, New York p.98
Roche 1990 Health and Safety Information Sheet BO3. October

Camelina oil

Scientific name
Camelina sativa
Family: Brassicaceae

Etymology
Sativa is from the Latin word for cultivated.

The plant is also known as weedseed, 'gold of pleasure', false flax, wild flax and linseed dodder; German sesame, Siberian oilseed.

Fr: Cameline cultivee Nor: *Oljedodre* Dnmk: *Sæd–Dodder* Fi: *Ruistankio* G: *Saat–leindotter* Sp: *Camelina pilosa*.

The plant and its environment
Camelina has been grown in Europe for about 3000 years; in the Iron and Bronze ages it was an important agricultural crop and this continued for some time, certainly it continued to be grown at the time of the Roman Empire (Robertson 1987) and was in northern Greece beyond the current range of the olive growing area (Clapham *et al* 1987).

A flowering plant of the Brassicaceae (which includes mustard, rapeseed, etc.), it is an annual or over wintering herb native to the Mediterranean and Central Asian areas where wild weedy forms survive. The plant appears very adaptable to climate and soil type.. Camelina is primarily a minor weed in flax and it possibly found its way to North America on account of this; it is today cultivated as an oilseed crop to produce vegetable oil and animal feed (in England to produce birdseed).

Camelina has branched smooth or hairy stems that become woody at maturity and range from 25–100cm high. Leaves are arrow–shaped, 5–8cm long with smooth edges. Each stem bears many small yellow flowers each with 4 sepals and petals. The seeds, borne in pear shaped capsules which are orange to brown in colour and result from self–pollination, although they can be cross pollinated by insects.

The oil
The oil has properties similar to those of sperm whale oil, for which it is increasingly being used as a replacement (cf jojoba wax qv). It has good levels of bonded essential fatty acids and an unusually high amount of bonded eicosenoic acid (C20:1).

Method of extraction

The seeds contain 35–40% oil and 30% protein but they are only 1–2 mm in length and 1 mm in width. This small size means it is difficult to extract the oil without the use of solvents.

Principal constituents

Type	Based on	Content – %
Saturated fatty acid units:		
C12:0	lauric acid	<0.5
C16:0	palmitic acid	3.0–8.0
C18:0	stearic acid	2.0–5.0
C20:0	arachidic acid	<2.0
C22:0	behenic acid	<0.5
C24:0	lignoceric acid	<0.5
Typical saturated fatty acid unit content		7–14
Monounsaturated fatty acid units:		
C16:1	palmitoleic acid	<0.5
C18:1	oleic acid	13–26
C20:1	ecosenoic acid	10–18
C22:1	erucic acid	0–4
Typical monounsaturated fatty acid unit content		26–41
Polyunsaturated fatty acid units:		
C18:2	linoleic acid	16–25
C18:3	α–linolenic acid	33–42
C20:2	dihom–gamma–linolenic	2
C20:3	eicosatrienoic acid	1
Typical polyunsaturated fatty acid unit content		46–64

Physical properties

Odour	slight odour
Specific gravity	0.915–0.925
Appearance	Clear bright yellow oil
Colour (Lovibond $5\frac{1}{4}$" cell)	2.0 red max
Acid value (mg KOH/g oil)	0.2 max
Peroxide value (meq/kg oil)	2.0 max
Refractive index at 40°C	1.4700–1.4750
Iodine values (Wijs)	145–170
Saponification value	180–195

Vitamin and mineral content

The oil contains many natural antioxidants, such as tocopherols, which make the oil stable, resistant to oxidation and rancidity.

The vitamin E content of Camelina oil is approximately 10mg/100g.

Folklore and traditional plant uses.

In Asia the seeds have long been used as a food source and in medical preparations for respiratory and metabolic disorders. Weedseed, as it is sometimes known, has been used for fattening poultry; the oil was also used in oil lamps, as an edible product and as a skin moisturiser. The protein rich pressed cake left after oil extraction was a valued livestock food. The plant stems were used for making brushes, packaging and thatching temporary buildings.

Therapeutic properties

Once the triacylglycerols have broken down, the longer chain fatty acids can be used by the body in the synthesis of cells.

Cosmetic use

The oil can be used in formulae for skin care creams, body lotions, bath foams and moisturisers as it is emollient, has good spreading properties and acts as a lubricant in both hair and skin preparations. It provides a protective coating to hair follicles (used by L'Oreal in hair products).

Camelina has a profile of bonded fatty acids which is similar to the oils present in marine fauna such as the shark and sperm whale (Press release 1991). Indeed, it can be used as a replacement for sperm whale oil in lipsticks and other solid products (see also jojoba oil).

Culinary use

The oil may be used in salad dressings with the nutritional advantage of having a low saturate content but a high total of unsaturated fatty acids. It has an aroma and flavour somewhat like the almond.

Cautions

As far as is known, camelina oil is non–irritant and non–sensitising.

Additional notes

1   Recently about 50ha of *Camelina sativa* were cultivated in Austria as a raw material for liquid biofuel production. (http://btgs.ct.utwente.nl/eeci/ countries)

2   Camelina has also been found to be a potential low cost crop for green manure.

3   Allelopathy: it has been shown to be allelopathic and is used in research areas to provide soil cover and competition and prevent seed mixture between adjacent plots (Robertson 1987).

4   Apart from cosmetic preparations the oil is used in the production of soaps, soft detergents and paints; it is also in the production of interesting lipopeptides and lipoaminoacids.

5   It is known that the seed and its components help to condition the plumage of canaries, giving a glossy sheen, and this led to research which showed that the oil has good skin softening properties (Product Information Sheet).

References

Press release 1991 Common weed seed oil aids sperm whale conservation. Anglia Oils, Kingston–upon–Hull 16 May

Product Information Sheet undated Gold of Pleasure Seed Oil. Anglia Oils, Kingston–upon–Hull

Bibliography

1   Clapham A R, Tutin T G, Moore D M 1987 Flora of the British Isles. 3rd Edn Cambridge University Press
2   Robertson R G 1987 Camelina: A useful research crop and a potential oilseed crop. Minnesota Agricultural Experiment Station, University of Minnesota, Station Bulletin 579–1987 (Item No. AD–SB–3275).
3   Smith N O 1994 Department of Agriculture, University of Reading, Letter to Mrs Blackburn, Alternative crops unit, MAFF, Room 405, 10 Whitehall Place, London, SW1A 2HH.
4   Askew M F 1992. A review of novel oilseeds and fibre crops and their potential for the UK. ADAS Wolverhampton WV6 8TQ.
5   Harvey J 1988 Alternative crops at Starcross experimental plots
6   Agegnehu M, Honermeier B 1997 Effects of seeding rate and nitrogen fertilization on seed yield, seed quality and yield components of False flax (Camelina sative Crtz). Die Bodenkultur. 48 (1).
7   Crowley J 1998 see web site http://www.teagasc.ie/research/reports/crops Teagasic project report 4320 Evaluation of Camelina sativa as an alternative oilseed crop.
8   Vollmann J A et al 1996 Improvement of Camelina sativa and under exploited oilseed. In Janick J (ed.), Progress in New Crops. ASHS Press, Alexandria, VA. p.357–362.
9   Marquard R, Kuhlmann H 1986 Investigations of productive capacity and seed quality of linseed dodder (Camelina sativa Crtz). Fette–Seifen–Anstrichmittel 88 p.245–249.
10   Robinson R G 1987 Camelina: a useful research crop and a potential oilseed crop. Minnesota Agricultural Experimental Station, University of Minnesota bulletin 579

Camellia seed oil

Scientific name

Camellia sinensis (*C. kissi*, *C. thea*, *Thea viridis*)
Family: Theaceae

Etymology
This tree is commonly known as tea plant or tea tree and Camellia oil is also called tea seed oil. The name tea tree has been applied not only to this plant but also to several other plants which are quite different from the Camellia tree. The word *sinensis* comes from the Latin for Chinese.

Chinese saying: – 'better to be three days without food than one day without tea'.

The plant and its environment

Native to Asia, the camellia plant grows wild and bears delicate white and pink flowers. It is native to southeast Asia and different varieties are grown in India and Sri Lanka (Ceylon), Cambodia, China, Japan and indeed today across the world's subtropical/tropical regions.

Camellia sinensis is the tea plant (nothing at all to do with tea tree essential oil from the quite different plant *Melaleuca alternifolia*); it is the plant species whose evergreen leaves (5 – 15cm long, 3 – 5cm wide) and leaf buds are used to produce tea. White tea, green tea, oolong and black tea are all harvested from this species, but are processed differently to attain different levels of oxidation.

This tree in the wild may reach 30m but when cultivated it is normally cut to prevent it growing above 2.5m (8ft) to facilitate collection of the leaves. It bears flowers (2.5–4cm) which are yellow to white with 7 or 8 petals. The fruit is a three celled capsule with one seed in each cell.

The oil

The seeds of Camellia sinensis are pressed to yield tea seed oil, a semi sweet oil which can be used as a cooking oil and for flavouring.

Extraction

The oil is cold pressed from the seeds of the camellia plant.

Principal constituents

Type	Based on	Content – %
C14:0	myristic acid	<1
C16:0	palmitic acid	8–10
C18:0	stearic acid	1–3.5
C20:0	arachidic acid	<1
Typical saturated fatty acid content		11
C16:1	palmitoleic acid	0.1
C18:1	oleic acid	78–86
Typical monounsaturated fatty acid content		80
C18:2	linoleic acid	7–10
C18:3	linolenic acid	0.2–0.8
Typical polyunsaturated fatty acid content		9

Physical properties

Colour	clear light yellow
Odour	none

Vitamin and mineral content

Camellia oil contains vitamins A and B.

Therapeutic properties – cosmetic uses

Camellia seed oil is:
- emollient and is regarded as having a similar action to jojoba oil; it is easily absorbed by the skin.
- claimed to help maintain a smooth, supple skin because of the oleic acid content but clinical studies are lacking to support this.
- a nourishing oil containing antioxidants which help protect the skin from free radical damage
- used for its nail strengthening property.

Culinary uses

The oil is used as a cooking oil and for seasoning, as it is slightly sweet tasting. It is a good seasoning for cold salad food, not having any particular aroma.

Folklore and traditional plant remedies

Camellia kissi oil has been used traditionally in far eastern hair and scalp treatments as it is an emollient, rich in unsaturated fatty acids.

71

The leaves are used in TCM (traditional Chinese medicine) to help asthma and circulatory problems.

Cautions

No contraindications are known. It has a useful shelf life of 2 years.

Additional notes

1   Fresh leaves of the camellia plant contain about 4% caffeine.
2   Historically, it was used in Asia to protect Samurai swords from rust and preventing corrosion of woodworkers' chisels, demonstrating its antioxidant properties.
3   Tea itself contains caffeine, theobromine, tannins, catechins and a volatile oil.
4   Chief components of the volatile oil (0.007–0.014% fresh weight of leaves) are hexenal, hexenol, butyraldehyde, isobuteraldehyde, isovaleraldehyde, and n–hexyl alcohol, benzyl alcohol, phenylethyl alcohol, phenols, cresol, hexoic acid, n–octyl alcohol, geraniol, linalool, acetophenone, benzyl alcohol, and citral.
5   Camellia seed oil helps a woman recuperate after bearing a baby.
6   The oil is 97% absorbed by the human digestive system, a higher rate than other cooking oils.
7   Tea bags have been used as a poultice on baggy or tired eyes, as a compress for headache and to soothe sunburn (Duke 1985 p.94).

References

Duke J A 1985 Handbook of medicinal herbs. CRC Press, Boca Raton

Castor oil

Scientific name
Ricinus communis
Family: Euphorbiaceae

Etymology
Also known as *Palma Christi, agno casto* (Spanish origin). *Ricinus* is the Latin name for a tick, which the seeds resemble; *communis* means general, common.

The plant and its environment
The castor oil plant has been cultivated for at least 6000 years, and is one of the few major crops with an African origin.

Castor oil is obtained from the seeds of Ricinus communis grown in India, Russia, Brazil, China and the Mediterranean countries. The plant was known to the ancient Egyptians, who burnt the seed oil in their lamps: they also used the oil as a base for perfumed ointments. On a recent visit to the Nile delta the plant was still to be seen growing and flourishing there, as it likes full sun and well drained soil: it is also to be seen in other Mediterranean countries e.g. southern Spain.

The castor oil plant presents itself in many forms, varying from 2–15m in height, perhaps an annual or perhaps a perennial. The large well known leaves (it is much used as a house plant) are alternate and the male and female flowers are both without petals and arranged in a cluster: the seeds have a mottled appearance and are bean shaped.

The demand for castor oil continues to rise and production now exceeds 500,000 tonnes each year, with Brazil producing 40% of the world supply, India 20% and Thailand 8%.

The oil
The seeds contain 50% of the fixed oil, which is a viscid fluid, almost colourless when pure, possessing only a slight odour and has a mild, yet highly nauseous and disagreeable taste. Castor oil dissolves in alcohol, ether and glacial acetic acid.

Method of extraction

Medicinal oil is obtained by cold pressure, the lower grades being obtained by hot pressure and finally by solvents, when the yield is higher at about 33%.

An industrial oil is made by roasting the seeds, then grinding and boiling them in water; the oil is skimmed off the surface, the yield being about 50%. Most types of castor oil yield a semi–solid deposit when exposed to the cold, which is not at all detrimental to the oil save for the somewhat unpleasant appearance.

Principal constituents

Ricinoleic acid (this is peculiar to the castor plant and occurs in combination with glycerine, making up the bulk of the oil)

Type	Based on
C16:0	palmitic acid
C18:0	stearic acid and hydroxystearic acid
C18:1	oleic acid
C18:2	linoleic acid

Physical properties

Castor oil is quite viscous and is not normally used in aromatherapy.
Its specific gravity is 0.96.

Folklore and traditional plant remedies

Dioscorides thought the oil suitable only for external application: today it is still regarded as being of no value in cooking. It is used industrially as a high temperature lubricant and in the manufacture of plastics, enamels and printers varnish. The oil does have the reputation of being fungistatic.

Ayurvedic medicine has long used the oil from the castor plant for lumbago, pleurodynia, sciatica and rheumatism. From India castor oil entered the Arab pharmacopoeia and was known as 'the sesame of India'. The leaves were and still are warmed and applied to Canary Island women's breasts to increase secretion of milk, the oil is used to prevent sore nipples and is also rubbed onto the scalp of nursing mothers to prevent post natal hair loss (Patnaik 1993, Bartram 1995). The seeds are ground up and applied to counteract gout (Schleifer 1973).

Castor oil has been used for centuries in India, China and Egypt as a cathartic (Leung & Foster 1996).

Therapeutic properties – internal use

- Castor oil is commonly used as a lubricant purgative, and has been listed in many pharmacopoeia since 1780, although known to Ayurvedic medicine as a purgative for millenia
- The oil is also used in cases of diarrhoea due to food poisoning
- Bartram (1995) gives castor oil as a galactogogue

Therapeutic use – external

- sores and abscesses (Leung & Foster 1996)
- recommended for cutaneous conditions such as ringworm, itch, etc.

Cosmetic uses

Castor oil is used in the making of brilliantine, nail polishes and removers, solid perfumes and lipsticks. For the bath, sulphated castor oil is water soluble and may be used as a base for essential oils; it will disperse in the water and not leave an oily ring around the bath. The lampblack produced by burning castor oil in lamps with wicks dipped in herbal preparations produced the eyeliner kohl.

Cautions

1 Ingestion of large amounts of the oil may cause vomiting, colic and violent purging. The bean meal can be fatal to cattle, but it makes an excellent fertilizer for grassland.
2 The seeds are extremely poisonous due to the presence of the albuminoid ricin (Bruneton 1995).
3 Ricin is not present in the oil.
4 The seeds are reported to have been used as an oral contraceptive in Algiers (Brondegaard 1973) and ricinoleic acid has been used in contraceptive jellies (Duke 1985).

Additional notes

1 Castor oil contains many chemicals, one of which is being investigated as a possible treatment for cancer. Though much of this oil is used medicinally, much more is used industrially for treating leather, for lubrication, and for the production of Turkey–red oil which is used in dyeing cotton.
2 The bean of the castor oil plant contains, as well as the useful oil, a highly toxic chemical, ricin, which is one of the most toxic substances known; fortunately the castor oil can be extracted free of this contaminant. The ricin molecule is extremely poisonous and as few as two seeds can be sufficient to kill a human.

3   Ricin impregnated metallic spheres, delivered via a sharpened umbrella–ferrule, was the toxic material used about 20 years ago in the 'Bulgarian umbrella' political assassination in London, using about 250 μg of the ricin poison (Knight 1979).

4   Both the seeds themselves and the cake left after the expression of the oil are violently purgative, a property which is due to the presence of the highly toxic albumin ricin.

5   The oil, or parts of it, can be used in the manufacture of soap, paint, varnish, candles, plastics, ointments, cosmetics, crayons and carbon–paper, in the dyeing of textiles, the preserving of leather and the waterproofing of fabrics. A most unusual use is the manufacture of Rilson, a nylon–type fibre made from the oil.

6   Combined with citron ointment, it is used as a topical application in common leprosy.

7   The oil is decomposed by the fat–splitting ferments of the intestinal canal liberating the irritant Ricinoleic acid, to which the purgative action is considered in all probability to be due.

8   Sodium ricinoleate, used by dentists for the treatment of gum problems, is extracted from the oil.

References

Bartram T 1995 Encyclopedia of herbal medicine. Grace, Christchurch pp 100–101
Brondegaard V J 1973 Planta Medica 23:167
Bruneton J 1995 Pharmacognosy, phytochemistry, medicinal plants. Intercept, Andover p.130
Duke J A 1985 Handbook of medicinal herbs. CRC Press, Boca Raton p.408
Knight B 1979 Ricin – a potent homicidal poison. British Medical Journal :350–351
Leung A Y, Foster S 1996 Encyclopedia of common natural ingredients used in food,
       drugs and cosmetics. Wiley, New York p.133
Patnaik N 1993 The garden of life. Aquarian, London
Schleifer H 1973 Sacred narcotic plants of the New World Indians. Lubrecht & Cramer,
       Monticello p.193

Cherry kernel oil

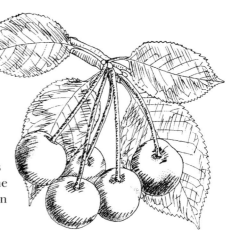

Scientific name
Prunus avium, Prunus cerasus
Family: Rosaceae

Etymology
Avium is from the Latin and means 'of birds', while *Prunus* is the Latin name for the plum tree and *cerasus* is the Latin name for cherry: *Prunus cerasus* is the sour cherry.

The plant and its environment
Cultivated cherries are derived from two species, the sour cherry *Prunus cerasus* (ancestor of the morello cherry) and *Prunus avium*, which grows wild in Britain and gives rise to the sweet cherries.

The oil
Cherry kernel oil is emollient and stable.

Persic oil is the fixed oil obtained from the kernels of various species (i.e. apricots, peaches, cherries, plums) by cold expression (see apricot oil). The French pharmacopoeia has a monograph for refined persic oil (Bruneton 1995).

Method of extraction:
The oil is expressed from the fruit stones of varieties of *Prunus cerasus*.

Principal constituents

Type	Based on	Content – %
C16:0	palmitic acid	4–9
C18:0	stearic acid	<4
Typical saturated fatty acid unit content		<15
C18:1	oleic acid	58–80
C18:2	linoleic acid	10–32
C18:3	linolenic acid	<0.1

Physical properties

Odour	mild, nutty
Acid value	2.0 max
Iodine value	95–115
Saponification value	182–202
Soluble	in isopropyl esters, mineral and other vegetable oils
Insoluble	in water

Cosmetic uses

Cherry stone oil imparts a long lasting emollient effect on the skin and gives a high gloss to the hair; used in emulsified and anhydrous conditioners. A rich natural emollient which spreads well and although benefits and uses are not yet well understood its use generally is as for almond oil.

Cautions

Cherry stone oil under occlusive patch is reported to be non–irritating to rabbit skin.

References

Bruneton J 1995 Pharmacognosy, phytochemistry, medicinal plants. Intercept, Andover p.126

Cocoa butter

Scientific name

Theobroma cacao

Family: Sterculiaceae

Etymology

Cacao is from the Mexican *cacauati*. Linnaeus gave the plant the name *theobroma* from the Greek, meaning 'food of the Gods'. Also known as cacao butter, *beurre de cacao* and kakao butter.

The word *cacao* itself derives from the Nahuatl (Aztec language) word *cacahuatl*.

The plant and its environment

The trees are native to Central and Southern America where they have been cultivated for centuries, and cocoa butter was first made in 1695. The seeds have always been prized; at one time they were even used as a form of currency. The tree flourishes in most tropical, moist countries and it is now grown in Central and Southern America, the West Indies, Ghana, Nigeria, Ceylon and Java.

Over the years this plant has been much developed, so much so in fact that the original trees no longer exist. The present one is a small evergreen tree varying in height from 4–6m (12–20ft).

The small yellow flowers characteristically grow directly on the trunk and older branches, producing brown fruits like large broad beans (or small cucumbers – 10–35cm long), each of which contains about three dozen 3cm (1?4 in) long seeds. These are the cocoa beans, which are odourless, very astringent and bitter when fresh; they take on their brown colour only after prolonged fermentation and desiccation; it is only after roasting and rolling that the unmistakable taste of cocoa appears (Bruneton 1995).

This wonderful taste (with a touch of vanilla) was experienced by Cortez in the hall of Montezuma in 1519 and was soon known and highly regarded in Europe.

The oil

Theobroma is a solid fat better known as cocoa butter. It is one of the most stable fats known and contains antioxidants so it can be stored for 2 to 5 years.

Method of extraction

Chemically the kernel of the cacao seed contains about 50% lipids (Bruneton 1995); the seeds are first fermented, then washed and dried before the final processing. This involves hulling, roasting and then hot expressing the oil (in the form of a solid fat) from the roasted seeds. This final step yields cocoa and cocoa butter. Solvent extraction is also commonly used.

Principal constituents

Type	Based on	Content – %
Saturated fatty acid units:		
C16:0	palmitic acid	25–29
C18:0	stearic acid	
C20:0	arachidic acid	small
Typical saturated fatty acid unit content		29
Monounsaturated fatty acid units:		
C18:1	oleic acid	34–36
Typical monounsaturated fatty acid unit content		36
Polyunsaturated fatty acid units:		
C18:2	linoleic acid	<4
Typical polyunsaturated fatty acid unit content		<4

(Leung & Foster 1996)

Physical properties

It is a firm but brittle yellowish mass which has a melting point of 34–38°C (93–100°F).

Folklore and traditional plant uses

The seeds have a diuretic and stimulant action due to the presence of caffeine (0.05–0.3%) and theobromine (1–3%), although theobromine does not affect the central nervous system (Stuart 1987). Theobroma 'oil' is used to treat wrinkles on the neck, around the eyes and the corner of the mouth. In European tradition it was used in combination with other ingredients for infectious intestinal disease, diarrhoea, bronchial expectorant in asthma, bronchitis, coughs and lung congestion; it has also been used to regulate the function of endocrine glands, especially the thyroid (Monograph 1991).

Therapeutic properties – internal use

Theobroma oil is used extensively as a base for suppositories and pessaries, because it melts at body temperature; it is also used as an ointment base (Leung & Foster 1996).

The purine alkaloids theobromine and caffeine are responsible for the stimulant effect of cocoa and chocolate and contribute to bitter cocoa flavour

Therapeutic properties – external use
- can be used in ointments and also as a massage lubricant, since it melts in the hand, and it softens and lubricates the skin
- said to enhance a suntan and help fade the appearance of scars and stretch marks

Cosmetic use

The 'oil' is a popular ingredient in cosmetics and skin care products and is employed in lipsticks, nail whiteners, rouge pastes, soaps, emollients, eyelash creams and massage creams.

Culinary use

The major use for ground cocoa beans is in chocolate; the fat extracted from the beans when making drinking chocolate is also used in the manufacture of chocolate. The drink is stimulating as, like coffee and tea, it contains caffeine. Cocoa is used to flavour certain meat and fish dishes, especially octopus, and is used with onion, garlic and tomatoes in Spain, Portugal and Italy. In some countries (Denmark, Ireland, UK) sal seed fat (*Shorea robusta*, Dipterocarpaceae) is allowed as a substitute for cacao butter up to a limit of 5%. Sal seed fat is also used in cosmetics.

Cautions

Theobroma oil may cause an allergic reaction on the skin. It is sometimes adulterated with waxes, stearins and animal or vegetable tallows (Trease & Evans 1983).

Additional notes

1   In Yucatan the seeds of *Theobroma cacao* were used as the currency until 1850 and they continued to be highly valued until the middle of the 1920's. At one time in Central America 100 beans would buy a slave.

2   The Aztecs discovered that by crushing the beans into a paste and adding spices, they could make a refreshing, nourishing but bitter drink. Travellers brought the drink back to Europe where it became popular, though expensive at the time.

3   Cocoa butter, which is extracted during the making of chocolate and cocoa powder, melts at around 97°F which is human body temperature so chocolate melts in the mouth: it has a mild chocolate flavour and is the

81

only cacao component used in white chocolate.

4   Chocolate contains the same 'happy' chemicals found in some recreational drugs but craving may be a symptom of addiction.

5   Research indicates that dark chocolate may have health benefits; a recent study claims that eating one square of dark chocolate a day tends to reduce blood pressure (Taubert et al 2007).

History of the first chocolate bars
- 1585 – cocoa exported to Europe
- 1800s – solid chocolate became popular with the invention of moulding processes
- 1825 – Dutchman Van Houten perfected the extraction of cocoa butter from cocoa beans
- 1848 – the first chocolate bar was made
- 1880s – Rudolphe Lindt of Switzerland started adding extra cocoa butter during chocolate manufacture, to make it smoother and glossier

References

Bruneton J 1995 Pharmacognosy, phytochemistry, medicinal plants. Intercept, Andover pp 889–891

Leung A Y, Foster S 1996 Encyclopedia of common natural ingredients. John Wiley & Sons, New York pp 181–184

Monograph 1991 Cacao semen. Bundesanzeiger no. 40 27 February. Cited in: Leung & Foster 1996

Stuart M (ed.) 1987 The encyclopedia of herbs and herbalism. Black Cat, London p.271

Tuabert D et al JAMA. 2007 Dark chocolate reduces blood pressure for short term. Journal of the American Medical Association 298:49–60.

Trease G E, Evans W C 1983 Pharmacognosy. 12th edition. Baillière Tindall, London p.335

Coconut oil

Scientific name
> *Cocos nucifera* L
> Family: Palmaceae

Etymology
> *Cocos* is Portuguese for monkey, as it was thought that the nut resembled a monkey's face: *nucifera* means bearing nuts.

The plant and its environment
> The palm tree grows to about 25m (80ft) and is of great commercial significance. The origin of the coconut is unknown, but it is believed to have spread from the Indian Ocean to Malaysia and Polynesia. The outer fibres of the coconut are impervious to salt water and when fruits from plants growing at the water's edge dropped into the sea they were taken by currents and tides throughout the South Sea Islands. Now, because of its economic importance, the coconut is cultivated in many tropical areas, especially Africa and south east Asia.

> The fruit is a large drupe with a hard endocarp and fibrous pericarp, the seed and its endocarp making up the commercial coconut. The seed albumin consists of the 'milk' and a solid – the copra, which contains about 65% lipids (Bruneton 1995).

> The tree, when fully grown at 30 years, will yield about 80 nuts a year, although it is reputed that some varieties can produce up to 200 nuts per year in bunches of 10–20. The extremely long leaves (up to 4–5m or 13–16ft) grow only at the top and so the trunk is ringed with the previous years' leaf scars.

> He who sees a straight coconut palm will go direct to heaven.
> **Indian saying**

The oil
> Coconut oil is a solid white, crystalline, highly saturated fat which melts at about 25°C, and has a distinctive, easily recognised odour. It is stable when exposed to air.

> When solid coconut oil is fractionated a clear liquid oil results. It is the fractionated oil which is commercially available but it is not a complete oil and its use in aromatherapy may therefore be questioned. Fractionated and

purified endosperm oil of the coconut (Thin Vegetable Oil of the BPC) contains triglycerides containing only the short and medium chain length fatty acids (e.g. octanoic, decanoic); it has low viscosity and solidifies at 0°C (Trease & Evans 1983)

Method of extraction

The extraction of oil from copra is one of the oldest seed crushing industries in the world.

Coconut oil can be obtained by cold pressing the flesh found inside the shell of the coconut.

The oil may be derived from the dried seed by boiling or pressure but it is often solvent extracted.

Principal constituents

Type	Based on	Content – %
C8.0	caprylic	11.0
C10.0	capric	8.0
C12.0	lauric	52.8
C14.0	myristic	16.0
C16:0	palmitic	6.0
C18:0	stearic	1.6
Typical saturated fatty acid unit content		86–95%
C18:1	oleic	3.5
Typical monounsaturated fatty acid unit content		3–6%
C18:2	linoleic	0.9
Typical polyunsaturated fatty acid unit content		1%

Glycerides: trimyristin, trilaurin, triolein, tristearin, tripalmitin also the glycerides of caprylic, capric and caproic acids.

Physical properties

Colour	white
Odour	odourless and tasteless
Melting point	25–27°C
Peroxide value	<3.0
Free fatty acid content	<1% max
Saponification value	258

Folklore and traditional plant uses

As it lathers easily coconut oil is used in the making of white soaps (especially those that will float in water); it is also a source of fatty alcohol for the manufacture of soapless detergent.

The hard shell is burned for charcoal and the coir (outer fibre) is a valuable raw material used in the manufacture of rope, mattresses, mats etc. Copra, the dried kernel of the coconut, no longer white but brown and shrivelled, yields two thirds by weight of the oil and the cake resulting from extraction provides animal fodder.

In India the coconut is considered to be the fruit of aspiration; a coconut is split at the beginning of functions to gain the blessing of the gods, whether launching a ship or making a film. The coconut provides milk, water, cream, and oil to Ayurvedic medicine for use in the treatment of burns, hair loss, dissolution of kidney stones, heart and circulatory problems (Patnaik 1993).

Therapeutic properties – internal use

The fractionated oil contains triacylglycerols with a medium chain length (principally C_{12} and C_{14}) and it is used in the diet of cystic fibrosis sufferers. This is because the high proportion of medium chain length fatty acids make the oil more easily absorbed by the gastrointestinal tract (Evans 1996).

It is used in suppositories because it softens and melts at body temperature.

Therapeutic properties – external use

The oil is frequently used in massage creams because of its emollient properties.

Cosmetic use

Coconut oil makes the skin smooth and satin–like, although it has been known to cause skin rashes. It is much used as an emollient for the skin and as hair pomade and because of its lubricating properties the oil is used in lipstick and soap formulations. Many hair conditioners contain coconut oil because it is beneficial to dry hair, and those tropical races who anoint their hair with coconut oil from childhood seldom go grey or bald. The oil aids tanning and does not filter the sun's rays.

Culinary use

The deodorized fat has been used as a substitute for butter and in the manufacture of margarine.

Cautions
Coconut oil can cause allergic skin rashes in some people (Winter 1999 p.134), especially the solvent extracted oil.

Additional notes
1   Cocos nucifera is a tree with many uses – but here we are concerned with the oil and the oil–rich copra that the tree produces.
2   The oil lathers well in both hard and salt water and it was first used in the western world for the manufacture of soap (first patented in 1841).
3   With the discovery of hydrogenation the margarine industry started using vegetable oil in preference to the more expensive animal fats; the first patent for making margarine from coconut oil was taken out in 1896. Coconut oil is still widely used in the manufacture of margarine.
4   The fact that it has good keeping qualities, due to its high saturated fat content, makes it attractive to industry because it prolongs the shelf life of products.
5   The coconut was the major source of vegetable oil until it was surpassed by soya beans in 1962 and since then it has been relegated to fifth place.
6   The oil is used in the production of margarine, soap, candles, cosmetics and a cocoa butter substitute.
7   It has been estimated that there are more than 500,000,000 coconut palm trees in plantations across the world, especially in India, Philippines, Indonesia, and Ceylon.
8   The fibre of the nut husk is called coir.
9   The white meat of the nut is eaten raw or is shredded and dried for use in confections. When dried for industrial purposes, it is called copra.
10   The liquid in the core of the nut, known as coconut milk, is a tasty beverage.
11   Palm wine, arrack, and vinegar are made from the sap of the flower stalk.
12   Baskets and mats are made from the leaves.
13   The trunk yields a useful timber.

References
Bruneton J 1995 Pharmacognosy, phytochemistry, medicinal plants. Intercept, Andover p.136
Evans W C 1996 Trease and Evans' pharmacognosy. Saunders, London p.187
Patnaik N 1993 The garden of life. Aquarian, London
Trease G E, Evans W C 1983 Pharmacognosy. Baillière Tindall, London p.333
Winter R 1999 A consumer's dictionary of cosmetic ingredients. Three Rivers Press, New York

Cohune nut oil

Scientific name

Attalea cohune, Orbignya cohune

Family: Palmaceae (Arecaceae)

Etymology

The genus Attalea was named after an ancient Middle Eastern king, Attalus III Philometor, who was very interested in medicinal plants. The species name, *cohune*, is the aboriginal name for this palm (new Latin, perhaps from American Spanish, from Mosquito *ókhún*). The tree has the common name 'rain tree' (due to the cascading leaves), *corozo, coquito, coco de aceite*: the oil is also called cohoun nut oil.

The plant and its environment

The cohune palm tree grows in western Central America from the Yucatán Peninsula to Honduras. The young palms grow with their trunk underground for many years and the adult tree has dark green, feather–shaped leaves extending almost straight up. A leaf can be up to 33ft (10m) long and the tree grows to a height of 20–50ft (6–15m) or more and 1–2ft (0.3–0.6m) in diameter. Cohune palms may have all male flowers, all female or both on the same tree. The cream coloured flower clusters are up to 5 ft (1.5m) long and the brownish yellow fruits are oval in shape; they may have three seeds and are carried on long drooping stalks (peduncles) from November to February.

The oil

The kernels are 65–70% oil, but they amount to only about 10% of the weight of the whole nut. There is little information on the therapeutic use of this oil, but the kernel oil is somewhat similar to coconut nut oil.

Extraction

Collection and transportation of the nuts is difficult; they are extremely hard, difficult to crack and there is a high ratio of shell to kernel. The pressure required to crack the nuts is estimated at between 4 and 9 tonnes. Many nuts are cracked by hand using sharp knives, an extremely laborious task, and the oil is extracted by small expellers. Some seeds are heated prior to expelling.

Principal constituents (Godin 1971)

Type	Based on	Content – %
Saturated fatty acids:		
C8:0	caprylic acid	7
C10:0	capric acid	4 – 7
C12:0	lauric acid	47
C14:0	myristic acid	16
C16:0	palmitic acid	10
C18:0	stearic acid	3
Total saturated fatty acid content		90
Monounsaturated fatty acid:		
C18:1	oleic acid	10
C18:2	linoleic acid	1
Total unsaturated fatty acid content		11

Cosmetic uses

The properties of cohune oil are similar to those of coconut oil: it is used in soap making.

Culinary

When refined the oil is suitable for margarine production, baking and biscuit making. The fruits of the cohune palm are made into sweet meats.

Cautions

The solvent extracted oil may cause a reaction in some people.

Additional notes

1   The cohune palm is a valuable source of oil and was one of the most important trees in the Mayan culture; all parts of the tree have their uses.
2   The seeds yield cohune oil which is used extensively as a lubricant, for cooking, soap making and lamp oil.
3   Damaged kernels can be used as cattle feed.
4   The shells are a good source of fuel.
5   The cake remaining after oil extraction is used as livestock feed.
6   The heart of the cohune palm, located in the last four feet of the trunk before the base of the leaf stems, is considered a delicacy.
7   Cohune leaves are used as thatching material for roofs.
8   Palm wine is produced from the sap of the heart of the cohune.
9   The related *A. funifera* of the Amazon region of South America yields a water–resistant fibre.

References

Godin N J, Spensley P C 1971 Oils and oilseeds. Crop and Product Digests: no. 1, Tropical Products Institute p.30–32

Corn oil

Scientific name
   Zea mays
   Family: Graminaceae, Poaceae

Etymology
   Also known as Indian corn and maize. *Zea* is
the Greek name for a related plant and *mays* is
from the Mexican.

The plant and its environment
   Corn or maize, which can grow to a height of about
4m (12ft) is native to the central Americas and was used by
the Aztecs, the Incas and the Mayans, who worshipped this
plant. No wild maize has ever been discovered and it is
assumed that our present day plants are hybrids dating back to pre–history. It
was one of the plants brought back to Europe by the modern discoverer of
America, Christopher Columbus. Once established in Europe it was not long
before this nutritious plant spread to Africa and the East.

The oil
   Pure corn germ oil is a clear light yellow and stores well as its high
vitamin E content (0.6%) helps to prevent oxidation. It is a semi drying oil.

Method of extraction
   Corn oil is usually extracted from the corn germ by means of steam and
pressure. An oil of a lesser quality may be derived from the whole kernel, when
the oil produced is of an orange hue. It is because of the practice of steaming,
bleaching and recolouring that this oil is not generally favoured for use in
aromatherapy. Cold pressed oil is not available, as there is only 6% oil in the
embryo.

Principal constituents
   Corn oil consists predominantly of unsaturated fatty acids (around
65%–80%) comprising about 58% linoleic acid and 1.5% alpha–linolenic acid,
oleic and arachidic acids, helping us to assimilate fat when used in cooking:
the saturated palmitic and stearic fatty acids are present only in small
quantities. It is a source of omega 6 fatty acids.

Type	Based on	Content – %
Saturated fatty acids:		
C12:0	lauric acid	<0.3
C14:0	myristic acid	<0.3
C16:0	palmitic acid	9.0–14.0
C18:0	stearic acid	0.5–4.0
C20:0	arachidic acid	<1.0
C22:0	behenic acid	<0.5
C24:0	lignoceric acid	<0.5
Total saturated fatty acid content		14
Monounsaturated fatty acid:		
C16:1	palmitoleic acid	<0.5
C18:1	oleic acid	24–42
Total monounsaturated fatty acid content		28
Polyunsaturated fatty acid:		
C18:2	linoleic acid	34–62
C18:3	α–linolenic acid	<2.0
Total polyunsaturated fatty acid content		58

Physical properties

Acid value (mg KOH/g oil)	0.2 max
Peroxide value (meq/k oil)	2.0 max
Refractive index at 40°C	1.4640–1.4690
Colour (Lovibond 5¼" cell)	2.5 red max
Iodine value (wijs)	103–131
Saponification value	187–193
Unsaponifiable matter (%)	2.0 max
Specific gravity at 25°C	0.915–0.920
Energy value Kcal/100ml	901

Vitamin and mineral content

The oil contains the vitamins A, B1, B2, C and E. The corn kernel germ surpasses wheatgerm with respect to its content of vitamin E, iron, zinc and fibre. It is also a good source of potassium, magnesium and copper.

Therapeutic properties – internal use

A tablespoonful (15ml) of this oil taken at meal times is reported to help such ailments as asthma, eczema, hay fever and migraine

The oil is said to be anticholesterol, and is also a great help for skin problems in small children and for neuro-dermatitis because it brings vitamins A and E to the body (Clergeaud & Clergeaud 2000).

91

Cosmetic uses

Corn oil is used mainly in emollient creams and toothpastes.

Culinary uses

Cheap and plentiful, this widely used cooking oil is produced on a large scale by the makers of corn flakes, cornflour and glucose. Used in margarine, chocolates, cheese spreads, and biscuits.

The best quality oil is delicate and should not be heated but used only for dressings

Contraindications

None known.

References

Clergeaud C, Clergeaud L 2000 Les huiles végétales. Atlantica, Biarritz

Cottonseed oil

Scientific name

Gossypium barbadense (plus various species)
Family: Malvaceae

Etymology

From the Latin *gossypinus*, gossypium–like, cotton–like.

The plant and its environment

Originally grown in India for the cotton fibre, the plant was introduced into China and Egypt about half a millennium BC and into the USA much later in 1774. There was a species grown in Peru predating the Egyptian cotton industry, and the use of cottonseed oil is mentioned in ancient Hindu writings. The plant forms a shrub growing to a height of 1.5m, bearing yellow flowers with a purple centre which lead to capsules containing the seeds and covered with trichomes, which are the source of cotton fibre.

The oil

Cotton oil is one of the big four (soy, corn, rapeseed/canola, cotton) genetically modified crops grown across the world. It must be treated to remove gossypol, a naturally occurring toxin that protects the cotton plant from insect damage.

Cottonseed oil is obtained from the seeds of *Gossypium barbadense* and other varieties; it is a bland, flavourless oil not liable to rancidity, being used for a great many purposes for external applications. Some seeds are almost bald and are known commercially as 'black', whereas others have a woolly lint on the outside and are known as 'white'; the former obviously produce more oil per seed weight (approximately 20–25%). Cottonseed oil has properties similar to *Hibiscus sabdariffa* (Malvaceae) which is used as a substitute for crude castor oil (Duke 1985).

Method of extraction

Cottonseed oil is extracted from the seeds after the cotton lint has been removed. The oil is hot expressed at high pressure (1500lb/in^2) resulting in a thick crude oil which must be refined.

93

Principal constituents

Type	Based on	Content – %
Saturated fatty acid:		
C16:0	palmitic acid	22–26
C20:0	arachidic acid	<4
C22:0	behenic	<4
C24:0	lignoceric	<1
Typical saturated fatty acid content		25
Monounsaturated fatty acid:		
C18:1	oleic acid	15–21
Polyunsaturated fatty acid:		
C18:2	linoleic acid	49–58
Typical unsaturated fatty acid content		75

Cosmetic use

Cottonseed oil is inexpensive and therefore it is used widely in soaps, creams, baby creams, nail polish remover and lubricants. It is not used in aromatherapy.

Culinary uses

As it is cheap it is used generally used for cooking e.g. in salad oils, for frying fish and is commonly used in manufacturing potato chips and other snack foods.. Kitchen tests show cottonseed oil to perform as well as or better than other oils, and to withstand higher temperatures than others.

Cautions

Cottonseed oil is known to cause allergies, but it is difficult to avoid this much used oil because it is so widely used in cosmetic preparations. The oil is cathartic, abortifacient; no part of the plant should be used internally unless prior medical advice is obtained.

Additional notes

1   Cottonseed oil has high antioxidant content and so has a long shelf life.
2   It costs less than many other oils, so it is attractive to restaurant owners and snack food manufacturers.
3   Unrefined cottonseed oil is sometimes used as a pesticide.
4   In its natural unhydrogenated state, cottonseed oil, like all vegetable oils, has no cholesterol. It contains no trans fatty acids but does contain over 50% omega–6 fatty acids and with trace amounts of omega–3 fatty acids, and this imbalance is considered unhealthy.

5   When processed, trans fatty acids are created which are cholesterol raising. CSIRO has used hairpinRNAi to silence the FAD2–1gene in cottonseed that normally converts oleic acid to polyunsaturated fatty acids. The resultant high–oleic cottonseed oil is suitable for cooking applications and does not contain the cholesterol raising trans fatty acids.

6   HairpinRNAi has also been successful in altering the proportions of saturated fatty acids in cottonseed oil so that stearate is produced rather than palmitate.

7   The ancient Chinese used the oil as a medicine and a lamp oil.

8   In Britain cottonseed oil used to be about 15% of the vegetable supply; in 1956 it was less than 3%.

9   Along with soybean oil, it is very often partially or fully hydrogenated. The growing consensus is that hydrogenated oils containing trans fatty acids are very unhealthy. Cottonseed oil was the first oil to be hydrogenated in mass production, originally intended for candle production, and soon also as a food

10   Researchers at the University of Michigan Comprehensive Cancer Center report that a compound used in Chinese medicine is to be found in cottonseed oil. This compound, (–)–gossypol, may help chemotherapy become more effective in patients suffering from cancers of the head and neck.

References

Liu *et al* 2002 Plant Physiology 129: 1732–1743
Duke J A 1985 Handbook of medicinal herbs. CRC Press, Boca Raton p.229
Reports on GM Canola from the Australian Department of Primary Industries

Cumin seed oil

Scientific name
Cuminum cyminum
Family: Apiaceae

Grind cumin seeds very fine. Add a drop of clarified butter and a pinch of sea salt. Grind fine
again. Wet and apply .... For scorpion stings
Treatise of Charaka – first century AD (quoted in Patnaik 1993 p.91)

Etymology
The name comes from the Greek word for the plant *kyminon*. It is known
as *jeera* in Hindi. Several kinds of cumin are recognised in India, the most
common being *safed* (white) and *kala* (black).

The plant and its environment
Cumin is native to Egypt and is a small annual plant growing to 30cm
(12in), with pink or white flowers (Chevallier 1996 p.194). The black cumin
plant comes from India, has blue flowers and forms a fruit pod with small
trihedral black seeds (Iburg 2004 p.287).

The Oil
This has a dark colour and is very rich in linoleic acid.

Extraction
The oil is cold pressed from the seeds

Therapeutic properties – internal use
It is said to regulate intestinal function and to have a positive influence
on allergies and stimulates the immune system (Lubinic 2003).

Therapeutic properties – external use
Cumin oil is indicated in cases of:
• skin irritation, prurigo
• allergic reactions
• dry skin, desquamation
• acne
• psoriasis
• eczema

Cosmetic uses

Used in creams, it softens the skin.

Culinary u ses

Cumin oil goes well with salads, vegetables and potatoes. It has a sharp spicy flavour, but is not suitable for heating because it loses its flavour very quickly and goes rancid (Iburg 2004 p.287). The seeds are used in curries and spice mixtures.

Folklore and traditional plant uses

Cumin seeds are advised in Ayurvedic practice for chronic dysentery and diarrhoea.

In India, they are considered a necessity in the diet of convalescents (Patnaik 1993 p.91).

In the east, cumin forms part of the diet for pregnant women to counter morning sickness.

Cautions

None known.

Additional notes

1   The plant contains cuminic aldehyde, which may have some antiviral properties (Winter 1999 p.147).
2   The aromatic oil was used for perfumes and liqueurs by neoclassical Europeans (Patnaik 1993 p.91)
3   Roasted cumin seeds are widely used in bread and cake recipes.
4   The seeds are used to make gripe water.
5   The seeds are lactogenic and are taken to improve breast milk production (Chevallier 1996 p.195).

References

Chevallier A 1996 The encyclopedia of medicinal plants. Dorling Kindersley, London
Lubinic E 2003 Manuel pratique d'aromathérapie. Vigot, Paris p.213
Iburg A 2004 Dumont's lexicon of oils and vinegars. Rebo, Lisse
Patnaik N 1993 The garden of life. Aquarian, London
Winter R 1999 A consumer's dictionary of cosmetic ingredients. 5th edn: Three Rivers Press, New York

Evening primrose oil

Scientific name
Oenothera biennis, O. glazioviana, (O. lamarkiana, O. riparia)
Family: Onagraceae

Etymology
Evening primrose is also known as 'king's cureall'; the name 'evening star' is less well–known and is due to the fact that the petals emit phosphorescent light at night.

The origin of the name Oenothera is uncertain but it may come from an older Greek plant name, *Oinotheras*, which signified that its roots were eaten to give an appetite for wine.

Glazioviana is after the botanist Glaziou (1828–1906), *riparia* means of the riverbank and *biennis* is Latin for biennial.

> It is an herbe good as wine to make the heart merry. Of such virtue is this herbe that if it be given to the wildest beast that there is, it will tame the same and make it gentle.
> **Pliny (quoted by Earle 1991)**

> It opens obstructions of the liver and spleen, provokes urine, is good for the dropsy if infused in common drink.
> **Culpeper 1650**

The plant and its environment
Native to North America, the evening primrose was introduced into Europe in 1619, and is now common in the Mediterranean; it is cultivated also in the UK. It has golden–yellow ephemeral flowers which burst into bloom in early evening and soon die, leading to the formation of pods containing tiny seeds (similar in size to mustard seed) from which the oil is obtained. The following evening the next circle of flowers blooms and so they progress toward the tip of the stem. It can grow almost anywhere – by riverbeds, on mountains, by the seashore and even in the desert.

The oil
Like borage oil, evening primrose oil is highly unsaturated (the seed contains up to 25% of an oil rich in unsaturated fatty acids) and is therefore more reactive and less stable than most other oils. It is yellow in colour and oxidizes on exposure to air and light, a process which is accelerated in the presence of heavy metals.

It must be emphasised that GLA is very fragile and can be rapidly destroyed by light, heat, humidity and the oxygen in the air. For this reason air should be excluded and the oil stored in a cool, dark place. GLA is rare in plants.

Method of extraction
The seeds are cold expressed to give a tiny quantity of oil.

Principal constituents

Type	Based on	Content – %
Saturated fatty acid units:		
C16:0	palmitic acid	6.5
C18:0	stearic acid	1.3
C20:0	arachidic acid	0.3
Typical saturated fatty acid unit content		8
Monounsaturated fatty acid units:		
C20:1	eicosenoic acid	0.2
Typical monounsaturated fatty acid unit content		0.2
Polyunsaturated fatty acid units:		
C18:2	linoleic acid	65–75
C18:3	α–linolenic acid	0.2
C18:3	gamma linolenic acid	8–10.5
Typical polyunsaturated fatty acid unit content		80

Physical properties

Acid value	1.0 max
Specific gravity	0.923
Colour	light yellow
Odour	pleasant
Taste	agreeable

Folklore and traditional plant uses
Native North Americans made an infusion of the seeds to be used for healing wounds. They also used the leaves and roots. Introduced to Europe in 1619 via the Padua Botanic Garden, the plant was described by the English herbalist John Parkinson in 1629, even though the evening primrose had rarely been used for medicinal purposes.

As late as the nineteenth century in Germany, pickled *O. biennis* roots were still eaten as an aperitif.

Therapeutic properties – internal use

Evening primrose oil contains gamma–linolenic acid (GLA) which is now known to lower blood cholesterol (Bartram 1996) and is therefore extremely useful in the prevention of heart disease. Both linoleic and gamma–linolenic acids are classified as 'essential fatty acids' – vitamin–like materials which are vital for cell and body function but which cannot be made by the body itself (WHO 1990).

Evening primrose oil is claimed to be useful in treating degenerative disease and is said to reduce blood pressure, inhibit thrombosis, control arthritis, treat atopic eczema (Lovell 1981, 1993), decrease hyperactivity in children and help in dealing with alcoholism (by reversing liver degeneration), PMT (Horrobin 1983) and schizophrenia (Barber 1988, Horrobin 1990, Li Wan Po 1991) (the Schizophrenia Association recommend evening primrose oil, vitamins B3, B6, and C, and zinc on a daily basis). Atopic eczema treatment using evening primrose oil is contested by Berth–Jones & Graham–Brown (1993).

It is now thought by some that evening primrose oil is of no real benefit in the small doses usually prescribed, although diabetics have used it to lessen the need for insulin; trials have shown that the oil has significantly improved sensory function in diabetics (Bartram 1996).

Gamma linolenic fatty acid is a direct precursor of E1 prostaglandins and opposes the effects of the protein prolactin which is implicated in premenstrual problems, abdominal bloating, migraines and water retention (Europhyto–Institut).

Evening primrose oil helps anxiety, insomnia and depression: workers in India have reported that evening primrose oil kills tumour cells in association with a marked increase in free radical generation (Ramesh 1992).

Therapeutic properties – external use
- useful for dry scaly skin
- dandruff conditions
- has benefited those with psoriasis (Ferrando 1986)
- helpful for eczema (Kerscher & Korting 1992)
- accelerates wound healing
- for hormone problems (e.g. menopause and painful periods because of its high vitamin F content)
- schizophrenia; it is used in a 25% dilution with a fixed oil e.g. grapeseed.
- premenstrual syndrome, but there is contradictory evidence (Collins *et al* 1993)

Cosmetic use

The oil can be used in anti wrinkle preparations at levels of around 20%; one recommendation is to apply one or two drops daily alternating with borage oil. Once the triacylglycerol is broken down the GLA is used by the body in the repair and maintenance of skin tissue.

Culinary use

Up to the 19th century the pickled roots were eaten as an aperitif in Germany. All parts of the plant are edible and the boiled young roots may be eaten hot or cold.

Cautions

1 As has been said, oils rich in GLA units can act as building blocks for powerful hormone–like substances that have far reaching effects on all body organs and processes, so oral intake of the oil for long periods of time is not recommended (Mindell 1991).

2 There are a few reports of unwanted side effects (headache, nausea, mild diarrhoea) when taking GLA supplements (Briggs 1986, Horrobin 1990).

3 Chevallier (1996) warns against taking evening primrose oil if suffering from epilepsy.

4 Borage oil has been used as an adulterant in order to increase the GLA content.

5 Because the flowers contain such a low content of oil, some producers are tempted to use solvents for extraction followed by a refining process, which completely denatures the product (Goëb 1998 p.44)

6 It is a fragile oil, sensitive to oxygen, heat and light and therefore must be stored properly (Goëb 1998 p.44).

Additional notes

1 It is thought that evening primrose contains a compound capable of reducing the rate of blood clotting or thrombosis information, and hence possibly acting as prophylactic against some forms of heart attack.

2 Uses of the fresh whole plant, fresh root and seeds are as antispasmodic, nutritive, demulcent, weak astringent, vulnerary, anticoagulant and may be applied externally as a poultice or in ointments in the treatment of minor wounds or skin eruptions: may be used internally for coughs, colds, gastric irritation and intestinal spasm.

3 A direct effect on the liver is suspected but not proven.

References

Barber H J 1988 Evening primrose oil: a panacea? Pharm Journal 240: 723–725

Bartram T 1996 Encyclopedia of herbal medicine. Grace, Christchurch p.175

Berth–Jones J, Graham–Brown R A C 1993 Placebo controlled trial of essential fatty acid supplementation in atopic dermatitis. Lancet 341:1557–1560

Briggs C J 1986 Evening primrose. Rev Pharm Canad, 119: 249–254

Chevallier A 1996 The encyclopedia of medicinal plants. Dorling Kindersley, London p.239

Collins A, Cerin A, Coleman G, Langren B M 1993 Essential fatty acids in the treatment of premenstrual syndrome. Obstetrics & Gynaecology 81:93–98

Earle L 1991 Vital oils. Ebury, London

Europhyto–Institut undated La phytothérapie: la santé par les plantes. Editions Alpen, Monaco p.60

Ferrando J 1986 Clinical trial of topical preparation containing urea, sunflower oil, evening primrose oil, wheatgerm oil and sodium pyruvate, in several hyperkeratotic skin conditions. Med Cutan Lat Am, 14(2): 132–137

Goëb Ph 1998 Connaître l'essentiel sur les huiles essentielles. IAPM, Tamil Nadu p.44

Horrobin D F 1983 The role of essential fatty acids and prostaglandins in the premenstrual syndrome. Journal Reprod Med. 28: 465–468

Horrobin D F 1990 Gamma linolenic acid: an intermediate in essential fatty acid metabolism with potential as an ethical pharmaceutical and as a food. Rev Contemp Pharmacother. 1: 1–45

Kerscher M J, Korting H C 1992 Treatment of atopic eczema with evening primrose oil: rationale and clinical results. Clinical Investigation Feb. 70(2): 720–721

Li Wan Po 1991 Evening primrose oil. Pharm Journal 246: 670–676

Lovell C R et al 1981 Treatment of atopic eczema with evening primrose oil. The Lancet 1(8214): 278

Lovell C R 1993 Plants and the skin. Blackwell Scientific, Oxford p.255

Mindell E 1991 Evening primrose oil: what is it? The Vitamin Connection, July/August p.38

Ramesh et al 1992 Effect of essential fatty acids on tumour cells. Nutrition, 8(5): 343–347

WHO 1990 Diet, nutrition and the prevention of chronic diseases. WHO

Grapeseed oil

Scientific name
Vitis vinifera
Family: Vitaceae

Etymology
Vinifera is from the Latin meaning wine bearing and *vitis* is Latin for the vine.

The plant and its environment
The plant is a deciduous climbing vine (with tendrils) which grows to a length of perhaps 20–30m (70–100ft). The cultivated vine has hermaphrodite flowers while wild forms are unisexual. There are about 3000 cultivated varieties, all with grapes that usually contain no more than two seeds.

The oil
First produced in France, grapeseed oil is now produced mainly in Spain, Italy, California and also Argentina. Grape seeds yield a high quality oil which is edible and it is now widely known thanks to its food and dietetic properties.

The refined oil keeps fairly well, is tasteless and almost colourless. A very fine oil, it is used to lubricate watches.

Method of extraction
Vine growing regions produce large quantities of grapes and after vinification and distillation the wasted grape seeds are washed, dried, ground and pressed with the aid of heat (necessary because there is only 13% oil in the seeds). The extracted oil may be refined to improve clarity and flavour. Many processes use chemical solvents in the extraction process and it is rarely available cold pressed at low temperature – typically below 80°C (176°F) – because of the poor yield.

103

Principal constituents

Type	Based on	Content – %
Saturated fatty acid units:		
C14:0	myristic acid	<0.3
C16:0	palmitic acid	5.0–11.0
C18:0	stearic acid	3.0–6.0
C20:0	arachidic acid	<1.0
C22:0	behenic acid	<0.3
Typical saturated fatty acid unit content		11
Monounsaturated fatty acid units:		
C16:1	palmitoleic acid	<1.0
C18:1	oleic acid	12–20
Typical monounsaturated fatty acid unit content		20
Polyunsaturated fatty acid units:		
C18:2	linoleic acid	58–81
C18:3	α–linolenic acid	<1.0
Typical polyunsaturated fatty acid unit content		69

Physical properties

Odour	little or no smell
Acid value	0.2 max
Specific gravity	0.915–0.925
Energy value Kcal/100ml	905
Iodine value	123–143

Vitamin

Contains vitamin E (0.8 to 1.2g/kg), vitamin C and β–carotene and perhaps vitamin D.

Folklore and traditional plant uses

It is believed that this oil was first produced during times of hardship in Napoleonic France. Michelet refers to a grapeseed oil mill in Tarn at a time when France was struggling to feed herself; an added bonus was that the oil could also be used for lighting.

Therapeutic properties – internal use

Grapeseed oil is easily digested and does not contain any cholesterol

It has been suggested that it may help increase HDL (good) and reduce LDL (bad) cholesterol

Therapeutic properties – external use

Grapeseed oil leaves the skin with a smooth satin finish without being greasy. It reduces the appearance of stretch marks.

Cosmetic use

Being non–toxic and hypoallergenic, grapeseed oil is much used in skin creams (Price 1987). It is used as a cosmetic ingredient for damaged tissues because it is alleged to have regenerative properties, said to be good for the skin around the eyes.

Culinary use

It is easy to digest and because it contains little or no cholesterol it is suitable for dietary and culinary use by those with hypertension or arteriosclerosis. The smoke point of grapeseed oil is 216°C (420°F) and so can be used in high temperature cooking. The neutral taste enables it to be used for salad dressings and for mayonnaise.

Cautions

Grapeseed oil has no known contraindications and is non–toxic (Winter 1999 p.226).

References

Price S 1994 Practical aromatherapy. Thorsons, London
Winter R 1999 A consumer's dictionary of cosmetic ingredients. 5th edn: Three Rivers Press, New York

Sources

Foster S, Tyler V E 1999 Tyler's Honest Herbal. 4th edn The Haworth Herbal Press, New York p.201–203

Hazelnut oil

Scientific name
  Corylus avellana
  Family: Corylaceae

Etymology
  Also known as the cobnut or filbert. The name in French is *noisette* and in German *haselnuss*. *Korylos* is the Greek name for the plant and *avellana* denotes that it is from Avella Vecchia in S. Italy.

The plant and its environment
  This small deciduous tree of 3m (10ft) is native to the whole of northern Europe, where it can be seen growing wild, although it may have originated in Greece. It is monoclinous (hermaphrodite) and so has both male and female flowers on the one tree. The male flowers, long, yellow catkins, which appear in February or March are a conspicuous feature. Female flowers are not so conspicuous; they are tight around the bud to give protection from the frost. 1, 2 or 3 nuts can develop in autumn from a female flower
  The Turkish hazel tree, which reaches a height of 20m and is pyramidal in shape, is the most grown tree in Turkey: the nuts are used for oil (Iberg 2004 p.176–178)

The oil
  Hazelnut oil is amber–yellow in colour and has a very pleasant taste. The oil is often used as a substitute for almond oil, to which it has a similar composition (Bruneton 1995) but is less viscous.

Method of extraction
  The oil is usually obtained by cold pressing, after which it is left for a few days for the sediment to settle before filtering. The yield is almost 40% by weight.

Principal constituents

Type	Based on	Content – %
Saturated fatty acid units:		
C14:0	myristic acid	<0.2
C16:0	palmitic acid	4.0–10.0
C18:0	stearic acid	1.0–4.0
C20:0	arachidic acid	<1.0
Typical saturated fatty acid unit content		9
Monounsaturated fatty acid units:		
C16:1	palmitoleic acid	<0.2
C18:1	oleic acid	70–84
Typical monounsaturated fatty acid unit content		74
Polyunsaturated fatty acid units:		
C18:2	linoleic acid	9–19
C18:3	α–linolenic acid	<1.0
Typical polyunsaturated fatty acid unit content		17

Physical properties

Odour	a pleasant, characteristic smell
Colour	orange–yellow
Acid value	0.2 max
Specific gravity	0.910–0.920
Energy value Kcal/100ml	893
Vitamin E /100ml	35mg

Therapeutic properties – internal use

Hazelnut oil is said to be digestive and vermifuge, and is used internally in cases of urinary stones, kidney colic and tapeworms. It is recommended for adolescents, old people, pregnant women and diabetics.

Therapeutic properties – external use

- said to penetrate the skin quickly (Goëb 1998) – (see Ch. 3)
- nourishing to the skin
- light astringent action
- stimulating to the circulation
- does not leave the skin feeling greasy
- often used for oily skins
- in cases of acne, sometimes diluted with grapeseed, sunflower or other base oil

107

- a good base for muscular problems (Goëb 1998 p.43)
- soothing to nappy rash
- relieves dry eczema

Cosmetic use

Studies, carried out for the Institute for Technological Research in Chile by Bio–Tox Labs in France (INTEC 1992), have shown that hazelnut oil acts as a natural sun filter with a factor equivalent to 10 in the FDA category. The oil is recommended for cosmetics such as sun lotions and creams, hair regenerators, shampoos, soaps etc.

Culinary use

For culinary use, the nuts are roasted before pressing, to increase the flavour. The resulting oil, tasting of hazelnuts, is excellent in salad dressings and baking. Noisette is much prized by French cooks and is found in many cakes and pastries.

It goes well with fresh or dried tomatoes and courgettes; mixed with a little lemon juice it adds flavour to shellfish and can also be used on fresh strawberries.

Cautions

1   Hazelnuts are reported as causing immunological contact urticaria and possibly anaphylaxis (Lovell 1993).
2   Cheaper oils are often added to this expensive oil, not always obvious from the label.

Additional notes

The nuts contain minerals (magnesium, potassium), vitamins (B1, B6, E, niacin, folic acid), fat (64/100g), MUFA (50/100g).

References

Bruneton J 1995 Pharmacognosy, phytochemistry, medicinal plants. Intercept, Andover p.124
Goëb Ph 1998 Connaître l'essentiel sur les huiles essentielles. IAPM, Tamil Nadu p.43
INTEC 1992 Gathering and industrialisation of Chilean hazelnut oil. Report sponsored by the Agricultural Planning Office (ODEPA): 13
Lovell C R 1993 Plants and the skin. Blackwell Scientific, Oxford p.36
Iberg A 2004 Dumont's lexicon of oil & vinegar. Rebo, Lisse

Hemp seed oil

Scientific name

Cannabis sativa

Family: Cannabinaceae

Etymology

Known as true hemp, *cannabis* is the Latin and the Greek name for the plant. It is known as *bhang* in Hindi. There are other plants which are given the name hemp: henequen, sisal, and bowstring hemp belong to the family Agavaceae; Manila hemp belongs to the Musaceae family; sunn hemp is obtained from *Crotalaria juncea*, Leguminosae.

The plant and its environment

Hemp is the common name for an Asian annual herb grown for cannabis and for its strong, pliable fibres. It is cultivated in Eurasia, United States and Chile. The plants may vary in height approximately from 1m (3ft) to 5m (15ft) depending upon the climate and soil type. The male plant bears flowers in axillary racemes and dies soon after pollination, while the female plant bears flowers in short, crowded spikes and dies after the seed matures: both are used for their fibres.

The oil

The hemp seed oil available does not contain the psychoactive substances present in the plant. The green colour of the oil is similar to dark olive oil.

Principal constituents

Type	Based on	Content – %
Saturated fatty acids:		
C16:0	palmitic acid	6
C18:0	stearic acid	2
Typical saturated fatty acid content		8
Monounsaturated fatty acid:		
C18:1	oleic acid	12
Typical monounsaturated fatty acid content		12
Polyunsaturated fatty acid:		
C18:2	linoleic	55
C18:3	linolenic	25
Typical polyunsaturated fatty acid content		80

Folklore and traditional plant uses

The flowers and leaves of hemp are used to produce the narcotics bhang, hashish, and marijuana.

The pain killing and antinausea properties of cannabis for those suffering from multiple sclerosis and cancer are widely known, but little is known of the beneficial properties of hemp seed oil.

A drink called bhang, based on hemp, milk, herbs, almonds, etc, was widely used in India in religious and other festivals (Patnaik 1993 p.34).

Culinary uses

The oil has a flavour similar to sunflower oil; it may be blended with other oils to produce a milder flavour (Iburg 2004 p.288). Hempseed oil can be ingested safely and used on salads and cold dishes but should not be heated because of the GLA content. It is thought that for optimum nutrition a ratio of omega–6 to omega–3 of 3:1 is desirable and hemp fits this requirement.

Additional notes

1   An 11 year old suffering from itchy eczema found that steroid treatment did not help, but found relief when she took 3 tsp of hemp oil three times a day; over a period of several weeks her skin became smoother and less irritable.

2   Hempseed yields an oil used in the manufacture of soap and oil paints and the seeds themselves are widely used as birdseed.

3   A resin, called charas, produced by female flower heads and seeds of hemp, is used in narcotic smoking mixtures in India. Hemp seeds can be used to make 'hemp butter', of greater nutritional value than peanut butter (Erasmus 1986)

4   Hempseed oil is subject to restrictions because of the tetrahydrocannabiol content, and it is only permitted to grow hempseeds that are free of this (Iburg 2004 p.288).

5   Ayurvedic medicine used hemp for the alleviation of migraine headaches and stomach spasms.

Sources and references

Notes from Dr. John Briffa and Encarta 95
Erasmus U 1986 Fats and oils. Alive, Vancouver p.232
Iburg A 2004 Dumont's lexicon of oil and vinegar. Rebo, Lisse
Patnaik N 1993 The garden of life. Aquarian, London

Jojoba wax

Scientific name

    Simmondsia sinensis (Link.) C K Schneider, *Buxus sinensis*
    Family: Buxaceae

Etymology

    Named after Mr Simmonds, *sinensis* means of or from China and *buxus* refers to the box plant. It is also known as the goat nut, and coffee berry.

The plant and its environment

    Simmondsia chinensis is a woody, evergreen, desert shrub indigenous to the American Sonoran Desert. This perennial leathery–leaved shrub grows well in arid and semi–dry areas, growing naturally in the desert regions of Southern California, Arizona and north–west Mexico. The plant, which is either male or female, grows slowly and the female bush only begins to bear seeds in its fifth year. It takes 12 years to achieve maturity, when it reaches a height of 0.5–2.0m (2–7ft).

    The jojoba plant is characterized by the blue–green leaves with a thick cuticle which limits water loss. The hulls of the fruit turn from green to brown before they crack and allow the seed to fall to the ground. The seeds produced in the summer are similar in appearance to coffee beans, being a dark, reddish–brown colour; they are about 1–1.5cm long.

The oil

    Jojoba is not an oil but a light golden coloured liquid wax. This is because it is not composed of triacylglycerols but of wax esters formed from long chain fatty acids and long chain fatty alcohols: thus jojoba is a complex mixture of naturally occurring long chain linear esters (97%) , with tocopherols, free sterols and other unsaponifiable material.

    The oil does not oxidize easily, has good thermal stability and does not become rancid, therefore it has a long shelf life and remains chemically unchanged for a period of years – it may be kept for 25 years without problem. If left in a very cold place or a fridge it will solidify, but will quickly liquefy at an ambient temperature of 10°C.

Method of extraction

    Approximately 50–60% of the weight of the seed is a liquid wax (consisting of a mixture of long–chain esters) which is extracted by mechanical

111

pressing. Extraction of jojoba from seeds in good condition yields a clean product that requires minimal processing and/or refining. There may be some small variation in the properties of the wax depending on the condition of the seed when crushed, although the properties do not vary greatly from year to year. After mechanical extraction jojoba is usually screened to remove tiny bits of sediment called 'footes' and then filtered: it is then pasteurized in an insulated tank to ensure product quality.

Four grades of jojoba are produced: apart from the natural, golden type other grades are produced for the cosmetics industry namely (1) refined and bleached (2) decolorized and deodorized (3) molecular distilled

Principal constituents

Type	Based on	Content – %
Saturated fatty acid units:		
C16:0	palmitic acid	11
C18:0	stearic acid	71
C20:0	arachidic acid	14
C22:0	behenic acid	1
Other		2
Typical saturated fatty acid unit content		93
Monounsaturated fatty acid units:		
C16:1	palmitoleic acid	0.1
C18:1	oleic acid	6.7
Typical monounsaturated fatty acid unit content		6
Polyunsaturated fatty acid units:		
C18:2	linoleic acid	0.3
C18:3	linolenic acid	0.2
Typical polyunsaturated fatty acid unit content		0.5
Fatty alcohol unit content:		
C18:0	octadecanol	1
C20:0	eicosanol	44
C22:0	docosanol	45
C24:0	tetracosanol	9
Other		trace
Typical fatty alcohol unit content		100

Physical properties

Odour	slightly sweet
Acid value	<1.0
Specific gravity	0.863–0.865

Colour Lovibond	50–60 yellow, 3.0–5.0 red
Iodine Value	78–90
Saponification Number	85–100

Folklore and traditional plant uses

Members of the Pueblo tribe, native to Mexico and south–western USA, crushed the jojoba seeds to produce an oil to use on their skin and hair to combat the drying effects of the desert sun. Warm jojoba oil eased their aches and pains, and was also used on skin abrasions. The Seri used jojoba to care for inflamed eyes, colds and sore throats, and it was used for wounds that refused to heal; it was topically applied to head sores (Duke 1985).

Early Spanish explorers and missionaries recorded that the native Amerindian inhabitants of the American Sonoran Desert used jojoba for sundry cosmetic and medicinal purposes, such as hair dressings, body oils, and skin salves. In addition, they attributed 'mystical' powers to jojoba, claiming that it could alleviate many ailments and cure cuts, scratches, and open sores. The Spanish missionaries also became jojoba users, with Father Valardes in 1716 referring to the plant as the 'wondrous gift of the desert'. Early settlers used the seeds as survival food and the seeds were roasted and used as a coffee substitute (Leung & Foster 1996).

Therapeutic properties – internal use
- The seeds have the reputation of being appetite depressant
- The oil is not readily broken down by the digestive juices, thus it has a more direct beneficial action on the intestines (Bartram 1996)
- Bruneton (1995) notes that if rats are fed jojoba oil, there are changes in histological and enzymatic activity observed in the small intestine, which probably preclude any dietary use

Therapeutic properties – external use
- contains myristic acid which is an antiinflammatory agent, thus the oil can be beneficial in mixes for arthritis and rheumatism
- beneficial to all types of skin
- dry scalp
- psoriasis
- eczema
- sunburn
- chapped skin and nappy rash (Bartram 1996)
- molecular structure similar to sebum which makes it useful in cases of *acne vulgaris*

113

- controls accumulation of excessive sebum and reportedly prevent its build–up (Anon 1983)
- it is claimed that jojoba can reduce superficial facial lines by 11% after eight hours

There is evidence that jojoba can permeate the skin. Photographs have been produced showing the oil in a 'pool' at the base of a hair and moving through the follicle wall into the corneal layer (Anon 1985). Jojoba is able to penetrate and dissolve any build up of sebum clogging hair follicles which perhaps may lead to problems and this may be because jojoba is comprised of monounsaturated fatty acids and alcohols, has a comparatively low saponification value, contains little lecithin, has a low viscosity and low saponification number.

Cosmetic use

Jojoba (like other wax esters in nature) resists hydrolysis and oxidation, giving it the properties of non–occlusive, moisture control and photo protection on the external surfaces of skin and hair (also the plant leaves).

After hydrogenation it remains solid up to 65°C and is second in hardness to carnauba wax, used for creams, lotions, soaps, and lipsticks; it is a good non–greasy lubricant. It forms a matrix with other waxes for holding pigments and oils in lipsticks, replacing petroleum waxes (Wilson 1992).

It is much used in skin care as it is balancing to the acid mantle of the skin, thus is useful dry, oily and mixed skin. It does not leave a greasy feel to the skin and it is beneficial on all skin types after depilation. Uses include:

- facial: moisturizers, cleansers, scrubs, masks, eye make–up remover, make–up, shaving lotions and after–shave creams
- body: bath oils, moisturisers, hand creams, foot care products and massage oils
- baby care: lotions, creams & oils
- hair care: jojoba is used in many commercial soaps, shampoos, hair conditioners, hair tonics, hair sprays, hair oils, scalp treatments, wave set lotions, stick pomades and hair creams
- sun care: sun protection and self–tanning products, tan extending products, after–sun creams and lotions and lip balm
- nail and cuticle care: cuticle oil, cuticle remover, nail hardener

Culinary

The oil is suitable for cooking because it remains essentially unchanged after repeated heating to temperatures above 285°C; there was no degradation in general composition and carbon chain length after being heated to 370°C for four days (Anon 1983).

Cautions

1 Jojoba oil may cause an allergic reaction (Winter 1999 p.265) and contact dermatitis has also been reported (Scott & Scott 1982). See internal use above.

2 CIR Expert Panel and Journal of the American College of Toxicology concluded that jojoba is safe as a cosmetic ingredient in concentrations from 0.1% to 25%.

Additional notes

1 At one time the sperm whale was killed for its spermaceti wax and was an endangered species. Spermaceti wax is a mixture of long chain esters and was much used in cosmetic preparations. Then it was discovered that jojoba could be used as an alternative to sperm whale oil (spermaceti) in cosmetics (cf camelina oil qv) and now for more than a quarter of a century the use of jojoba oil, instead of the wax formerly extracted from the whale, has saved thousands of these animals.

2 Jojoba seeds were originally hand picked from bushes growing in the wild and supply was limited but the plant has been grown commercially since 1979 and today there is a reliable supply of the oil from many millions of jojoba trees grown in irrigated orchards.

3 It can be planted to help prevent arid land from becoming desert.

4 University of Michigan studies revealed that jojoba does not support the growth of common micro organisms including pathogens such as *Staphylococcus aureus*, *Pseudomonas aeruginosa*, and *Candida albicans*.

References

Anon 1983 Botanicals in cosmetics. Jojoba: a botanical with proven functionality. Cosmetics & Toiletries June 98:81–82

Anon 1985 Jojoba: new crop for arid lands, new raw material for industry. US National Research Council. National Academy Press, Washington.

Bartram T 1996 Encyclopedia of herbal medicine. Grace, Christchurch p.258

Scott M J, Scott M J Jr 1982 Jojoba oil (Letter). Journal American Ac of Dermatol. 6: 545

Bruneton J 1995 Pharmacognosy, phytochemistry, medicinal plants. Intercept, Andover p.146

Duke J A 1985 Handbook of medicinal herbs. CRC Press, Boca Raton pp 444–445

Leung A Y, Foster S 1996 Encyclopedia of common natural ingredients. John Wiley & Sons, New York pp 322–323

Wilson R 1992 Drug & Cosmetics Industry 43

Winter R 1999 A consumer's dictionary of cosmetic ingredients. Three Rivers Press, New York

Bibliography

Brown J, Dwyer K 1988 The jojoba potential: an overview. Proceedings from the Seventh International Conference on Jojoba and Its Uses, Phoenix, AZ.

Christensen, M.S. and E.W. Packman, Skin Surface Softening Effects of Jojoba and Its Derivatives, Proceedings from the Seventh International Conference on Jojoba and Its Uses, Phoenix, Az. 1988.

Johnson W Jr 1992 Final report on the safety assessment of jojoba oil and jojoba wax. Journal of the American College of Toxicology 11(1)

McClatchey, K.D., in Jojoba: New Crop for Arid Lands; New Raw Material for Industry, National Academy Press, Washington D.C., 1985.

McClatchey, K. D., W.J. Ferrell, and C. L. Pierson, Percutaneous Absorption of Jojoba Oil, Proceedings from the Fourth International Conference on Jojoba and Its Uses, Hermosillo, Sonora, Mexico, 1980.

Purcell, H., Natural Jojoba Versus Dryness and Free Radicals, Cosmetics and Toiletries Manufacture Worldwide, Aston Publishing Group, Hertfordshire, U.K., 1993.

Taguchi, M., Test results on safety on jojoba oil to be used for cosmetics. Proceedings from the Second International Conference on Jojoba and Its Uses, Ensenada, Baja California, Mexico, 1976.

Wisniak, J., Recent Advances in the Chemistry and Properties of Jojoba Oil, Proceedings from the Seventh International Conference on Jojoba and Its Uses, Phoenix, Az., 1988

Kukui nut oil

Scientific name
Aleurites moluccans
Family: Euphorbaceae

Etymology
Moluccans means of or from the Moluccas (Indonesia – also known as the Spice Islands). Kukui nut oil is also known as candlenut oil and lumbang oil

The plant and its environment
This plant was probably brought to Hawaii by early Polynesian settlers, and it is now grown there extensively; in 1959 it was named as the official state tree. The tree has pale leaves, silver grey on the underside so it is easy to distinguish from other trees growing on the lower mountain slopes, where it has adapted well to the climate and volcanic soil. The kukui fruits have a hard covering about 6mm (¹⁄₄in) thick: inside is a hard wrinkled nut (perhaps 2) and as it matures it turns progressively from white to brown to black. Each tree yields about 35–45k (75–100lb) of nuts per year.

The oil
Kukui oil is derived from the nut; it is high in linoleic and linolenic essential fatty acids. It is expeller pressed; solvents are not used. In its natural state the oil has a distinctive odour and steam is pumped through under vacuum to deodorize it. It is then bleached and filtered. Most of the free fatty acids are taken out by mixing the oil with caustic soda, which turns the free fatty acids into soap.

Method of extraction
Traditionally in Hawaii the nuts were shelled by the natives and the kernels lightly roasted before pressing to produce the clear oil.

Principal constituents

Type	Based on	Content – %
Saturated fatty acid:		
C16:0	palmitic acid	6.4
C18:0	stearic acid	2.8
Typical saturated fatty acid content		9

Monosaturated fatty acid:		
C16:1	palmitoleic acid	0.1
C18:1	oleic acid	19
C20:1	eicosenoic acid	0.6
Typical monosaturated fatty acid content		21
Polyunsaturated fatty acid:		
C18:2	linoleic acid	41
C18:3	linolenic acid	<29
Typical polyunsaturated fatty acid content		70

Physical properties

Colour	light yellow
Specific gravity	0.926
Acid value	0.55
Iodine value	160–170
Saponification no.	190–195
Unsaponifiable	<1%
Melting point °C	−12
Freezing point °C	−22
Flash point °F	655
Boiling point °F	600
Peroxide value	<5

To stabilize the oil and extend its shelf life vitamins A, C and E may be added.

Folklore and traditional use

Kukui nut oil has been used by Hawaiians for centuries to protect and heal skin exposed to harsh sun, drying winds and salt water: other uses are for psoriasis, acne and other common skin problems (Winter 1999 p.269) New born babies used to be anointed with this oil to protect their skin from sun and sea.

Therapeutic properties – external use
- a penetrating oil, easily absorbed while not blocking skin pores
- acne
- eczema
- psoriasis
- haemorrhoids

Cosmetic use

Used for sunburn and dry or wrinkled skin. It affords the skin good protection during outdoor pursuits

Cautions

1   Kukui nut oil has no known toxicity and is regarded as non–irritant even to the eyes.
2   Shelf life is six to eight months providing it is kept away from direct light and high temperatures.

Additional note

Used in skin care, pharmaceuticals, soaps, foods, paints etc.

References

Winter R 1999 A consumers dictionary of cosmetic ingredients. 5th edn: Three Rivers Press, New York

Linseed oil, flaxseed oil

Scientific name

Linum usitatissimum
Family: Linaceae

Etymology

Linum is the Latin name for flax, and it is from where we get our word linen. *Usitatissimum* is the Latin superlative of useful, and this plant finds a host of uses.

The existence of two common names for products from the same plant (flax and lin) is due to a deliberate attempt to discriminate between the plant products which are intended for human use (under the banner of flaxseed) and those products which are aimed at commercial exploitation (using the name linseed). This has come about because, although flax has been used for thousands of years, it is only fairly recently that the benefits of this oil have been brought to light in connection with improving the health of people.

The plant and its environment

Flax is one of the oldest cultivated plants, a native of Central Asia, and for 7,000 years has always been grown for the useful fibres taken from the stem of the plant, with which cloth was made, a tradition which started off in ancient Mesopotamia and was carried on by the Egyptians (they wrapped their mummies in linen), Greeks and so on. The Romans introduced it to the rest of Europe. Manufacture of Irish linen started about 1,500 years ago. It was introduced into the Argentine – a very large producer – after 1850.

Today many cultivars of flax are grown, long stemmed varieties for the fibres, others for the seed and short stemmed plants bearing large seeds dedicated to the production of oil. Originally Asian, linseed oil is now obtained from flax seed cultivated in Russia, North America, India, Morocco, Argentina and Brazil. It is a tall slim annual ranging from 0.5–1.5m (1.5–5 ft) in height, with alternate leaves and attractive blue flowers; the plant grows best in the cool, longer days of the northern climes.

The linseed oil of commerce

Owing to the property that this oil has of uniting with oxygen to form a sticky, and ultimately a dry hard film, it is called a 'drying oil', and therein lies its value as a major component of linoleum (note that the word itself means oil of lin) and its use in paints, varnishes (very useful in the case of cricket bats!), wood preservatives, oil stains, concrete sealers, printing inks, putty, gum erasers, brake linings and hardboard. Boiled linseed oil dries more rapidly than the raw oil because boiling partially oxidises the oil. (Only one oil, *Aleurites moluccana*, dries more quickly (Duke 1985)). It is one of the few oils that has a high content of α–linolenic acid similar to the omega–3 polyunsaturated fatty acids found in fish oils.

Method of extraction

Flaxseed oil: The seeds must be cold pressed (below 40°C) to achieve a good oil, and the oil must be unrefined, unfiltered and not have gone through a deodorising process.

Linseed oil: The seeds are softened by steam, and the oil pressed out by hydraulic pressure. The yield of oil can exceed 40% by weight of the seed. When the process is complete the exhausted seed cake is used as fodder for cattle.

Principal constituents

Type	Name	Content %
Saturated fatty acid units:		
C16:0	palmitic	3.0–7.0
C18:0	stearic	2.0–5.0
C20:0	icosanoic	< 0.5
C22:0	docosanoic	< 0.5
Typical saturated fatty acid content		9.5
Monounsaturated fatty acid units:		
C16:1	palmitoleic	<1.0
C18:1	oleic	18–24
C20:1	icosenoic	< 0.5
Typical monounsaturated fatty acid content		19
Polyunsaturated fatty acid units:		
C18:2	linoleic	14–17.5
C18:3	α–linolenic	50–60
C18:3	γ–linolenic	<0.5
Typical monounsaturated fatty acid content		70

Physical properties

Iodine value	170–190
Free fatty acid (% as oleic)	< 3.0
Peroxide value	< 2.0

The use of linseed oil is limited by the practical consideration of its keeping qualities; 4 or 5 months is the limit under good storage conditions (cool, dark, exclusion of air) before the oil starts to break down with respect to its nutritional qualities, although it can be used after this time for massage.

Oxygen must be excluded to prevent rancidity, light must be excluded to prevent the formation of free radicals and heat must be excluded to prevent the formation of trans–fatty acids, which do not occur in nature.

Vitamin content
Flaxseed oil contains vitamin E and β–carotene, a precursor to vitamin A.

Folklore and traditional plant remedies
Hippocrates noted that linseed oil was helpful for skin disorders, but in the past it has been little used in pharmacy (it is an ingredient in Liquor Cresol Saponatus – Lysol); as an ingredient in paints enormous quantities are consumed. Charlemagne (8th century) decreed that flax seeds should be consumed in order to maintain good health (Bown 1995). In Iran a paste made from Linum, Malva and Papaver is applied to boils (Duke 1985 p.344).

The seeds are used as a laxative by providing bulk, and when ground they can be used in poultices for drawing out and for healing. A decoction of the seeds helps allay coughs. Flax also contains lignans (phenolic compounds) which have anti–oestrogenic action; these compounds are found in high quantities in the urine of vegetarian women who have low risk of developing breast cancer.

Therapeutic properties – internal uses
The oil contributes to the nutrition of the brain, aids cellular exchanges and diminishes the level of cholesterol (Europhyto–Institut). A veterinary use of the oil is as a purgative in animals.

Therapeutic properties – external uses
Linseed oil may be used:
- as an ingredient in poultices for burns and scalds (Bartram 1995)
- to ease the elimination of gallstones

Cosmetic uses

Linseed oil is soothing to the skin and is used in cosmetic preparations such as shaving creams, medicinal soaps and emollients. It is said to improve the quality of the skin.

Culinary use

The use of linseed oil in cooking is strictly limited as high temperatures, for example in frying, will lead to break down of the oil and the formation of toxic substances.

Cautions

1   It is dangerous to ingest more than 50 g of the seeds. Flaxseed contains a glycoside, linamarin, which can, in theory, release hydrocyanic acid in the acid environment of the stomach. However no case of this has ever been reported, and millions of animals have eaten linseed over a long period of time.
2   Can cause allergic reaction (Winter 1999 p.279).

Additional notes

1   The drying oil produced from the seeds is used in food processing and waterproofing, in the manufacture of paint, varnish, printing ink and soap.
2   The oil has been recommended as an aid to eliminating unwanted metals from the body.
3   Three tablespoonfuls of crushed flaxseed daily ensures an adequate supply of omega 3 fatty acids (Bartram 1995).

References

Bartram T 1995 Encyclopaedia of herbal medicine. Grace, Christchurch p.271
Bown D 1995 Encyclopaedia of herbs and their uses. BCA, London p.152
Duke J A 1985 Handbook of medicinal herbs. CRC Press, Boca Raton p.29
Europhyto–Institut undated La phytothérapie: la santé par les plantes. Editions Alpen, Monaco p.52
Winter R 1999 A consumers dictionary of cosmetic ingredients. 5th edn: Three Rivers Press, New York

Macadamia oil

Scientific name
Macadamia ternifolia, *M. integrifolia*
Family: Proteaceae

There are two species – the smooth–shelled macadamia (*Macadamia integrifolia* Maiden & Betche) and the rough–shelled macadamia (*M. tetraphylla* L. Johnson) and hybrid forms exist between the two species.

Etymology
Ternifolia refers to the fact that the leaves are grouped in threes, whereas integrifolia means with entire uncut leaves. *Tetraphylla* means four–leaved. The name macadamia was given by von Mueller in honour of John Macadam. Common names are Australian bush nut, Queensland nut, bauple nut and popple nut and to the aboriginal people it is *kindal–kindal*.

The plant and its environment
The macadamia tree is native to Australia, and grows naturally in the sub–tropical forests of northeast New South Wales and southeast Queensland. Macadamia nuts were eaten by the aborigines and the original trees were discovered by Europeans in 1877.

The tree is evergreen and lives for about 80 years, producing nuts in the seventh year. The tree eventually reaches 11–20m (36–65ft) and yields 25–45kg (55–100lb) of nuts. The nut kernel is within a hard shell which is within a green outer husk. Australia accounts for about 40% of the world production of macadamia nuts although the tree is also grown Brazil, Costa Rica, Hawaii, Kenya, S. Africa. The production of macadamia nuts is not enough to fulfil world demand.

The oil
Today the oil comes from nuts which come from hybrid plants developed from the original trees. The nut contains 72–75% oil, which is mostly made up of triacylglycerols that contain monounsaturated fatty acid units (80%), and has good resistance to rancidity. Macadamia oil is particularly unusual in having a high proportion of palmitoleic acid units (these units are also found in whales, dolphins etc at about 12–15%).

Method of extraction

The oil is cold pressed (at the low temperature of 30–35°C) and is available either refined or unrefined. In both cases solvents are not used and the oil retains its natural properties.

Principal constituents

Type	Based on	Content – %
Saturated fatty acid units:		
C12:0	lauric acid	0.1
C14:0	myristic acid	0.6–1.6
C16:0	palmitic acid	7.0–9.5
C18:0	stearic acid	2.0–5.5
C20:0	arachidic acid	1.5–3.0
C22:0	behenic acid	<0.3
Typical saturated fatty acid unit content		15
Monounsaturated fatty acid units:		
C16:1	palmitoleic acid	18–25
C18:1	oleic acid	55–67
C20:1	eicosenoic acid	<2.5 max
Typical monounsaturated fatty acid unit content		83
Polyunsaturated fatty acid units:		
C18:2	linoleic acid	1–3
C18:3	linolenic acid	trace–2.4
Typical polyunsaturated fatty acid unit content		2

Physical properties

Odour	faint, slightly nutty aroma
Acid value	0.2
Specific gravity	0.910–0.929
Vitamin E/100ml	19mg

Vitamin and mineral content

Contains magnesium and thiamine (Winter 1999 p.283)

Therapeutic properties – internal use

Macadamia oil has a mild laxative action.

Monounsaturated oils, such as macadamia, are effective in reducing the level of low density lipoprotein cholesterol (LDL) without lowering the high density lipoprotein cholesterol (HDL); it also decreases the susceptibility of LDL to oxidation (Reaven *et al* 1991).

Therapeutic properties – external use

- The oil makes a pleasant massage oil with good keeping properties as it has a good resistance to rancidity
- It is a skin lubricant and is easily absorbed by the skin ? it has been described as a 'vanishing' oil
- Goëb (1998) describes the oil as one of the best vegetable oils for massage as it has an exceptional power to penetrate the skin, leaving it non greasy and supple
- The high levels of palmitoleic acid units present in macadamia oil are not found in any other known plant oil although they are found in human sebum, especially in the young. As ageing takes place the concentration falls, so it may be that macadamia oil could be beneficial for the skin of older people (Anon 1991)
- Iberg (2004) writes that the oil is alleged to slow down the ageing process of the skin but this has not been proved
- There is some (very little) anecdotal evidence to suggest that macadamia oil may be useful in reducing scarring after surgery

Cosmetic use

Macadamia oil is used in products that afford protection from the ageing effects of the sun; it may replace shark liver and mineral oil in skin care products. In hair care, it is utilized in brilliantine and hot oil conditioning treatments.

Culinary use

The oil has a pleasant flavour, which enhances salad dressings and the nuts can be used in any recipes that call for nuts, including stuffings, fruit salads, cakes, etc. – they can also be frozen.

Cautions

Skin tests carried out over 4 years on a range of subjects (different skin types and ages) have failed to reveal any toxic effects, irritation or allergic reactions (Minroba undated).

Additional notes

1   The macadamia nut is nutritious, containing vitamins niacin, riboflavin and thiamine and is a rich source of minerals – potassium, phosphorous, magnesium, calcium, iron and zinc in descending order of value.
2   Macadamia nuts are excellent raw or roasted.
3   To home–roast macadamia nuts, place shelled nuts (whole kernels or

halves only) in a shallow tin in an oven set at 250°C for 5–8 minutes. Remove from the oven as soon as they start to brown. The nuts store well in airtight containers.

References

Anon 1991 Cosmetics & Toiletries, February vol. 106

Goëb Ph 1998 Connaître l'essentiel sur les huiles essentielles. IAPM, Tamil Nadu p.43

Iberg A 2004 Dumont's lexicon of oil & vinegar. Rebo, Lisse p.192–184

Minroba Undated Macadamia nut oil: the miracle of the 90's. Information Leaflet. Minroba Pty Ltd, Ballina

Reaven P, Parthasarathy S, Khoo J et al 1991 Oleate rich diets reduce LDL susceptibility to oxidation. Circulation (suppl. 2) 84:681

Bibliography

Butterfield, H M 1963 A History of Subtropical Fruits and Nuts in California. University of California, Agricultural Experiment Station

California Macadamia Society. Macadamia Nut Trees for California Gardens. Undated.

California Macadamia Society. Yearbook 1955 to date.

Facciola S 1990 Cornucopia: a Source Book of Edible Plants. Kampong Publications p.380–381.

Hamilton R A, Fukunaga E T 1959 Growing Macadamia Nuts in Hawaii. University of Hawaii, Agricultural Experiment Station Bulletin 121. 1959.

Page P E 1984 Tropical Tree Fruits for Australia. Queensland Department of Primary Industries. p.150–160.

Rosengarten F Jr 1984 Book of Edible Nuts. Walker and Co.

Samson J A 1986 Tropical Fruits. 2nd ed. Longman Scientific and Technical. p.282–284.

Winter R 1999 A consumers dictionary of cosmetic ingredients. 5th edn: Three Rivers Press, New York

Mango seed oil

Scientific name

Mangifera indica
Family: Anarcardaceae

Boy, cut these mangoes and prepare them in slices, because in that way they have a better taste, and the chief thing is to soak them in wine, like nectarines.
Garcia de Orta 1563 The Simples and Drugs of India

Etymology

The scientific name *Mangifera* is composed of the word mango and the Latin *ferre* = to bear and so means mango bearer. *Mangi* is Latinised mango which probably comes from the Tamil word *man–kay*, referring to the unripe mango fruit. In Tamil (the main language of southern India) the mango is called *mamaran* or *mampalam*. These names come from Sanskrit, *amra* = mango and Hindi *aam*. French (*mangot, mangue*), Portuguese (*manga, mangueira*), and Dutch (*manja*). In some parts of Africa, it is called *mangou*, or *mangoro*.

The plant and its environment

Mango trees, which are native to southern Asia, especially India and Burma, were already cultivated in the Indian state of Assam 4000 years ago. Buddhist monks are believed to have taken the mango to Malaya and eastern Asia in the 4th century BC and it is claimed that the Persians took it to East Africa in the 10th century AD. The Portuguese introduced it to West Africa and to Brazil in the 16th century, thence to the West Indies about 1742. It reached Jamaica about 1782 and in the 19th century it reached Mexico.

The tree is long–lived, some specimens being known to be 300 years old and still fruiting and there are today approximately 1500 different cultivars. The tree has glossy green long, oblong leaves up to 30cm (12in) in length which hang in clusters at the branch ends. The mango tree can reach 30m (100ft) and the small pink flowers give off a lily–like fragrance. The fruit is up to 25cm (10in) long and can weigh up to 2 kg ($4\frac{1}{2}$ lb). The juicy flesh holds a large, smooth stone, which is the source of the oil. The yield of fruit varies with the cultivar and the age of the tree. At 10 to 20 years, a good annual crop may be 200 to 300 fruits per tree. At twice that age and over, the crop will be doubled. In Java old trees have been known to bear 1,000 to 1,500 fruits in a season.

The oil

Mango seed oil is extracted from the fruit kernels (seeds) of the mango tree (Mangifera indica). It is produced during the oil fractionation process in the production of mango butter. The oil is refined and deodorized to obtain an oil which is a soft, yellow solid at 15°C. The seed residue after fat extraction is usable for cattle feed and soil enrichment

Principal constituents:

Type	Based on	Content – %
Saturated fatty acid:		
C14:0	myristic	<1
C16:0	palmitic	4–9
C18:0	stearic	34–48
Typical saturated fatty acid content		53
Monounsaturated fatty acid:		
C18:1	oleic	38–50
Typical monounsaturated fatty acid content		42
Polyunsaturated fatty acid:		
C18:2	linoleic	4–6
C18:3	α–linolenic	<1
Typical polyunsaturated fatty acid content		5

Physical properties

Iodine value (wijs)	40–60
Saponification value	180–195
Unsaponifiable matter	0.5% min
Appearance	soft yellow, semi–solid oil
Odour	characteristic fatty odour
Free fatty acid	1% max
Melting Point	23–27°C

Vitamin and mineral content

The oil contains vitamin E; also phytosterols and phospholipids.

Therapeutic properties – external use

Mango seed oil:

- has emollient and antioxidant properties
- is used for protection against UV rays
- is useful for dry skin after exposure to the sun or other weather conditions unfriendly to the skin

Cosmetic uses

It is suggested as an ingredient in skin creams and lotions, balms, bar soaps, hair products and massage oils.

Culinary uses

Summer drinks are made from pulped mangoes, sometimes mixed with salt, molasses and cumin, or with milk. The ripe fruits can be eaten fresh or dried, the unripe fruits can be eaten with lemon juice and salt, dried and ground as a spice, or processed into chutneys.

Folklore and traditional plant remedies

Mangoes are rich in vitamin C and are used in India all year round. In summer, when the body is losing salt through perspiration, raw mangoes are sliced and eaten with salt; they are pickled in oil and used in winter months as an antidote to colds (Patnaik 1993 p.96). The pulp of the fruit is used for the treatment of diabetes and blood pressure problems.

In times of food scarcity in India, the kernels are roasted or boiled and eaten. After soaking to dispel the astringency (tannins), the kernels are dried and ground into flour in which is mixed with wheat or rice flour to make bread; it is also used in puddings.

Cautions

Keep dry and cool, preferably below 25°C, out of direct light in sealed container.

Additional notes

1   In Ayurvedic medicine the twigs, which are antiseptic, are used like toothbrushes for oral hygiene and infusions of the bark are used for diarrhoea and excessive menstrual flow.

2   The seed is ground to a powder to counteract vaginal discharge and the kernel has long been acknowledged as a cure for dysentery (Patnaik 1993 p.96).

3   The kernel is a major by–product of the mango processing industry.

4   Immature mango leaves are cooked and eaten in Indonesia and the Philippines.

5   The flesh of the mango fruit contains carotenoids, violaxanthin, quercetin glycosides, and polysaccharides.

6   The kernel fat contains fully saturated glycerides 14.2%, mono–oleoglycerides 24.2%, di–oleoglycerides 60.8%, tri–unsaturated glycerides 0.8%

References

Morton J, 1987 Mango. In: Morton J F Fruits of warm climates. Miami, FL p.221–239
Patnaik N 1993 The garden of life. Aquarian, London

Meadowfoam oil

Scientific name
Limnanthes alba
Family: Limnanthaceae

Etymology
Limnanthes comes from two Greek words, *limne* meaning marsh and *anthos* meaning a flower; *alba* is Latin for white. The English common name is said to be on account of its resemblance of the flowers in full bloom to the white foam blowing on the ocean.

The plant and its environment
Meadowfoam is a low growing herbaceous winter annual, native to the Pacific north west coast of N. America.

The oil
Meadowfoam oil was developed to replace sperm whale oil in the 1970s, in an effort to protect the species. The oil is unusual in that the majority of it consists of fatty acids which are chains of 20 or more carbon atoms (more than rapeseed oil). It is a very stable oil due to the presence (0.07%) of vitamin E (α–, β– and γ–tocopherol). Meadowfoam seed oil is very stable because it contains about 97% long carbon chain fatty acids and is characterized by very high levels of mono–unsaturation and very low levels of polyunsaturation. It is reputed to be one of the most stable lipids known, even when heated or exposed to air, and will help extend the shelf life of less stable ingredients.

Method of extraction
Extracted from the seeds, which are about 2–3 mm in length and contain 20–30% oil by weight, the oil is expeller pressed, solvent extracted and refined.

Principal constituents

Type	Based on	Content – %
Saturated fatty acid:		
C16:0	palmitic acid	<1.0
C18:0	stearic acid	<0.5
C20:0	arachidic acid	trace
C22:0	behenic acid	trace

Typical saturated fatty acid content		1
Monounsaturated fatty acid:		
C16:1	palmitoleic acid	<0.5
C18:1	oleic acid	0–4
C20:1	eicosenoic acid	60–65
C22:1	erucic acid	8–11
Typical monounsaturated fatty acid content		77
Polyunsaturated fatty acids		
C18:2	linoleic acid	0–4
C18:3	α–linolenic acid	trace
Typical polyunsaturated fatty acid content		22
Other constituents		
C22:1	delta–linolenic acid	2–4
C22:2	docosadienoic acid	15–23

Physical properties

Acid value (mg KOH/g oil)	0.2 max
Peroxide value (meq/k oil)	2.0 max
Refractive index at 40°C	1.4645–1.4655
Colour (Lovibond 5¼" cell)	3.0 red max, 50 yellow
Iodine value (wijs)	90–102
Saponification value	165
Specific gravity at 25°C	0.910–0.920
Energy value Kcal/100ml	900 (3700kJ)
Shelf life	2 to 3 years
Odour	none

Meadowfoam oil remains liquid at room temperature despite its high molecular weight.

Therapeutic properties – external

Meadowfoam is emollient and one of the most penetrating oils available because of the small molecular structure. This oil:

- helps to heal bruising
- affords ultra violet protection (sunscreen applications)
- has a non greasy feeling because of its skin penetration ability
- it is alleged to reduce wrinkles and delay signs of aging

133

Cosmetic uses

It is an ingredient in products such as massage oils, lotions, face creams, sun screens, hair/scalp products, and shaving creams. When used in hair products it adds shine and helps repair dry or damaged hair; used in lip balms for dry, cracked lips.

Cautions

None known for use on the skin.

Additional notes

1   Meadowfoam oil is of interest because it contains a high proportion of the 20 and 22 carbon chain fatty acids.
2   In field tests *L. alba* ssp. *alba* produced 8% 22:1 and 30% 22:2, whereas *L. alba* ssp. *versicolor* plant produced 24% 22:1 and 9% 22:2.
3   The pressed seeds are fed to cattle and other livestock.
4   The plants are a renewable crop and are grown as a rotation crop for grass seed farmers.
5   It is a stable refined oil which may be refrigerated, although this is not necessary.

Mustard seed oil

Scientific name
Sinapis alba
Family: Brassicaceae (cabbage family)
Synonyms are *Brassica alba*, *B. hirta*. Related species are Chinese mustard, *S. cernua* (syn. *Brassica cernua*), and rocket *Eruca sativa* (syn. *Brassica eruca*).

With a few spoonfuls of mustard, a cold and lazy woman can become an ideal wife.
Pliny the Elder

Etymology
Sinapis is Latin for mustard and *alba* is Latin for white.

The German *Senf* has the same derivation, as well as the Old English *senep* (preparation of mustard paste was introduced to central and Northern Europe by the Romans). The Latin term is probably from Greek (*sinapi*, but its ultimate origin is not known. Similar names in other European languages include Italian *senape*, Swedish *senap* and Yiddish *zeneft*. *Sinapi* is also the word used in the New Testament for "mustard"; it appears in the famous parable of the mustard seed found in all synoptic gospels

The word mustard probably comes from the Latin *mustum* ardens meaning burning must because in France the seed was originally ground with grape must

The plant and its environment
White mustard probably originates from the Mediterranean region, but many cultivars are grown in Northern, Central and Eastern Europe. It is a small annual plant which grows up to a height of one metre with some branches. It has round stem with long internodes, simple, alternate and very soft yellowish green leaves. The fruit is a pod (2.5cm, 1in) long containing seeds (1mm diameter) which are light brown.

The oil
The oil contained in the mustard seed is edible but it is mostly used in making pharmaceutical products, soap, leather and wool articles.

Extraction
Mustard oil is cold pressed, yielding 28–35% of a fixed oil.

135

Principal constituents

Type	Based on	Content – %
Saturated fatty acid:		
C18:0	stearic	<0.5
C20:0	arachidic	9–12
C22:0	behenic	9–12
C24:0	lignoceric	30–40
Typical saturated fatty acid content		55
Monounsaturated fatty acid:		
C16:1	palmitoleic	1.5–3
C18:1	oleic	0.5–1.5
C20:1	eicosenoic	<1.5
C22:1	erucic	<1.5
C24:1	nervonic	<1.5
Typical monounsaturated fatty acid content		5
Polyunsaturated fatty acid:		
C18:2	linoleic	20–30
C18:3	α–linolenic	2–4
C18:3	gamma linolenic	10–14
Typical polyunsaturated fatty acid content		40

Physical properties

Peroxide value (meq/kg oil)	<5 max
Refractive index at 20EC	1.4750–1.527
Optical rotation	inactive
Iodine value (wijs)	95–120
Specific gravity at 20EC	1.014–1.030
Free fatty acids (% as oleic)	<0.5
Colour	medium–dark yellow

Therapeutic properties

The oil is used in many prescription for the treatment of various ailments. Mustard oil boiled with henna leaves is useful in healthy growth of hair and regular head massage with this oil will encourage hair growth.

Culinary uses

Used in pickles and salads (because it is a powerful preservative effective against mould and inhibiting bacterial growth). In Punjab, Delhi and Western Uttar Pradesh, the young leaves are used as a vegetable.

Usage of white mustard seeds as a spice is relatively minor, but the whole seeds are popular in pickled vegetables; for this usage, they may be combined with allspice and bay leaves. The ground seeds are a popular spice mixed with water and added to stews and sauces. Many recipes have been compiled for mustard seed or mustard–containing sauces, pickles and chutneys used with meat and fish dishes, and even in breads, confectionery items and sweets (Man and Weir, 1988).

Folklore and traditional plant remedies

The oil extracted from the seeds is used in North India as a hair oil, for frying and other cooking purposes. White mustard seeds can be used beneficially as a beauty aid. A handful of these seeds are roasted in a litre of sesame or coconut oil, which when strained and cooled can be applied with a little water on the face to cure pimples and whiten the complexion.

Mustard is a rubefacient which causes reddening and warming of the skin. A paste made with water is applied as an analgesic in rheumatism, sciatica, and other muscular pains: a layer of lint should be placed between the mustard paste and the skin to prevent blistering. Mustard paste as an external application is beneficial in the treatment of ringworm

Cautions

1   Extremely hazardous in case of eye contact (irritant). Inflammation of the eye is characterized by redness, watering, and itching.

2   Very hazardous in case of skin contact (irritant, corrosive, permeator – skin inflammation is characterized by itching, scaling, reddening, or, occasionally, blistering.), of ingestion, of inhalation. [The oil is used diluted as a counter irritant and rubefacient (Winter 1999 p.306)]

3   Severe over exposure can result in death.

Additional notes

1   Mustard seeds have emetic properties which cause vomiting, useful in drunkenness and other poisonings. The seeds contain about 1% of a volatile oil which is used as a counter–irritant when greatly diluted. White mustard has less volatile oil and the flavour is milder than that of black mustard seeds

2   Besides proteins (28%) and fatty oil (35%), white mustard seeds contain approx. 2.5% sinalbin, a thioglycoside–like compound of glucose and p–hydroxy–benzyl–isothiocyanate ($HO–C_6H_4–CH_2–NCS$). On cell damage, the enzyme myrosinase hydrolyzes the sinalbin and produces free p–hydroxy–benzyl–isothiocyanate, a pungent and non–volatile

substance. Isothiocyanates are also the main ingredients in black mustard, horseradish, cress, rocket and wasabi, all of which belong to the same plant family.

3   In the 17th century, the vinegar maker Maille distributed mustard to the poor of Dijon to help protect them from chilblains. During the great yellow fever epidemics along the banks of the Mississippi which brought about thousands of deaths, mustard sold for the price of gold, since it was believed to afford protection.

4   There is also a black mustard (*Brassica nigra*) which is a native to Eurasia and was used by the Romans, Greeks and Indians since ancient times. The plant is cultivated as a field crop in most temperate countries and has been grown in Europe for centuries, but has largely been replaced in modern times because the plant is not suitable for mechanical harvesting. This was the first species to provide table mustard for use as a condiment and it is much more pungent than white mustard.

References

Man R, Weir R 1988 The compleat mustard. Constable, London
Winter R 1999 A consumers dictionary of cosmetic ingredients. 5th edn: Three Rivers Press, New York

Olive oil

Scientific name
Olea europaea
Family: Oleaceae

Etymology
Also known as Florence oil
or Lucca oil (Florence and Lucca are towns
in Tuscany which are important trading
centres for olive oil). The olive tree dates back
several thousand years; in ancient Egypt the tree
was called the *bak*, whereas to the Romans it was the
olea, derived from *oleum* meaning oil.

> Then the Lord said unto Moses: Take the following fine spices – 500 shekels of liquid myrrh, half as much (that is, 250 shekels) of fragrant cinnamon, 250 shekels of fragrant cane, 500 shekels of cassia – all according to the sanctuary shekel – and a hin* of olive oil. Make these into a sacred anointing oil, a fragrant blend, the work of a perfumer. It will be the sacred anointing oil.
> **Exodus 30:22 25 (1491 BC), The Holy Bible, NIV**
> *About 4 litres*

The plant and its environment
The silvery green olive branch has always been a token of peace: the dove messenger to Noah, the wearing of olive leaf garlands by the Greeks, the use of olive branches in the Jewish Feast of Tabernacles, the symbol of the United Nations flag etc.

The trees are not large, growing to a height of about 8m (25ft), but they do live to a great age, which can be some hundreds of years. It is native to the Mediterranean region but has been successfully introduced into many other places.

Cultivation of the evergreen olive is recorded from the earliest times (5000 BC) and the oil has always been an important product. The chief centres of olive cultivation are Italy, southern France, Spain, Portugal, Greece, Turkey, Israel, Morocco and Tunisia and, more recently, California, Mexico and Australia.

Olive trees begin to produce fruit after 15 years and continue to do so for literally hundreds of years. Contrary to popular belief, both the black and the green olives come from the same trees, as the fruits (drupes) turn from green to black progressively as they ripen.

139

The oil

Olive oil is slightly green owing to the retention of trace amounts of chlorophyll – the green colouring matter of plants. Like avocado oil, olive oil is prone to congealing when cold, thus it is usually filtered in the warm countries where the tree is grown. The fruits yield about 18–20% oil and it is relatively expensive; the average yield per tree is 20kg of olives which yield about 4–5kg of oil.

A million tonnes of oil are produced annually and, apart from cooking purposes, olive oil is used in lubrication, lighting and soap.

Some olive oils have an uncharacteristic taste or colour and these are frequently the result of the chemical refining of genuine but poor quality material. Obviously, this type of oil should not be used therapeutically.

Method of extraction

Like avocado oil, olive oil is obtained from the flesh of the fruit and not from the stone or kernel. The picked fruits are left in the sun until they begin to ferment, whereupon they are gently crushed (so as not to fracture the stones, which are then removed) and the flesh is pressed. The resulting oil is centrifuged and filtered for clarity. This first portion of oil is known as virgin oil and the oil obtained at the very beginning of this pressing is known as extra virgin oil or first pressing.

Water is then mixed with the pulp, which is pressed again to produce oil of second quality. The refuse is allowed to accumulate in pits and more oil is extracted by boiling or by dissolving in carbon disulphide and recovery of the solvent. Such oil is only fit for the roughest purposes, such as low quality soaps.

Principal constituents

Type	Based on	Content – %
Typical saturated fatty acid unit content		10
Monounsaturated fatty acid units:		
C18:1	oleic acid	55–83
Typical monounsaturated fatty acid unit content		74
Polyunsaturated fatty acid units:		
C18:2	linoleic acid	11
C18:3	α–linolenic acid	0.7
Typical polyunsaturated fatty acid unit content		16

Physical properties

Odour	typically slightly fruity smell
Acid value	extra virgin: <1
	virgin: <2
Specific gravity	0.916–0.919
Energy value Kcal/100ml	892
Vitamin E/100ml	14mg

Folklore and traditional plant uses

The leaves have antiseptic, febrifuge, hypoglycaemic, diuretic and hypotensive properties. The oil has traditionally been taken with lemon juice in 5ml doses to treat gallstones (Chevallier 1996).

> The yelow and freshe olive is beter for the stomack, but it is hard for the belly. The blak that is rype is disposed to corruption and is evel for the stomack. ... it is good to wash the goumes that are vexed with a filthy moysture, with the oyle of the wild olive. It maketh fast louse tethe. Take ye oyle and put it in to woll, or a fyne cloth and lay it hote unto the waterishe goumes until they be whyte, and it will help them.
> **William Turner 1562 A new herbal. Part II p.67**

Therapeutic properties – internal use

There are indications that olive oil lowers the blood pressure more than other highly publicised polyunsaturated oils and this is borne out by the findings of the Finnish vs southern Italian investigation into the effect of diet on heart/circulatory diseases and deaths. It was shown that the Finnish high animal fat diet was responsible for their high levels of blood cholesterol. The southern Italian diet is practically meatless and, although the amount of olive oil consumed causes some weight problems, there is a very low incidence of heart problems. It appears that olive oil lowers the amount of LDL (low density lipoprotein) cholesterol in the body (Bartram 1996), and perhaps high cholesterol levels may be reduced more by ingesting olive oil than by following a fatless diet.

Olive oil has also been recommended for disorders of the liver and hyperacidity (it reduces the amount of acid produced in the stomach), and it is mildly purgative. It is considered a healthy food oil because it increases the secretion of bile and acts as a laxative through its contracting effect on the muscles of the bowel. Recommended as a part of a diabetic diet, the oil has also been used as a preventative agent for osteoporosis in the St Louis Hospital, Paris.

Therapeutic properties – external use

Olive oil has the properties of being calming, demulcent and emollient. It is effective in the following ways:

- burns
- sprains
- bruises
- insect bites
- relieving itching of the skin
- weakly astringent
- weakly antiseptic
- has been used to massage the gums of people suffering from pyorrhoea

The refined oil appears in the French pharmacopoeia as a solvent for parenteral preparations.

Although olive oil can be used for massage but it is somewhat fatty and heavy; also the characteristic odour is not always acceptable to client or therapist as it may tend to overpower the essential oils. It could be better used in the same way as avocado and wheatgerm oils, by adding around 20% to the basic carrier oil.

Cosmetic use

Olive oil is used in shampoos, soaps, face powders, hair colouring, lipsticks, emollients, brilliantines, anti–wrinkle oils and eyelash oils. It is beneficial to dry skin; when mixed with honey, lemon juice and egg yolk it makes an anti–wrinkle mask. Replacing the honey with lemon zest gives a mask suitable for oily skin (Stier 1990). Olive, sesame and avocado oils mixed together in equal proportions makes a blend which affords some protection from the sun.

Culinary use

Olive oil of first quality is nutritious and easy to digest. It is often used in salads and is ideal for low temperature cooking, as it does not smoke under 200°C, although the flavour begins to change at 140°C.

Choosing an olive oil can be confusing. Extra virgin oil denotes oil produced at the beginning of the first pressing, with an acidity of <1% and a strong flavour. Virgin oil is taken from the middle stage of the first pressing and it has a good flavour with an acidity of <2%. There is even another virgin oil from the last stage of the first pressing which has an acidity of <3.5%.

Cautions

At one time this oil was frequently adulterated with cheaper cottonseed oil which is known to cause allergies. Dandruff is made worse if olive oil is applied to a dry scalp, and the oil may cause an allergic reaction (Malmkvist Padoan 1990). The oil may also sensitise when applied topically (Sutton 1943, van Joost *et al* 1981). The oil may cause allergic reactions and smarting occurs if the oil gets into the eyes (Winter 1999 p.321).

Additional notes

1   A press report by Monell Chemical Senses Centre states that a compound found in olive oil is a natural antiinflammatory and may also reduce the risk of getting Alzheimer's disease and some cancers (Stein 2005). Named oleocanthal by the researchers, the compound inhibits activity of cyclooxygenase (COX) enzymes, a pharmacological action shared by ibuprofen (Beacham *et al* 2005).

2   It has been observed from animal studies that cholesterol becomes toxic when oxidised, i.e. reacts with oxygen, and olive oil contains some compounds, including oleuropein and squalene, which inhibit this oxidation and may also bring other benefits to the health.

3   A bread containing a concentrated component of olive oil has been launched in Spain as an anti–ageing food. The bread contains a concentrated hydroxytyrosol, an antioxidant extracted from olives, which, it is claimed, can help prevent ageing (Brett 2005).

4   Spanish researchers now say that the plant chemicals in olive oil, rather than the fatty acids, may be responsible for the good heart health widely observed in Mediterranean populations. In a study on blood vessel function in human volunteers, it was found that a polyphenol rich olive oil caused a significant improvement, but there was little effect after subjects consumed an oil that had many of the phenols removed. The work by the Reina Sofia University Hospital in Cordoba is one of a number of investigations going on to understand better why olive oil protects the heart. It was noted that not all olive oils have a high phenolic content, but the results support increasing consumption of olive oil as a way of preventing progression of atherosclerosis (Brett 2005).

5   Monounsaturated fatty acids, such as oleic acid, are as effective in reducing serum total and low–density lipoprotein (LDL) cholesterol levels as polyunsaturated fatty acids such as alpha–linoleic acid (Vessby 1994).

References

Bartram T 1996 Encyclopedia of herbal medicine. Grace, Christchurch p.318

Beauchamp G K, Keast R S J, Morel D, Lin J, Pika J, Han Q, Lee C–H, Smith A B III, Breslin P A S 2005 Ibuprofen–like activity in extra–virgin olive oil. Nature 437: 45–6

Brett K 2005 An ancient source of oil. The Iberian Times 18–24 November p.20

Chevallier A 1996 The encyclopaedia of medicinal plants. Dorling Kindersley, London p.239

Malmkvist Padoan S, Petterson A, Svensson A 1990 Olive oil as a cause of contact allergy in patients with venous eczema, and occupationally. Contact Dermatitis 23: 73–76

Stein L 2005 Olive oil contains natural anti–inflammatory agent. Press release 31st August Monell Chemical Senses Center

Stier B 1990 Secrets des huiles de première pression à froid. Self published, Quebec p.78

Sutton R L 1943 Contact dermatitis from olive oil. Journal American Medical Association 122: 34–35

van Joost T, Sillevis Smitt J H, van Ketel W G 1981 Sensitization to olive oil (Olea europaea). Contact Dermatitis 7: 309–310

Vessby B 1994 Inform 5(2):182–185

Winter R 1999 A consumer's dictionary of cosmetic ingredients. Three Rivers Press, New York

Palm kernel oil

Scientific name

Elaeis guineensis

Family: Palmaceae

Common names: Palm oil, German *Palmöl*, *Palmfett*, French *Huile de palme*, Spanish *Aceite de palma*.

Etymology

The generic name *Elaeis* is from the Greek *elaia* = olive because it is rich in oil and the specific name refers to the area of origin for this species, Guinea; *guineensis* is the Latinized form.

The plant and its environment

A solidly built, tall (15–30m, 50–100ft) palm, which grows wild in Nigeria, is native to West Africa, and is now grown also in other areas near the equator, (i.e. between 10 degrees north and 10 degrees south), for example in the East Indies and in Brazil. Widely produced – Europe, Africa East and West Africa, Indonesia, Malaysia, India, America, Australia; Malaysia is the largest producer of both palm and palm kernel oil followed by Indonesia, Zaire and the Ivory Coast. The United Kingdom is the biggest importer of palm oil products.

The wild palm does not produce fruit until approximately 15 years old, unlike the cultivated variety which yields fruit at 4 years, and is smallish when young so that climbing is not necessary until the tree is about 12 years old. The fruit grows at the top among the fronds in bunches of about 15–18 Kg containing 700–900 palm fruits. The thin yellow to reddish skin covers the pulpy pericarp which yields palm oil; this is chiefly used for soap making, although an edible oil is now produced in modern plantation mills.

The oil

The palm fruit is the source of both palm oil (extracted from palm fruit) and palm kernel oil (extracted from the fruit seeds).

Palm kernel oil is obtained from the kernels of the cracked nuts and usually exported to and processed in Europe (this first happened in 1850): this oil is used mainly as an edible oil, but is also used in soaps. The kernel yields an oil greatly different from that extracted from the fleshy pericarp of

145

the ripe fruits, expressed to yield palm oil; both oils are solid in temperate climates (Bruneton 1995). Palm oils contribute about 20% of the world oil production. It is, along with soybean oil, the most widely produced edible oil.

Palm oil is reddish because it contains a high amount of beta–carotene but boiling it a few minutes destroys the carotenoids and the oil becomes colourless.

Principal constituents – Palm kernel oil

Type	Based on	Content – %
Fatty acid:		
C8:0	caprylic	2.4–6.2
C10:0	capric	2.6–5
C12:0	lauric	41–55
C14:0	myristic	14–18
C16:0	palmitic	6.5–10
C18:0	stearic	2.5
Total Saturated		82
C18:1	oleic	12–19
C18:2	linoleic	2.3

Principal constituents – Palm oil

Type	Based on	Content – %
Fatty acid:		
C14:0	myristic	0.5–2
C16:0	palmitic	41–47
C18:0	stearic	4.5–6
Total Saturated	50	
C18:1	oleic	36–44
C18:2	linoleic	6.5–12

Physical properties

Density	0.920–0.940
Acid value	palm kernel oil <5%
Shelf life at 30°C	6 months
Palm oil is semi–solid at room temperature	

Vitamins

A, E (natural palm oil contains alpha, beta, gamma, and delta–tocopherols and alpha, beta, gamma, and delta–tocotrienols).

Therapeutic properties and uses

Palm kernel oil resembles coconut oil in its constituents, properties and application.

Palm oil is used together with the seeds of *Physostigma venenosum* (Fabaceae) to kill lice (Duke 1985).

Culinary use

Palm oil is processed to produce edible fats (margarine), used in baking and confectionery, and is also used in the manufacture of ice cream and mayonnaise

Other uses

Used in toilet soap, soap powder, detergents and candles; also used in pharmacy and cosmetics and it is an important raw material in oleochemistry (fat chemistry).

Cautions

No toxicity is known.

Additional notes

1   Soap making has become a community industry, helping people affected by leprosy regain some financial independence and dignity. The outer skins are removed and the inner kernels left in the sun to dry. These are then ground to extract the whiter oil for cooking. The yellow oil is mixed with caustic soda by hand, but because the hands of people with leprosy are insensitive, the mixing is done by people who do not have leprosy.

2   Unrefined palm and coconut oils do not increase the risk of atherosclerosis.

3   Palm oils are rich in beta carotenes, most notably red palm oil which has about 15 times more than in carrots.

4   Minor nutrients in palm oil are about 10% linoleic acid, which is an unsaturated omega–6 fatty acid, and small amounts of squalene (possible cholesterol lowering and anti–cancer properties) and ubiquinone (energy booster). Red palm oil is rich in co–enzyme Q10.

5   In some tropical cities some buses and taxis are fuelled with palm oil diesel.

6   Napalm derives its name from naphthenic acid, palmitic acid and pyrotechnics (i.e. simply a recipe using naphtha and palm oil.

7   The oil palm gives its name to the 16 carbon saturated fatty acid palmitic acid found in palm oil.

References

Bruneton J 1995 Pharmacognosy, phytochemistry, medicinal plants. Intercept, Andover p.365

Hornstra, 1990 Effects of dietary lipids on some aspects of the cardiovascular risk profile. In Ziant G ed Lipids and health.

Koh C S 2006. Comments on draft document: diet, nutrition, and the prevention of chronic diseases. http://www.who.int/dietphysicalactivity

Ang C Y W, KeShun L, Yao–Wen Huang eds. 1999 Asian Foods. WHO 2003 Diet, nutrition and the prevention of chronic diseases. Technical Report Series 916. Geneva p.82, 88

Bibliography

United States Department of Agriculture, Agricultural Statistics 2004. Table 3–51.

Malaysian Oil Palm Statistics 2005. Malaysian Palm Oil Board.

Peach kernel oil

Scientific name

Prunus persica Stokes
Family: Rosaceae
Synonyms are *Amygdalus persica* L.,
Persica vulgaris Nutt.

Etymology

Prunus is the Latin for plum tree,
and persica means coming from
Persia. Peach kernel oil is also
known as persic oil.

The plant and its environment

The peach tree is a
small deciduous tree
growing to a maximum height
of only about 8m (25ft) with its
origins in China. It was Alexander
the Great who brought news of the
peach from Persia and by the first century AD
peaches were being enjoyed by the Romans, who
knew them as Persian apples; it was the Romans
who brought the peach to Europe.

California and Texas are now the world's major
producers, even though the tree was not introduced to America until the 17th
century. The tree grows well, sometimes for centuries, in an alkaline soil with
plenty of sun.

The oil

Chemically and physically peach kernel oil is similar to apricot kernel
and sweet almond oils, but it is more expensive than sweet almond, possibly
because it is not produced in such large quantities and is mostly cold pressed.
Persic oil is expressed from the seeds of *P. persica* and *P. armeniaca* (apricot)
and is largely used in the manufacture of toilet preparations and as a
substitute for almond oil (Wren 1975).

Method of extraction

The best quality oil is obtained by cold pressing the kernels.

Principal constituents

Type	Based on	Content – %
Saturated fatty acid units:		
C14:0	myristic acid	trace
C16:0	palmitic acid	5
C18:0	stearic acid	1
C20:0	arachidic acid	<0.5
C22:0	behenic acid	trace
C24:0	lignoceric acid	trace
Typical saturated fatty acid unit content		6
Monounsaturated fatty acid units:		
C16:1	palmitoleic acid	0.7
C18:1	oleic acid	62
C20:1	ecosenoic acid	<0.5
Typical monounsaturated fatty acid unit content		61
Polyunsaturated fatty acid units:		
C18:2	linoleic acid	29
C18:3	α–linolenic acid	<0.8
Typical polyunsaturated fatty acid unit content		28

Physical properties

Odour	essentially odourless
Acid value	1.1
Specific gravity	0.913

Folklore and traditional plant uses

The plant – bark, leaves, expressed oil – has been used for its sedative, diuretic and expectorant properties. It has been used in coughs, whooping cough and chronic bronchitis and also for irritation and congestion of the gastric surfaces (Wren 1975). Culpeper advises the application of the milk or cream of the kernels on the forehead to bring rest and sleep to sick persons and writes that

> ...the oil drawn from the kernels, and the temples anointed therewith doth the like
> **Culpeper**

Therapeutic properties – internal use

As with both sweet almond oil and apricot kernel oil, peach kernel oil may be used in laxative preparations and is said to be effective in reducing blood cholesterol levels.

Therapeutic properties – external use

- skin protection (emollient, nourishing and is slowly absorbed)
- relieves itching
- eczema

Cosmetic use

Peach kernel oil is suitable for sensitive, dry and ageing skins and makes a good facial massage oil. It is often used in skin care creams.

Cautions

Non–irritating and non–sensitizing to the skin, it is considered safe for cosmetic use and has no known toxicity (Winter 1999 p.330).

Additional note

The pressed oil cake is not used as animal feed because of the amygdalin it contains, but it is used as an organic fertiliser (Stier 1990 p.73).

References

Culpeper's complete herbal. Undated. Foulsham, London p.262–263
Wren R W (ed.) 1975 Potter's new cyclopaedia of botanical drugs and preparations. Health Science Press, Bradford nr. Holsworthy p.230–231
Stier B 1990 Secrets des huiles de premier pression à froid. Self published, Quebec
Winter R 1999 A consumers dictionary of cosmetic ingredients. 5th edn: Three Rivers Press, New York

Peanut oil

Scientific name

Arachis hypogaea
Family: Fabaceae, Leguminosae

Etymology

Also known as monkey nut, groundnut, pig nut, earth nut, ground pea, Spanish nut (Swiss), cameroon (German), katchung and arachis oil. *Arachis* is Latin based on Greek *arakis*, a diminutive of arakos, a legume. *Hypo* is the Greek for under and *ge* means the earth, describing the underground characteristic. Known as a peanut in the USA because of the pea shaped flower of the plant. Groundnut comes from the fact that the nut grows and develops underground.

The plant and its environment

It was not until 1814 that these nuts were pressed for their oil, although the plant previously had been cultivated for hundreds of years. It is native to S. America (chiefly Brazil) and the W. Indies, but now it is grown extensively throughout the world in tropical and sub–tropical areas, especially in the USA, Africa, India and China. The slave traders used it as food for their prisoners on the South Atlantic voyages and introduced it to W. Africa in the early 16th century. Magellan took monkey nuts from Peru to the Moluccas and Philippines in 1519, whence they spread to Japan, Indo China and Southern Asia.

The peanut plant is an annual legume (rather than a nut, strictly speaking) growing 25–59cm (1–2ft) tall. The pods are produced from small insignificant flowers an inch or two above the ground, and after the yellow flowers have died off the stem bends to the soil and then – a remarkable thing happens. The young pod containing up to four seeds begins a rapid growth, forcing it under the soil (geocarpy) at a depth of 5–8cm (2–3in) where it remains until dug up 3–4 months after the nuts have matured; there are 2 nuts with thin brown skins inside the brittle shell. Each plant produces 40 or more pods; an upright variety and a low spreading variety also exist. Note that this is a ground nut, in contradistinction to a tree nut.

The oil

Peanut is the expressed oil of the seeds (nuts) and is used as a cheap substitute for almond oil. It has a distinctive odour and for massage is perhaps too 'oily' for some therapists.

152

Method of extraction

The oil is pressed from the nuts and the residue is a protein rich cake, which is a nutritious food for animals. About 42% of the decorticated nut is extractable as an edible oil.

Principal constituents (Bruneton 1995)

Type	Based on	Content – %
Saturated fatty acid:		
C18:0	stearic acid	1.3–6.5
C20:0	arachidic acid	1–3
C22:0	behenic acid	1–5
C24:0	lignoceric acid	0.5–3
Typical saturated fatty acid content		17
Monounsaturated fatty acid:		
C18:1	oleic acid	35–72
C20:1	ecosenoic acid	0.5–2.1
Typical monounsaturated fatty acid content		63
Polyunsaturated fatty acid:		
C18:2	linoleic acid	13–43
C18:3	linolenic acid	<0.6
Typical polyunsaturated fatty acid content		20

Physical properties

Energy value Kcal/100ml is 898

Vitamin and mineral content

The nuts contain vitamins B1, B6, E, niacin, folic acid and the minerals magnesium and potassium with about 46% fat with 20% MUFA.

Peanut oil is almost always refined to a high degree, and therefore any vitamin (eg vitamin E 0.2%) and mineral content is lost.

Therapeutic properties – external use

- said to be effective in helping arthritis and rheumatism
- has properties similar to olive oil (Trease & Evans 1983)

Cosmetic use

Used in the manufacture of soaps, shampoos, night creams, emollients, brilliantines, and sunburn creams. Popular with pharmacists for use in the preparation of ointments because of its stability, relative cheapness and ability to spread easily. Used in soothing ointments because it does not absorb too quickly; used as a carrier (an oily excipient) for some substances (Bruneton 1995) e.g. vaccines.

Culinary use

It is a nutritive oil, good for cooking and serves in many instances as a cheap substitute for olive oil. Can be used for shallow frying as it has a high smoke point.

Caution

Allergy to peanuts has increased steadily over the last two decades, and 6 occurrences of fatal anaphylaxis in 1993 were reported in the UK due to peanuts; the UK situation has been reviewed (Hourihane, Dean & Warner 1996, Ewan 1996). Ingestion can cause sensitization in young children, therefore this should be borne in mind for baby massage, also the use of creams and lotions for nursing mothers. Of nut allergies, that of peanut is the commonest, followed by Brazils, almonds, and hazelnuts, and any such allergy should be brought to light at the consultation stage of aromatherapy or massage. Peanut oils may contain carcinogenic substances made by a fungus which grows in damp peanuts (Erasmus 1986).

The oil is reported as a mild irritant in soap, but is considered harmless to the skin (Winter 1999 p.330).

Additional notes

1   Peanuts were cultivated about 3000 years ago in S. America and after Columbus peanuts quickly became crops all around the tropical areas of the world.
2   Oil production began in France in the middle of the 19th century where it was used in place of olive oil for frying because it did not degrade at high temperatures.
3   Refined oil is tasteless and has a shelf life of 18 months. The cold pressed oil has a slight peanut flavour with a shelf life of 12 months. Peanut oil kept at temperatures below 46F 8C becomes more viscous.
4   Peanuts are about 30% protein and oil content is approximately 50%.

References

Ewan P W 1996 Clinical study of peanut and nut allergy in 62 consecutive patients: new features and associations. British Medical Journal. 312(7038):1074–1078

Bruneton J 1995 Pharmacognosy, phytochemistry, medicinal plants. Intercept, Andover p.125

Erasmus U 1986 Fats and oils. Alive, Vancouver p.234

Hourihane J O, Dean T P, Warner J O 1996 Peanut allergy in relation to heredity, maternal diet and other atopic diseases: result of a questionnaire survey, skin prick testing and food challenges. British Medical Journal. 313(7064):1046

Iburg A 2004 Dumont's lexicon of oil and vinegar. Rebo, Lisse p.170–173

Trease G E, Evans W C 1983 Pharmacognosy. Baillière Tindall, London p.329

Winter R 1999 A consumers dictionary of cosmetic ingredients. 5th edn: Three Rivers Press, New York

Pecan oil

Scientific name
Carya illinoinensis (Wangenh.) K. Koch
Family: Juglandaceae

Etymology
The common name is American walnut. Most sources list it as *C. illinoensis* but there are synonyms: *Hicoria pecan*, *Carya pecan*, *Carya oliviformis*, *Caryocar nuciferum*.

Carya is the ancient Greek name for walnut; *illinoinensis* refers to Illinois, the state where the species was first described. *Nuciferum* has the meaning of bearing nuts. The Juglandaceae family comprises walnuts and hickories.

History
The pecan was an important source of food for native Americans and was planted as far away from its habitat in floodplains and uplands as central Mexico in pre–Columbian times. It has been extensively planted over a long period of time and it is the state tree of Texas.

The plant and its environment
The pecan is a large, spreading tree which attain a height of more than 20m (65ft) and living up to 300 years. It is cultivated principally in southern USA but also in Mexico, South Africa and Australia.

The alternate leaves are very large, up to 50cm (20in) long, and the flowers are greenish yellow catkins which appear in the Spring, male flowers (up to 10cm/4in) long are larger than the female. The nuts are thin shelled and are similar in appearance and size to walnuts and occur in clusters, which fall when mature.

The oil
Pecan nuts contain about 65–70% oil, of which there is less than 10% saturated fat, which is less than that contained by olive oil, peanut oil or corn oil.

Method of extraction
The highly unsaturated oil is edible and is available cold pressed from the pecan nut. It is also produced by refining the oil which has been expeller pressed from pecans, yielding a bland, odourless, product.

Principal constituents

Type	Based on	Content – %
Saturated fatty acid:		
C14:0	myristic	<0.1
C16:0	palmitic	6.5–8.0
C18:0	stearic	2–2.5
C20:0	arachidic	<0.5
Typical saturated fatty acid content		9–11
Monounsaturated fatty acid:		
C16:1	palmitoleic	<1.0
C17:1	9–heptadecenoic	<0.1
C18:1	oleic	43–51
C20:1	ecosenoic	<1
Typical monounsaturated fatty acid content		47–53
Polyunsaturated fatty acid:		
C18:2	linoleic	37–45
C18:3	α–linolenic	1.5–2.5
Typical polyunsaturated fatty acid content		37–43

Physical properties

Peroxide value (meq/kg oil)	0.5 max
Refractive index at 40EC	1.4650–1.4652
Colour (Lovibond 5¼" cell)	6 yellow/ red 1.1
Iodine value (wijs)	110–120
Saponification value	190
Unsaponifiable matter (%)	0.0 max
Specific gravity at 25EC	0.915
Colour	light amber to clear
% FFA (as Oleic)	0.05 max
Smoke Point	460°F (240°C)
Flash Point	630°F (330°C)
Fire Point	680°F (360°C)
Aroma	very little, slight nutty tones
Shelf life	6 to 8 months

Vitamin and mineral content

Vitamins E (24mg/100g), B1 and zinc.

Therapeutic properties

Pecan oil is not easily absorbed and will leave an oily film on the skin, therefore in massage therapy it is usually blended with other oils.

Cosmetic uses

It is used in preparations for mature and dry skins.

Culinary uses

Pecan oil goes well with balsamic vinegar and is very good in salad dressings. It adds character to rice dishes, corn and polenta and is also good with hard cheeses, mushrooms, fish and shellfish.

Cautions

1 The cold pressed oil is to be preferred to the highly refined oil.
2 As pecan oil easily goes rancid, refrigeration after opening is recommended.

Additional notes

1 The nutritious seeds are eaten not only by people but also many species of wildlife.
2 Pecan oil should be avoided by individuals with nut allergies.
3 A colouring for use in cosmetics is made from pecan shells.

Perilla seed oil

Scientific name

Perilla frutescens var. *frutescens*, *Perilla frutescens* var. *crispa shiso*
Family: Lamiaceae

Etymology

The derivation of *perilla* is obscure, but it is thought by some people that it may be connected to pearl; *frutescens* means shrubby.

In Korea the plant is called *tul–kkae* which means wild sesame plant and in Japanese the name is egoma derived from their word for sesame. There is no close connection between perilla and sesame plants.

The plant and its environment

Perilla was introduced to the United States in the late 1800s by Asian immigrants and quickly naturalized itself, soon becoming a common weed. It is annual herb of the mint family native to E. Asia, perilla is a traditional crop of China, India, Japan, Korea, Thailand, and other Asian countries. The plant is 120cm (4ft) tall, the stems are square, reddish–purple and the leaves are large, perhaps 15cm (6in) diameter, dark green tinted red to purple – occasionally so large and red that they give rise to the name beefsteak plant. The flower spikes are about 4cm (10in) long, although the numerous flowers themselves are small, about 6mm (¹⌷₄in) long, tubular and coloured pink to lavender.

The oil

Perilla frutescens egoma is valued for its oil extracted from the seeds, which is highly unsaturated and includes linolenic, linoleic, and oleic acids.

Extraction

The oil is cold expelled from the perilla seeds, which contain 35–45% oil.

Principal constituents

Type	Based on	Content – %
Monounsaturated fatty acid:		
C18:1	oleic	15
Polyunsaturated fatty acid:		
C18:2	linoleic	15
C18:3	α–linolenic	50–60

Physical properties

Iodine value (wijs)	185–208
Colour:	bright yellow – golden
Odour:	bland characteristic odour
Shelf life	1 to 2 years

Vitamin and mineral content

It is an oil rich in vitamins and amino acids.

Cosmetic uses

Perilla oil is used in soap making and is known to have antiseptic properties; it helps:
- the skin and hair retain moisture
- in the treatment of skin disorders such as dry eczema and psoriasis

Culinary uses

The plant also supplies a nutritious cooking oil from the seed, as well as giving colour and flavour to many pickled dishes.

The entire perilla plant is nutritious, is edible and medicinal. The leaves have a sweet taste (an aldehyde isomer in perilla is 2,000 times sweeter than sugar) and are used as a spice in dishes with fish, rice, vegetables, soups and also root ginger, which is then added to stir–fries and salads in many Asian countries.

Folklore and traditional plant remedies

The plant has been used for centuries in Oriental medicine as an antiasthmatic, antibacterial, antidote, antimicrobial, antipyretic, antiseptic, antispasmodic, antitussive, aromatic, carminative, diaphoretic, emollient, expectorant, pectoral, restorative, stomachic and tonic.

Infusion of the plant is useful in the treatment of asthma, colds, cough and lung afflictions, influenza prevention, nausea, vomiting, abdominal pain, constipation, food poisoning and allergic reactions (especially from seafood), and to restore health and balance. The stems are a traditional Chinese remedy for morning sickness and restless foetus in pregnancy, though some say the herb should be avoided by pregnant women.

The oil from the seeds is used in Shintoist ceremonies.

Cautions

There are no known contraindications.

Additional notes

1 Perilla seeds contain a drying oil (40%) with high content of unsaturated fatty acids; however, their medicinal value has sometimes been greatly exaggerated.

2 A drying oil similar to tung oil or linseed oil, perilla seed oil has been used for paints, varnishes, linoleum, printing ink, lacquers, and for protective waterproof coatings on cloth.

3 Perilla oil can also be used for fuel.

4 In parts of Asia, perilla oil is used as an edible oil, valued more for its medicinal benefit than its flavour. Perilla oil is a very rich source of the omega–3 fatty acid alpha–linolenic acid.

5 Perilla is a very aromatic plant, with a strong minty smell has deep purple stems and purple to red tinted leaves and attracts butterflies.

6 It is often confused with purple Basil and used for the same purposes.

7 Perilla yields a dark purple colouring.

8 Volatile oils of the plant are also used in aroma therapy and for perfume. Perilla leaves contain about 0.2% of an essential oil. In the most frequently cultivated chemotype, the main component is perillaldehyde (p–menthadien–1,8(9)–al(7), 75%) Its minor constituents are limonene (13%), linalool, β–caryophyllene, l–menthol, limonene, α–pinene, perillene (2–methyl–5–(3–oxolanyl)–2–pentene) and elemicin.

9 Perillaldehyde can cause skin allergies.

10 The crushed plant makes an effective insecticide

11 The oxime of perillaldehyde (perillartin) is used as an artificial sweetener in Japan as it is about 2000 times sweeter than sucrose.

12 Perilla ketone is toxic to some animals.

13 Perilla contains the pseudo tannins and antioxidants typical for the mint family.

14 The essential oil of the plant is used for flavouring food and dental products; it used to be an ingredient in sarsaparilla.

References and bibliography

He–ci Yu. "Perilla: The Genus Perilla", Medicinal & Aromatic Plants, Industrial Profiles. ISBN 90–5702–171–4.

Hao Zheng, Yun Wu, Jianqing Ding, Denise Binion, Weidong Fu and Richard Reardon (September 2004). "Perilla frutescens (Perilla)", Invasive Plants of Asian Origin Established in the US and Their Natural Enemies. USDA Forest Service, 129–130. Retrieved on 2006–11–17.

David Brenner (1995). Perilla. Purdue University New Crop Fact Sheet. Retrieved on 2006–11–17.

Gernot Katzer (September 19, 2006). Perilla (Perilla frutescens) L. Britton. Spice Pages. Retrieved on 2006–11–17.

Perilla (Japanese, Vietnamese and Korean Shi–So, Zi Su, Beefsteak). Evergreen Seeds. Retrieved on 2006–11–17.

http://www.uni–graz.at/~katzer/engl/Peri_fru.html

http://altnature.com/gallery/perilla.htm

Pistachio oil

Scientific name
Pistacia vera, Pistacia chinensis
Family: Anacardiaceae

Etymology
From the Greek word for the nut *pistake* (Latin *pistacium*); *vera* means true.
The Latinized *chinensis* indicates coming from China.

The plant and its environment
The deciduous Eurasian tree originates from southern Europe and Asia
Minor and is grown in France, Turkey, Italy, Iran and the USA. The pistachio
tree gives fruit every other year and its leaves are oval shaped and have a
grey–green colour. The nuts contain an edible greenish kernel.

The oil
Used mainly in the food industry.

Principal constituents (Kamangar *et al* 1975)

Type	Based on	Content – %
Saturated fatty acid:		
C14:0	myristic	trace
C16:0	palmitic	9.2–13.4
C18:0	stearic	0.5–1.1
C20:0	arachidic	trace
Typical saturated fatty acid content		12–14
Monounsaturated fatty acid:		
C16:1	palmitoleic	0.5–1.0
C18:1	oleic	55–65
Typical monounsaturated fatty acid content		49–52
Polyunsaturated fatty acid:		
C18:2	linoleic	22.6–31
C18:3	linolenic	0.1–0.4
Typical polyunsaturated fatty acid content		36–37

Physical properties

Unsaponifiable matter	0.72–0.96%
Saponification value	189.0–193.6

Refractive index	1.4635–1.4643
Iodine value	98.1–100.5
Energy value Kcal/100ml	895
Colour	green/amber

Culinary use

Used generally in many Middle Eastern dishes, the oil has a powerful, sweet flavour which does not go with everything, but it does go well with all sorts of green salads, especially those containing citrus. It is used also in mayonnaises, vinaigrettes, on smoked or grilled fish and as a glaze for grills and oven roasts. It works well with avocadoes, beetroot, apples and pears.

Cautions

None known.

Additional notes

1   The composition of pistachio oil extracted from seeds grown in Italy, Turkey, Iran and Greece is quite similar to that of olive oil, having high contents of oleic acid and ,–sitosterol (Arena *et al* 2007)

2   Solvent extracted oils in Turkey yielded 57–62% oil and were found to contain 55–65% oleic acid, the main fatty acid component: pentadecanoic acid, (Z)–7–hexadecenoic acid, margaric acid, Z–7–octadecenoic acid, arachidic acid, 11–eicosenoic acid, and behenic acid were detected (Satill *et al* 2003).

3   Ten pistachio samples from various Iranian cultivars were examined and the kernels were found to contain 55–61% oil (Kamangar *et al* 1975); presumably solvent extracted.

4   The essential oils of the fruits and the leaves of pistachio (Pistacia vera L.) were analyzed and the fresh unripe pistachio fruits were found to contain 0.5% essential oil and the leaves 0.1%. Twenty one compounds were identified in the essential oil of the fruits and the major components were (+)–·–pinene (55%) and terpinolene (31%). Thirty three compounds were identified in the essential oil of the leaves and the major components were found to be ·–pinene (30%), terpinolene (18%) and bornyl acetate (11%) (Tsokou *et al* 2007).

5   Essential oil of pistachio is not generally available.

References

Arena E, Campisia S, Fallicoa B, Maccaronea E 2007 Distribution of fatty acids and phytosterols as a criterion to discriminate geographic origin of pistachio seeds. Food Chemistry 104(1): 403–408

Satil F, Azcan N, Baser K H C 2003 Fatty acid composition of pistachio nuts in Turkey. Chemistry of Natural Compounds 39(4): 322–324

Kamangar T, Farrohi F, Mehran M 1975 Characteristics of pistachio kernel oils from Iranian cultivars. Journal of the American Oil Chemists' Society 52(12): 512–513

Tsokou A, Georgopoulou K, Melliou E, Magiatis P, Tsitsa E 2007 Composition and enantiomeric analysis of the essential oil of the fruits and the leaves of Pistacia vera from Greece. Molecules 12: 1233–1239

Poppy seed oil

Scientific name

Papaver somniferum

Family: Papaveraceae

Not poppy, nor mandragora,
Nor all the drowsy syrups of the world,
Shall ever medicine thee to that sweet sleep
Which ow'dst yesterday
Othello, Shakespeare

Etymology

The common name is opium poppy. *Papaver* is the Latin name for the flower; *somnus* is sleep and *ferre* is to carry, so *somniferum* means bearing sleep.

Summer set lip to earth's bosom bare,
And left the flushed print in a poppy there.
The Poppy, Francis Thompson (1859–1907)

History

It is difficult to determine the source of the opium poppy exactly as it has been cultivated since the Stone Age, but it is supposed to have its origin in Asia Minor and the Mediterranean. The history of the opium poppy predates written history; images of opium poppies have been found in ancient Sumerian artefacts (ca. 4000 BC) and it is mentioned in the Ebers Papyrus. The ancient Greeks gave it its modern name of opium and later Charlemagne ordered an increase in poppy cultivation. Poppy oil production began in Germany after knowledge of oriental cooking was spread during the Crusades and today it is grown widely.

The plant and its environment

The annual plant grows to a height of 75–120cm (2¹⁄₄–4ft) and has light green leaves and white, violet or red flowers. The round poppy seeds are contained in a golf ball size capsule which is formed on the blossom. There are three varieties of poppies grown for oil:

- the white poppy – Berlin poppy – with white or red petals and white seeds, which have the highest oil content of all poppies
- the closing poppy has light red petals and blue seeds, which produce a moderate amount of oil

• the grey poppy has light red petals with grey seeds having a low oil content

There are many varieties of the species Papaver somniferum. Some of the varieties (e.g. the Norman and Przemko varieties) have a low morphine content. The European poppy producers are Hungary, Austria, France, Poland, the Czech Republic, Slovakia, Greece; it is also grown in Turkey, the Middle East and India

The oil

No opiates can be found in poppy seed oil (Iberg 2004 p.250–251) but while the oil has no narcotic properties opiates are present in quantities large enough to be detectable by urinalysis. The poppy seed oil normally sold is cold pressed.

Extraction

Poppy seed oil is obtained by pressing the seeds of the poppy flower.

Principal constituents

Type	Based on	Content – %
Saturated fatty acid:		
C16:0	palmitic	12
C18:0	stearic	3
Typical saturated fatty acid content		15
Monounsaturated fatty acid:		
C18:1	oleic	16
Typical monounsaturated fatty acid content		16
Polyunsaturated fatty acid:		
C18:2	linoleic	68
C18:3	α–linolenic	1
Typical polyunsaturated fatty acid content		69

Physical properties

Shelf life	6 months to 1 year
Colour	yellow to reddish
Odour	none

Vitamin and mineral content

5mg vitamin E/100ml.

Cosmetic uses

Poppy seed oil is considered to have good moisturizing properties and can be used to make a wide variety of cosmetic products. It absorbs into the skin fairly slowly leaving a slight oily feeling. It is highly emollient and possesses characteristics similar to hemp seed oil, for which it can be used as a substitute. Poppy seed oil is a suitable choice for inclusion in balm, hair conditioner, soap and other formulations.

Culinary uses

Dieticians do not consider this oil particularly suitable because of the ratio of linoleic to linolenic acid, which is not ideal.

However, the seeds of the poppy plant are edible and non–toxic, and have been used for cooking (particularly baking) since ancient times.

Folklore and traditional plant remedies

Opium (not the oil) has been used for treating asthma, stomach illnesses, and bad eye sight.

Cautions

None known.

Additional notes

1   The Opium Wars between China and the British Empire took place in the late 1830s when the Chinese attempted to stop the British selling opium in China.

2   Cultivated poppies are regulated by narcotics laws, but generally it is legal for gardeners to cultivate low morphine varieties, i.e. when the capsules contain less than 0.01% morphine.

3   The fluid in the bud which is a precursor to opium is present only before the seeds are formed, therefore poppy seeds have no narcotic properties.

4   Poppy seed oil is used as a lubricant in fine machinery (Winter 1999 p.354)

References

Iberg A 2004 Dumont's lexicon of oil & vinegar. Rebo, Lisse
Winter R 1999 A consumers dictionary of cosmetic ingredients. 5th edn: Three Rivers Press, New York

Pumpkin seed oil

Scientific name
Cucurbita maxima, *C. pepo*
Family: Cucurbitaceae

Etymology
Cucurbita is the Latin name for a gourd, and *maxima* means largest: *pepo* is Latin for large pumpkin or marrow.

The plant and its environment
The pumpkin grows in the warmer climes and is an ancient vegetable (fruit). It is said to have grown continuously in the Americas for some 9,000 to 10,000 years! Pumpkins were introduced into England in the 17th century where they grow quite well on compost heaps, and these huge vegetables captured the popular imagination, even to the extent of being incorporated into a fairy tale. Pumpkin pie is popular in the USA, where the hollowed out shell with candlelight shining through the pierced eyes and mouth is ubiquitous at Halloween.

Method of extraction
Pumpkin seeds are cleaned and dried and then, usually, are cold pressed to produce the oil, which is a dark reddish–green colour with a delicious, sweetish taste.

Principal constituents

Type	Based on	Content – %
Saturated fatty acid:		
C16:0	palmitic acid	6–21
C18:0	stearic acid	3–8
C20:0	eicosanoic	<1
C24:0	tetracosanoic	<1
Typical saturated fatty acid content		15
Monounsaturated fatty acid:		
C18:1	oleic acid	24–41
C20:1	eicosenoic	< 0.5
C24:1	tetracosenoic	<1
Typical monounsaturated fatty acid content		31

Polyunsaturated fatty acid:		
C18:2	linoleic acid	42–60
C18:3	α–linolenic acid	<2
Typical polyunsaturated fatty acid content		45

Physical properties

Iodine value	110–130
Colour	dark green
Peroxide value	<4

Vitamin and mineral content

Pumpkin seeds are rich in zinc. The oil contains vitamins B, C, E (18g/100ml) and phytosterols which inhibit inflammation of prostate tissue (Europhyto–Institut p.34).

Folklore and traditional plant remedies

Pumpkin seeds are about 30% protein and contain a significant amount of zinc. They are eaten by some Romany men to maintain their virility. The seeds are used for travel sickness and together with Senna alexandrina for tapeworms and round worms (Bown 1995). Bartram (1995) states that pumpkin seeds are ground and mixed with honey as an anthelmintic and because of their antimitotic effect they are used to maintain the health of and arrest enlargement of the prostate gland.

Therapeutic properties – internal

Pumpkin seed oil is:

- reputed, as a winter food supplement, to be good for the lungs and the mucous membranes
- slightly diuretic for urinary complaints, is used as a demulcent and as a general vermifuge (Duke 1985) (due to the presence of curcubilin (Europhyto–Institut)
- healing to the digestive tract (Stier 1990)
- emollient, calming, laxative and is employed in cases of demineralisation. It is only necessary to use it in small quantities (1 dessertspoonful for an adult)
- placed among the top nutritional oils (Stier 1990) – along with hemp seed oil and flax seed oil – providing the highest EFAs (omega 3 and omega 6) required for healthy mind/body functioning
- said to provide increased energy, to aid the maintenance and improvement of sexual health and optimum brain function

169

- known to give excellent results, when used orally, for men suffering from prostate troubles and women with urinary infections (Europhyto–Institut)
- given for general fatigue, intestinal parasites, high cholesterol, tooth decay, mouth ulcers and vascular problems (Clergeaud & Clergeaud 2000 p.104–105)

Cosmetic uses

Pumpkin seed oil maintains a smooth skin and is useful for skin problems such as sores and ulcers.

Culinary uses

Pumpkin seed oil is best used in its raw state. Most people use 1 or 2 tablespoons straight or blended in a protein drink, shake, or smoothie. It can also be used in the making of salad dressing.

Cautions

This oil is often diluted with cheaper refined oils. There are no known contraindications.

Additional notes

1 Pumpkin seed oil keeps well and rarely goes rancid but must be kept in the refrigerator
2 The oil should never be never heated.
3 Pumpkin seed oil is believed to be a good tonic for men because of its zinc, calcium, iron, magnesium and B complex vitamins which are needed for enzyme production, cell division, growth, reproduction and a healthy immune system. Zinc is believed to help men with benign prostate disease, apparently inhibiting the production of the hormone involved in the enlargement of the prostate gland.

References

Bartram T 1995 Encyclopedia of herbal medicine. Grace, Christchurch p.361
Bown D 1995 Encyclopedia of herbs and their uses. BCA, London p.269
Duke J A 1985 Handbook of medicinal herbs. CRC Press, Boca Raton p.195
Europhyto–Institut undated La phytothérapie: la santé par les plantes. Editions Alpen, Monaco p.34
Stier B 1990 Secrets des huiles de première pression à froid. Self published, Quebec p.63
Clergeaud C, Clergeaud L 2000 Les huiles végétales. Atlantica, Biarritz

Rapeseed oil

Scientific name

Brassica napus, Brassica campestris
Family: Cruciferae

Etymology

From the Latin (*napus*) and Greek words for turnip. *Brassica* is the Latin name for cabbage, while *campestris* means of the fields.

Common names are rape, oilseed rape, rapa, rapaseed and canola (an artificial variety). The common name is derived from the Old English word *rapum* for turnip. *Canola* comes from the initials of Canadian Oilseed Low Acid.

The plant and its environment

The plant has intense yellow flowers which are so remarkable a feature of the British countryside in early summer. It grows to a height of about 1.5m (5ft), is produced in China in great quantity and is widely grown as a forage crop in the USA.

Method of extraction

The seeds contain 35–40% oil, and after extraction the exhausted seeds are used as cattle fodder. Almost 50 million tonnes are produced each year. A very small amount of cold pressed oil is made.

Principal constituents

Type	Based on	Content – %
Saturated fatty acids:		
C14:0	myristic	trace
C16:0	palmitic	4.2
C18:0	stearic	1.5
C20:0	arachidic	<1
C22:0	behenic	<1
C24:0	lignoceric	trace
Typical saturated fatty acid content		6–8
Monounsaturated fatty acids:		
C16:1	palmitoleic	<1
C18:1	oleic	58
Typical monounsaturated fatty acid content		55

171

Polyunsaturated fatty acids:		
C18:2	linoleic	20
C18:3	α–linolenic	10
Typical polyunsaturated fatty acid content	30–37	

Physical properties

Energy value Kcal/100ml	897
Colour	brownish yellow
Odour	unpleasant
Shelf life	6 months to 1 year
Energy	3344kj 813kcal

Minerals and vitamins

Sodium 0.4g/100ml, vitamin C 28mg/100ml.

Therapeutic properties

Only a highly refined oil is available which has no significant therapeutic properties. Contains omega–6 and omega–3 acids in the ratio of 2:1.

Cosmetic use

Rapeseed oil has no particular merit for either aromatherapy or cosmetic purposes; it is suitable for use in soft soaps.

Culinary use

The oil is used commercially in food production and is also used to a small extent in the home. It is not a stable oil for frying and so is best used in salad dressings, but suffers the disadvantage that it has no taste or flavour.

Cautions

This oil, not generally regarded as edible, can cause acnelike skin eruptions (Winter 1999 p.371).

Additional notes

1 Canola oil – processed rape seed oil – may contain erucic acid, a highly toxic substance which is known to cause heart damage and cancer (Anon 1997).

2 High erucic (acid) rapeseed oil contains 50% erucic acid, but oils for human consumption have been genetically modified so that the plants contain little or no erucic acid (Stier 1990).

3 The oil is used in additives for the plastics industry, antifoaming agents and detergents (Bruneton 1995).

4 Refrigeration after opening is recommended.

5 A proportion of rapeseed oil is treated and used to lubricate farm machinery.

Reference

Anon 1997 Townsend Letter for Doctors and Patients. May :17
Bruneton J 1995 Pharmacognosy, phytomedicine, medicinal plants. Intercept, Andover p.132
Stier B 1990 Secrets des huiles de première pression à froid. Self published, Quebec p.61
Winter R 1999 A consumers dictionary of cosmetic ingredients. 5th edn: Three Rivers Press, New York

Rice bran oil

Scientific name
Oryza sativa
Family: Poaceae, Graminaceae

Etymology
Oryza is the Latin word for rice and *sativa* is the botanical term for cultivated.

Method of extraction
Ice bran is a refined oil extracted from the bran of the rice kernel.

Principal constituents

Type	Based on	Content – %
Monounsaturated fatty acid:		
C18:1	oleic acid	43.6
Polyunsaturated fatty acid:		
C18:2	linoleic acid	36.6
C18:3	linolenic acid	1.8
Typical fatty acid content		16.3

Physical properties

Colour Lovibond	3.0 R max / 30.0 Y max
Free fatty acids	0.05% max
Iodine value	98–108
Peroxide value	1.5 max
Saponification value	185–195
Unsaponifiable matter	2.5% max
Smoke point	>500°F
Specific gravity @ 25°C	0.913–0.919
Refractive index 25°C	1.470–1.473

• This oil is difficult to obtain on a retail basis
• Naturally high in tocopherols and ferulic acid (an antioxidant)

Culinary
As far as cooking is concerned, in its unrefined state it has characteristics similar to those of wheatgerm oil (Emmerson & Ewin 1996). Foods cooked

174

with rice bran oil absorb less oil, which results in food which is lower in calories and with a better taste. A very high smoke (burn) point makes it ideal for pan or stir frying.

Additional notes

1   It contains Essential Fatty Acids (EFA), can help to lower cholesterol and contains a many vitamins, antioxidants and other nutrients.

2   It has a high level of components with nutraceutical value such as gamma–oryzanol and tocotrienols.

3   Rice bran oil is said to reduce cholesterol more efficiently than olive oil, reducing harmful cholesterol (LDL) without reducing good cholesterol (HDL).

4   A natural component of rice bran oil lowers cholesterol in rats, and ongoing research also shows it may have potential as an anticancer and antiinfection agent in humans (Minhajuddin 2005)

References

Emmerson M, Ewin J 1996 A feast of oils. Thorsons, London p.141
Minhajuddin M 2005 Rice bran oil to cut cholesterol. Food Navigator. 13 May

Rose hip oil

Scientific names

Rosa species – *Rosa canina* L., *R. rubiginosa*, also *R. acicularis* Lindl., *R. cinnamomea*, *R. rugosa*, *R. villosa*, *R. rubiginosa*.

Family: Rosaceae

Etymology

Rosa canina is known as the dog rose or the moquette rose. *Canina* is from the Latin meaning dog–like, perhaps from the sharp toothed leaves, or, as some think, from the old belief that the root of the plant was a cure for rabies resulting from the bite of a rabid dog. *Acicularis* means needle like, *villosa* means soft–haired, *rubiginosa* means rusty red, *rugosa* means wrinkled and *cinnamomea* means cinnamon brown.

The plant and its environment

Rosa rubiginosa is a species of wild rose originating in Asia and later introduced into Chile, where the bush grows wild in the Andes, principally in Chile and Peru, and is found in poor soil in mountainous areas, where it reaches a height of up to 2.5m (8ft). It bears white and pink flowers of 3–6cm diameter which ultimately form hips (amarilla). The rose hips owe their colour to carotenoids (Bruneton 1995); technically they are the swollen receptacles, *Fructus cynosbati* (Schauenberg & Paris 1990); cyno comes from the Greek *kyon* meaning dog.

The oil

The oil is a golden reddish colour, due to the carotenoids in the hips, and is produced from the fruits or berries of wild bushes.

Method of extraction

Seeds make up 70% by weight of the fruit and these are the source of the oil. It is extracted and refined using adaptations of conventional methods. The hips are first dried at temperatures which are kept below 80°C in order to avoid possible degradation. They are then split in order to obtain the seeds which are themselves broken down via a grinding process.

In Chile a rosehip oil is produced by simple expression without the use of solvents and can be said to be an organic oil.

Crude rose hip oil is produced by solvent extraction (hexane), which can then be further refined in order to obtain a material with an extended shelf life.

Principal constituents

Type	Based on	Content – %
Saturated fatty acid units:		
C12:0	lauric acid	trace
C14:0	myristic acid	trace
C16:0	palmitic acid	3.6
C18:0	stearic acid	1.7
C20:0	arachidic acid	0.7
C22:0	behenic acid	trace
Typical saturated fatty acid unit content		6
Monounsaturated fatty acid units:		
C16:1	palmitoleic acid	trace
C18:1	oleic acid	13.4
C20:1	eicosenoic acid	trace
Typical monounsaturated fatty acid unit content		13
Polyunsaturated fatty acid units:		
C18:2	linoleic acid	43.6
C18:3	α–linolenic acid	27–36
Typical polyunsaturated fatty acid unit content		78

Physical properties

Odour	faint, slightly castor oil–like
Acid value	0.16
Specific gravity	0.927
Colour	golden–orange

Folklore and traditional plant uses

Rose hips contain about twenty times as much vitamin C as oranges and children in the 1930's and 40's were given rose–hip syrup to supplement their intake of Vitamin C. The hips themselves have a tonic effect and the seeds were once used as a diuretic, although one study has shown that an infusion of the hips does not have a diuretic effect (Jaretzky 1941). The hips and leaves are mildly laxative (Tyler 1993) and have an astringent action (Stuart 1987). Phytopharmaceutical drugs based on rose hips have been traditionally used in functional asthenia, and to facilitate weight gain (Bruneton 1995).

Therapeutic properties – internal use

Rose hip oil contains small amounts of trans–retinoic acid which gives it therapeutic properties. The oil is antiscorbutic, antihaemorrhagic and diuretic.

177

Therapeutic properties – external use

* skin regeneration
* scars
* wounds
* burns
* eczema
* for ulcers and acne one or
  two drops can be applied
  to the skin

Cosmetic use

Rose hip oil may be used in cosmetic creams and lotions.
In Chile it has been found that the oil is a tissue regenerator,
having an effect on the skin to prevent premature ageing, minimize wrinkles
and reduce scar tissue. It is recommended for use (up to 10%) in a blend with
macadamia and sweet almond oils.

Culinary use

As a fitness tea, rose hips help maintain healthy collagen (Bartram 1996).

Rosehips were a popular sweetmeat in the Middle Ages (Chevallier 1996)
and today jellies, syrups, jams and herbal teas are produced from the fruits
(Schauenberg & Paris 1990).

Cautions

1   Trans–retinoic acid presents benefits without harmful secondary effects,
    except in the case of overdose, when irritation may be caused.
2   There are two qualities available on the market, one unrefined and the
    other refined and which may have been subjected to temperatures up to
    250°C.
3   The oil is fragile, susceptible to heat, light and oxygen and so should be
    suitably stored.

References

Bartram T 1996 Encyclopedia of herbal medicine. Grace, Christchurch p.376
Bruneton J 1995 Pharmacognosy, phytochemistry, medicinal plants. Intercept, Andover pp 21–23
Chevallier A 1996 Encyclopedia of medicinal plants. Dorling Kindersley, London p.261
Jaretzky R 1941 Pharm. Zentralh. 82:229 cited in: Bisset N G (ed.) 1994 Herbal drugs and
    phytopharmaceuticals. Medpharm, Stuttgart pp 424–426
Schauenberg P, Paris F 1990 Guide to medicinal plants. Lutterworth Press, Cambridge p.67
Stuart M (ed.) 1987 Encyclopedia of herbs and herbalism. Black Cat, London p.253
Tyler V E 1993 The honest herbal. Pharmaceutical Products Press, New York p.263

Safflower oil

Scientific name

Carthamus tinctorius L.
Family: Asteraceae (Compositae)

Etymology

Tinctorius means of dyes or belonging to dyers. *Carthamus* is modern Latin and is derived from the Arabic *qurtum* and the Hebrew *qarthami*, meaning to dye, to colour (Reader's Digest 1985). Synonyms are American saffron, false saffron, bastard saffron and dyers' saffron.

The plant and its environment

The safflower is a tall, annual plant resembling a thistle with red or orange–yellow flowers – hence its English name, which is a shortened form of saffron flower. It is related to the lettuce, sunflower, artichoke, chicory and daisy, and is sometimes referred to as American saffron (indeed, it has been used to adulterate genuine saffron, hence the common name 'bastard saffron'). It is a plant of antiquity, and has always been highly regarded; safflower seeds have been discovered in Egyptian tombs up to 3000 years old. Both the flowers and the seeds have been used in the dyeing of material.

Producers include Mexico, India and the United States, although the quantities produced, while by no means insignificant, are far below that of the chief oil crops (Bruneton 1995).

The oil

A fluid, unsaturated oil which is a pale to rusty yellow in colour and with a make up similar to that of sunflower oil. It thickens and becomes rancid on exposure to air.

Method of extraction

Produced by cold expression of the seeds.

Principal constituents

Type	Based on	Content – %
Saturated fatty acid:		
C16:0	palmitic acid	6–7.5
C18:0	stearic acid	2–2.5

179

Typical saturated fatty acid content		9
Monounsaturated fatty acid:		
C16:1	palmitoleic acid	0.5
C18:1	oleic acid	20 (high 72–79)
Typical monounsaturated fatty acid content		16
Polyunsaturated fatty acid:		
C18:2	linoleic acid	77 (55–81)
C18:3	linolenic acid	trace
Typical polyunsaturated fatty acid content		76

Physical properties

Odour	bland, little odour
Energy value	903
Iodine value	140 150 (87 94 high oleic)

Folklore and traditional plant uses

The natural pigments safflomin and carthamine (or vegetable red) have a long history in dyeing and in the manufacture of paints and cosmetics. The leaves and seeds are capable of making milk curdle, thanks to a special enzyme. The oil has been used as a lamp oil. The flowers are laxative and diaphoretic (Wren 1975).

Therapeutic properties – internal use

Use of safflower oil aids prevention of chronic degenerative diseases such as arteriosclerosis, arthritis and coronary thrombosis (Bartram 1996). It prevents cholesterol from hardening and normalizes its metabolism (Stier 1990). The oil is a purgative (Reader's Digest 1985). Both the seeds and the extracted oil are beneficial to diabetics (Bartram 1996) or those suffering with angina and circulatory problems. The oil is also helpful in cases of bronchial asthma and nephrosis. Safflower is reputed to have diuretic properties and safflower tea has sudorific properties (i.e. it promotes sweating).

Therapeutic properties – external use

Helpful against eczema and rough skin (Bartram 1996).

Cosmetic use

Safflower oil is used in:
• the making of rouge and other make–up in Algeria
• creams and lotions to soften the skin
• hair conditioners

Culinary use

The keeping qualities are poor and it is unstable at elevated temperatures: it is therefore not good for most culinary purposes except as a salad dressing. It is however useful as a food supplement as it is a rich source of essential fatty acids.

Cautions

Safflower oil has no known contraindications and is safe as a cosmetic ingredient (Winter 1999 p.378).

Additional note

People on long term parenteral alimentation may be deficient in EFA and develop redness and scaling in the scalp and eyebrows and suffer hair loss (Skolnik *et al* 1977). These changes may be reversed by the topical application of safflower oil, because of its high content of linoleic acid (Rook & Dawber 1991 p.149).

References

Bartram T 1996 Encyclopedia of herbal medicine. Grace, Christchurch p.379
Stier B 1990 Secrets des huiles de première pression à froid. Self published, Quebec p.59
Bruneton J 1995 Pharmacognosy, phytochemistry, medicinal plants. Intercept, Andover p.134
Reader's Digest 1985 Secrets et vertus des plantes médicinales. Sélection du Reader's Digest, Paris p.101
RookA, Dawber R eds 1991 Diseases of the hair and scalp. 2nd edn Blackwell Scientific, Oxford
Skolnik P, Eaglstein W H, Zibouh V A 1977 Human essential fatty acid deficiency. Archives of Dermatology 113: 939
Wren R W (ed.) 1975 Potter's new cyclopaedia of botanical drugs and preparations. Health Science Press, Bradford, nr. Holsworthy p.264
Winter R 1999 A consumers dictionary of cosmetic ingredients. 5th edn: Three Rivers Press, New York

Sesame oil

Scientific name

Sesamum indicum DC
Family: Pedaliaceae

Etymology

The name comes from *simsim* (Arabic), *semsem* (Coptic) and *semsemt* (Egyptian). It is also known as gingelly (or gingili) oil, teel oil, benne oil and thunderbolt oil. Sesame is mentioned in the *Ebers Papyrus* which dates from about 1800 BC. In Hindu mythology sesame relates to the god *Yama*, the judge of the dead, and is the symbol of mortality.

The plant and its environment

The sesame plant, originating from the tropical regions of the East Indies, is an upright annual with long bell–like flowers resembling those of the foxglove. The flowers are white with just a tinge of red, blue or yellow.

The seeds are difficult to harvest as the keel shaped seedpods shatter easily, so they need to be gathered by hand. However, there are now several different modern varieties, varying in height from 0.6–2.5m (2–8ft) which allow machine harvesting. As a result, sesame is grown world wide, especially in China, India, Africa and South America (where it was introduced by the Portuguese). Sesame has been cultivated for at least 4000 years in Mesopotamia and is documented somewhat later in India and China. It was one of the plants found in the tomb of Tutankhamun 1370–1352 BC (Chevallier 1996).

The hulled seeds are waxy, measuring approximately 3mm in length, with a shape like a flat teardrop. Their colour varies from white, through reddish brown to black; in fact, they are known commercially as 'white and black'. The white seeds yield the superior oil. The seeds escape spontaneously from the ovary at maturity and this may be the source idea behind Ali Baba's exclamation in the Arabian Nights – 'Open sesame'.

The oil

The oil has properties similar to those of olive oil. It is very stable as it contains a natural antioxidant system made up of sesamol and sesamolinol formed from sesamolin; these reduce the rate of oxidation significantly (Houghton 1995).

Method of extraction

The seed contains up to 55% oil and the best grade is obtained by single cold pressing and filtering. It is a clear pale yellow colour. A lesser quality oil is available which has been hot pressed at high pressure, and then refined and deodorised before being suitable for use. Most sesame oils have some colour and sometimes they are bleached, but such oils tend to be somewhat acid.

Principal constituents

Type	Based on	Content – %
Saturated fatty acid:		
C14:0	myristic acid	<0.5
C16:0	palmitic acid	7.0–12.0
C18:0	stearic acid	3.5–6.0
C20:0	arachidic acid	<1.0
C22:0	behenic acid	<0.5
Typical saturated fatty acid content		16
Monounsaturated fatty acid:		
C16:1	palmitoleic acid	<0.5
C18:1	oleic acid	35–50
C20:1	eicosenoic acid	<0.5
C22:1	erucic acid	<0.1
Typical monounsaturated fatty acid content		40
Polyunsaturated fatty acid:		
C18:2	linoleic acid	35–50
C18:3	α–linolenic acid	<1.0
Typical polyunsaturated fatty acid unit content		44

Physical properties

Odour	almost odourless
Acid value	0.3 max
Specific gravity	0.915–0.925
Energy value Kcal/100ml	898

Vitamins

The oil is high in vitamins A, B and E, and in calcium, magnesium and phosphorus.

Folklore and traditional plant uses

The seeds are helpful in cases of constipation and, when ground up with water, can be used to treat haemorrhoids. In India a liquid extract is made by boiling the seeds with water to use as an emmenagogue (Stuart 1987). Sesame oil may be used as a drug solvent. The cosmetics industry uses an extract as an antioxidant, radical scavenger and regenerating agent (Bruneton 1995).

The seeds were ground in ancient Egypt to produce a flour and today throughout the East and the Mediterranean they are made into a paste called tahini, supposed to give long life. The women of ancient Babylon ate halva, a mixture of sesame and honey, to retain their youth and beauty; Roman soldiers mixed sesame seeds with honey for energy during their campaigns.

Therapeutic properties – internal use

Sesame oil is said to improve the blood platelet count and combat anaemia (Bartram 1996). It is said that 20 drops taken daily double the count in children in three to four weeks. It is also said to be effective against spleen disorders. The oil is soothing to the digestive tract (high in calcium, not acid forming) and is a mild laxative.

Therapeutic properties – external use
- excellent for massage when used at around 20% in the base carrier
- beneficial for rheumatic and skin conditions
- in Scandinavia it is used for psoriasis, dry eczema, broken veins (Thomsen 1986)
- protects skin from UV rays (Lubinic 1997)
- it is a skin softener
- the oil contains elements which are active against lice (Winter 1999 p.385)

Cosmetic use

Sesame oil is used in brilliantine, sun screens, shampoos, hair conditioners, soaps and lubricating creams. Mixed with olive oil it can be used to counteract dandruff.

Culinary use

The natural oil does not have a definite taste and is suitable for flavoured dips, salad dressings and deep frying: it is used in the manufacture of margarine. Toasted sesame oil is also available which adds flavour to salad dressings and eastern dishes. Both tahini and halva (see above) are now available in some supermarkets and stores. The toasted oil is used sparingly in crudities and mayonnaise and gives the flavour to humus.

Cautions

Sesame oil has been reported as causing hypersensitivity (Torsney 1964). It may cause allergic reaction, primarily contact dermatitis (Winter 1999 p.385). It is safe as a cosmetic ingredient (CIR Expert Panel).

Additional note

The oil contains antioxidants and lecithin and is said to be good for the nervous system.

References

Bartram T 1996 Encyclopedia of herbal medicine. Grace, Christchurch p.389
Bruneton J 1995 Pharmacognosy, phytopharmacy, medicinal plants. Intercept, Andover p.130–131
Chevallier A 1996 Encyclopedia of medicinal plants. Dorling Kindersley, London p.268
Houghton C 1995 Essential facts about speciality oil. Cosmetics & Toiletries Manufacturers & Suppliers, Dec 1995/Jan 1996: 21
Lubinic E 1997 Handbuch Aromatherapie. Ätherische Öle und ihre Anwendung. Hüthig Medizin Verlag, Stuttgart
Stuart M (ed) 1987 Encyclopedia of herbs and herbalism. Black Cat, London p.263
Thomsen S 1986 Personal communication
Torsney P J 1964 Hypersensitivity to sesame seed. Journal of Allergy 35: 514–519
Winter R 1999 A consumers dictionary of cosmetic ingredients. 5th edn: Three Rivers Press, New York

Shea butter

Scientific name

Vitellaria paradoxa, (*Butyrospermum parkii*)
Family: Sapotaceae

Etymology

Shea comes from the Bambara word *si*; Bambara is spoken in Mali. Other common names are karité butter, bambuk butter.

The plant and its environment

The karité nut trees, also known as mangifolia, grow in the semi–arid wooded savannah regions of tropical West and Central Africa (e.g. Nigeria, Togo). The dried fruit consists of a thin shell, having an egg shaped seed. The seeds are about 3g in weight. The kernels contain about 50% of a non–drying fat. Both nuts and the fat are exported to Europe as well as used locally (Magness *et al.* 1971). The mangifolia tree can live up to 300 years.

The oil

Shea butter is a slightly greenish natural fat extracted from nuts of scattered wild shea trees.

There are two kinds of shea butter available, unrefined and refined, and most shea butter available outside West Africa is white and odourless; in other words it has been refined to remove the odour and colour of the natural product. In the process, the majority of the effective healing agents are also removed.

Extraction

The fruits of the shea tree are dried and then pulverized into a fine paste and boiled, when the shea butter floats to the top.

In addition, refined shea butter has usually been extracted from the shea kernels with hexane or other petroleum solvents. The extracted oil is boiled to drive off the toxic solvents, and then refined, bleached, and deodorized, which involves heating it to over 205°C (400°F) and the use of harsh chemicals, such as sodium hydroxide. Some undesirable solvent residues remain and antioxidants or preservatives such as BHA (butylated hydroxyanisole) or BHT (butylated hydroxytoluene) may be added. This results in an odourless, white butter that lacks some of the moisturizing, healing and nutritive properties of unrefined shea butter. The refined product has an extended shelf life.

Physical properties

	Off white	Semi solid
Melting point	32	45
Iodine value	50	70
Saponification value	165	195

Therapeutic properties of the unrefined oil

An antiinflammatory agent, shea butter has healing effects on the following conditions:

- scars and stretch marks.
- eczema.
- burns, rashes, scrapes, small wounds.
- dry skin, skin irritations, and ulcerated skin.
- rheumatism and aching muscles.

It displays a protective role against UV rays because of the cinnamic acid and latex content.

Cosmetic uses

Shea butter helps cell regeneration and capillary circulation and so is good for ageing skin and dry, fragile hair. It is a humectant (absorbs moisture from the air) and so is good for dry skin; it is an ingredient in soaps, lotions, suntan gels and creams, indoor tanning preparations, hair conditioners and lipsticks.

Culinary uses

Shea butter is edible. In Europe, the fat is used as a cooking fat, in the manufacture of margarine and as a substitute for cacao butter

Folklore and traditional plant remedies

Shea butter has many useful properties and has been traditionally used as a decongestant, an antiinflammatory for sprains and arthritis, a healing salve for babies' umbilical cords, a lotion for hair and skin care, as a cooking oil and for lamp fuel. In central Togo, shea butter is applied to the skin and hair as a moisturizer and is also a main ingredient in traditional black soaps.

Cautions

Shea butter does not normally trigger any allergic reaction but in a case of latex allergy a patch test is recommended. Winter (1999 p.387) states that there is no known toxicity.

Additional notes

1   It is consumed in traditional cuisine and used in the chocolate industry as a substitute for cocoa butter.
2   Scarcity of supply results in an erratic market price.
3   Followers of the Holy Spirit Movement rebel group of Uganda smeared their bodies with shea butter in the belief that it would stop bullets.
4   It is used in Togo, West Africa for ceremonies among the Fulani ethnic group.
5   Sometimes called 'women's gold' because extracting the butter from the nuts gives employment and income to hundreds of thousands of rural African village women.
6   The extracted meal is fed to cattle.

References

Magness J R, Markle G M, Compton C C 1971 Food and feed crops of the United States. Interregional Research Project IR–4, IR Bul. 1 (Bul. 828 New Jersey Agr. Expt. Sta.)
Winter R 1999 A consumers dictionary of cosmetic ingredients. 5th edn: Three Rivers Press, New York

Sisymbrium oil

Scientific name

Sisymbrium irio, (syn. *Sisymbrium orientale*, *Erysimum irio*)
Family: Brassicaceae (Cruciferae)

Etymology

In English the common name is London rocket; other common names are Asalio, Khubkata (Rajasthan, western India)

The plant and its environment

This is a herbaceous plant found in certain regions of Asia. It is an annual weed introduced in California and the eastern U.S. The plant grows to 0.5m (18in) tall, with petiolate lower leaves and sessile upper leaves The flowers are pale yellow, 2.5–4mm (1–1^1⁄$_2$in) long, the pods are cylindrical, 3–4cm (1^1⁄$_4$–1^1⁄$_2$in) and the seeds are oblong, about 1mm (0.05in) long.

The oil

The seeds contain 22–30% by weight of a fixed oil which is a clear yellow–green colour with a distinctive odour and taste.

Method of extraction

Sisymbrium oil is a fixed oil obtained from the seeds of the plant by cold pressing.

Principal constituents

Type	Based on	Content – %
Monounsaturated fatty acid:		
C14:0		0.7
C16:0	palmitic acid	6–15
C18:0	stearic acid	1.9–3.5
C20:0	arachidic acid	1.7
C22:0	behenic acid	9.5
C24:0	lignoceric acid	0.9
Typical saturated fatty acid content		20
Monounsaturated fatty acid:		
C16:1	palmitoleic acid	0.2
C18:1	oleic acid	12–17

C20:1	ecosenoic acid	9.2
C22:1	erucic acid	0.2–10
Typical monounsaturated fatty acid content		22
Polyunsaturated fatty acid:		
C18:2	linoleic acid	15.6–16.6
C18:3 omega 6	α–linoleic acid	0.6
C18:3 omega 3	gamma linoleic acid	37
C22 others		0.9
Typical polyunsaturated fatty acid content		55

Physical properties

Specific gravity at 20°C	0.913
Refractive index	1.465–1.470
Saponification value	160–180
Iodine value	96–103 [191]
Acid Value	2.5

Folklore and traditional plant remedies

As early as Roman times sisymbrium oil was used as a massage oil for the body. Today, in certain regions of India, sisymbrium seeds are brewed to treat skin ailments. It is interesting to note that around the regions of Hyderabad and Lahore, not far from Kashmir, the seeds themselves are applied to the face for between 15 and 20 minutes: this is reputed to give excellent results in improving the texture and appearance of the skin. The oil is used as a tonic

Cosmetic use

An oil giving beneficial properties to skin care preparations.

Culinary

The plant is eaten raw in salads in Sicily (Lentini & Venza 2007) and the seeds are used as a base for a refreshing, cooling drink. In Arizona (USA) the green parts are eaten by the native American Mohave and Yuma tribes.

Cautions

No known toxicity.

References

Lentini F, Venza F 2007 Wild food plants of popular use in Sicily. Journal of Ethnobiology & Ethnomedicine. 2007; 3: 15.

Soya oil

Scientific name

Glycine max, Glycine soja, Glycine hispida
Family: Leguminosae

Etymology

Also known as soja, soybean and soy oil. Hispida
from the Latin *hispidus* means bristly, coarse, having
short stiff hairs. *Glycine* is from the Greek *glukus*
meaning sweet, as the leaves and roots of some species are sweet. Soy is
derived (probably) from the Chinese *sou* meaning big bean.

The plant and its environment

Soya has been grown in China for some 5000 years; it was referred to in
Chinese materia medica over 4500 years ago and because of this long
continuous use and development there are now several hundred varieties.

The soya bean was not grown in Europe until the 18th century and not
used greatly in the western hemisphere until the late 19th century. It was first
imported into England in 1908, but not to the USA until 1924. Now the USA
is the biggest producer and exporter of soya beans (they grow 60% of the
world's 110 million ton harvest). The second largest producer is China and it
is also grown extensively in Brazil and Japan.

The soya plant, an annual, grows to about 1.2m (4ft) and bears hairy
pods, each containing 3 or 4 yellow beans which are now the single most
important source of seed oil in the world. The bean seed contains
approximately 48% protein, 18% lipids, 11% carbohydrates and 16% other
(Iberg 2004 p.221)

The oil

The oil is an edible semi–drying oil used extensively in the Far East.

Method of extraction

Soya beans have a comparatively low oil content (17–20%) and therefore
very little oil is produced by pressing, thus the bulk of oil is obtained
commercially by solvent extraction. Pressing of the beans gives a thick golden
liquid which is a mixture of oil and lecithin which is separated by decantation
(Europhyto–Institut): cold pressed soybean oil has a distinctive taste, used in
Oriental cuisine and contributes to the formation of lecithin due to the high
(3%) content of phosphatides (Iberg 2004 p.222).

Principal constituents

Type	Based on	Content – %
Saturated fatty acid:		
C16:0	palmitic	10
C18:0	stearic	5
Typical saturated fatty acid content		17
Monounsaturated fatty acid:		
C18:1	oleic acid	19–26
Typical monosaturated fatty acid content		23
Polyunsaturated fatty acid:		
C18:2	linoleic acid	50–55
C18:3	α–linolenic acid	6–9
Typical polyunsaturated fatty acid content		60

Physical properties

Peroxide value (meq/k oil)	1.0 max
Colour (Lovibond 5.25" cell)	1.5 red max
Iodine value (wijs)	125–140
Saponification value	180–200
Energy value Kcal/100ml	898

Vitamin content

Soya bean oil is a good source of vitamin E (23mg per 100ml), although not as rich as wheatgerm or sunflower oils. Soya beans contain vitamins A and B complex and soya is one of the few foods to have all 22 health giving amino acids (Bartram 1995). The seeds also contain appreciable amounts of phytosterols (stigmasterol and sitosterol) which are used for synthesizing steroids.

Therapeutic properties – internal use

Soya beans are free of cholesterol, rich in lecithin, and have a low content of saturated fats. This makes it an easily assimilated oil, helpful against arteriosclerosis and cholesterol build up, maintaining suppleness in the vascular system. Purified soybean oil is used in pharmacy for parenteral feeding (Bruneton 1995).

Cosmetic use

Soya oil is used in manufacturing soaps, shampoos, bath oils and is used as a dermoprotector (Lubinic 1997). Reputed to have a beneficial effect on aging skin.

Culinary uses

The beans, being high in protein (soya beans are sometimes known as 'boneless meat') and containing vitamin A and B complex, constitute an important food source for many people throughout the world. The beans and the oil are especially important to vegetarians as from them can be made soy flour, tofu, tempeh, miso, soya milk, cottage cheese and cheese; many of these have been made since the 2nd century BC, but there is no record of the oil having been used. The strongly flavoured soya sauce (which contains a high proportion of salt) is produced from fermented beans (the main use for this oil is dietary). The oil is unsuitable for frying because of its high content of polyunsaturates, but is used in the manufacture of margarine.

Folklore and traditional plant remedies

Originally used only for soap and for burning in lamps. Also used for adhesives, plastics, paper size, textile fibre, animal food, paint, printing inks and fertilizer.

Cautions

On the debit side soya oil is prone to oxidation and may cause allergic reactions, pimples and hair damage (Winter 1999 p.411). Much soya is now genetically modified.

Additional notes

1   In the USA, where 75% of the home production is used, the oil is used as a salad oil and in the manufacture of margarine and shortening. Industrially the oil is used in the manufacture of paints, linoleum, printing inks, soap, insecticide and disinfectant. A by–product of the soya oil industry is lecithin, which is used as a wetting and stabilizing agent in the food, cosmetic, pharmaceutical, leather, paint, plastic, soap and detergent industries.

2   Debittered soybean flour contains practically no starch and is widely used in diabetic foods.

3   Soybean is used in many products – MSG, Lea & Perrins sauce, Worcester sauce, soy sauce, salad dressings, pork sausages, luncheon meats, sweets, coffee substitutes, etc. (Winter 1999 p.411)

References

Bartram T 1995 Encyclopedia of herbal medicine. Grace, Christchurch p.398
Bruneton J 1995 Pharmacognosy, phytochemistry, medicinal plants. Intercept, Andover p.133
Iberg A 2004 Dumont's lexicon of oil & vinegar. Rebo, Lisse
Lubinic E 1997 Handbuch Aromatherapie: Ätherische Öle und ihre Anwendung. Hüthig Medizin Verlag, Stuttgart
Winter R 1999 A consumers dictionary of cosmetic ingredients. 5th edn: Three Rivers Press, New York

Sunflower oil

Scientific name
Helianthus annuus L.
Family: Asteraceae

Etymology
Helios is the Greek word for sun and *anthos* means flower. *Annuus* is from the Latin and means yearly. In France, the plant is called tournesol and in Spain tornasol, both of which mean 'that which turns toward the sun' but this has no foundation in fact and the plants do not show this behaviour; although the flowers do all face the same way, toward the morning sun in the south of France – they do not turn.

The plant and its environment
The plant originated in South America, where the flower was worshipped by the Aztecs as a representation of the sun; the seeds were eaten toasted or turned into meal and the plant was brought to Europe at the end of the 16th century. The major countries in which sunflowers are grown are Russia, Eastern Europe, India, Argentina, Romania, the Mediterranean countries and the USA.

Sunflowers can grow to a height of 5m (15ft) and the flower heads can vary from 7.5cm (3in) in diameter to an impressive 35cm (15in)! This tremendous growth takes place in a relatively short period of time (the plant is an annual) and requires lots of water, so sunflowers can be used to drain soggy areas. They will grow in almost any soil as long as there is plenty of full sun and they are watered daily in dry areas.

Before collection the seeds are allowed to ripen in the flower head until black, and each head yields on average about 0.25kg (0.5lb) of seeds.

'High oleic' type sunflowers are also grown and here the triglycerides contain at least 80% oleic acid. The oil from these is more heat resistant than the usual 'linoleic type' sunflower oil.

The oil

Sunflower seeds contain around 30% of oil (although some modern varieties contain 50% (Bruneton 1995)) which is light and slightly sweet. Organic sunflower oil is often used as the macerating medium for calendula and other plants. Sunflower seed oil forms a 'skin' after drying (Winter 1999 p.423).

Method of extraction

All oil extracted from organically grown plants is obtained by cold pressing. The oil obtained from non–organically grown plants and sold commercially in large quantities is produced by solvent–based refining.

Principal constituents

Type	Based on	Content – %
Saturated fatty acid:		
C14:0	myristic acid	<0.5
C16:0	palmitic acid	1–10
C20:0	arachidic acid	0–1.5
C22:0	behenic acid	0–1
C24:0	lignoceric acid	<0.5
Typical saturated fatty acid unit content		12
Monounsaturated fatty acid:		
C16:1	palmitoleic acid	<1
C18:1	oleic acid	14–35 (high 78–83)
C20:1	eicosenoic acid	<0.5
C22:1	erucic acid	<0.3
Typical monounsaturated fatty acid unit content		24
Polyunsaturated fatty acid:		
C18:2	linoleic acid	55–70*
C18:3	α–linolenic acid	<0.3
Typical polyunsaturated fatty acid unit content		64

* the value increases with cooler growing conditions

The 'high oleic' sunflower oil has the approximate composition:

saturated	10%
monounsaturated	80%
polyunsaturated	10%

Physical properties

Odour	essentially odourless
Acid value	0.4 max
Specific gravity	0.915–0.920
Energy value Kcal/100ml	900

Vitamins

Sunflower oil contains vitamins A, D and (principally) E, and minerals calcium, zinc, potassium, iron and phosphorus.

Folklore and traditional plant uses

The oil was used by the indigenous population of America to help with rheumatism, whereas in Russia the leaves and flowers were used for the treatment of chest problems, bronchitis, coughs and even malaria. The dried leaves have been smoked like tobacco.

The petals can be steeped in water to produce a yellow hair dye and the stalks are used in papermaking. The oil burns well and may be used in oil lamps. It has also been used in the manufacture of resins and soap. Sunflower seeds, together with a decoction of morning glory (*Ipomoea pandurata*), are used as a sacrament by the Iroquois Indians in spring and autumn rituals (Chevallier 1996).

Therapeutic properties – internal use

Sunflower oil has slight diuretic properties and also favours the development of healthy teeth in growing children. It aids cholesterol metabolism (Bartram 1996) and may be used to counteract arteriosclerosis (Stier 1990). Sunflower oil is expectorant and, as it contains inulin, it is useful in the treatment of asthma (Mabey 1988 p.14). It has been reported as being helpful in the treatment of multiple sclerosis (Anon 1990, Millar *et al* 1973, Swank & Dugan 1990). A homoeopathic sunflower tincture is used in cases of constipation.

Oleic type sunflower oil is included in mixtures designed to balance the lipidic diet (Bruneton 1995): the current recommendations are 25%/50%/25% of saturated, monounsaturated and polyunsaturated oils respectively.

Therapeutic properties – external use

- beneficial for skin complaints and bruises
- alleged to be helpful in cases of leg ulcers
- included in preparations for skin disorders, haemorrhoids, acne, seborrhoea, rhinitis and sinusitis (Reynolds 1993)

Cosmetic use

The oil has a softening and moisturizing effect on the skin (Mabey 1988 p.145) and is used for massage.

Culinary use

It is a good cooking oil and is used in frying and to make margarine, cheese and salad dressings. Mixing the seeds with water in a blender produces very palatable vegetarian milk. The seeds can be roasted and eaten or ground for use as a coffee substitute. The flower buds can be cooked and eaten with butter, just like artichokes.

As the smoke point is below 220°C the oil is suitable for low temperature cooking.

Sunflower seeds are thought to be helpful for debilitated and cold lungs and for people with a tendency to colds and 'flu, particularly during the winter. Their richness in nutrients, particularly B vitamins, makes them useful for a weak and stressed nervous system. Because of its high polyunsaturated fat content, sunflower seed oil is recommended for lowering cholesterol and reducing atherosclerosis.

The seeds can be added to cooked rice, salads and sprinkled over cooked vegetables; they make a palatable milk substitute simply liquidised in water.

Cautions

The oil used in blended cooking oils has been highly refined and should not be used for aromatherapy/massage. The unrefined oil should not be used at high temperatures as it breaks down and produces toxic elements when heated (Earle 1991). Otherwise, there are no other known contraindications (Winter 1999 p.423).

Additional notes

1   Apart from its use as a cooking oil and for margarine, because the oil is semidrying it is blended with linseed oil and used as a base for some paints and varnishes. It can also be used as a lubricant and for lighting.

2   Linoleic sunflower oil is the original sunflower oil and until recently has been the most common type available. It is a polyunsaturated oil with low saturated fat levels, a clean, light taste and is high in Vitamin E. This type of sunflower oil is predominantly polyunsaturated (65%) with monounsaturated fats (oleic) at 21% and a saturated fat level of 11%.

3   High oleic sunflower oil has a minimum 80% oleic acid (monounsaturated). The patent on high oleic sunflower oil and seed has expired.

4 Substitution of foods rich in saturated fat with foods rich in high–oleic–acid sunflower oil and margarine has favourable outcomes on blood lipids and factor VIIc; the oil presents a useful source of MUFA for diets aimed at prevention of heart disease (www.adajournal.org July 2005 p.1071–1079).

5 Sunflower seeds are a treasure of a highly digestible, polyunsaturated oil and contain as many as seventeen different vitamins, twelve minerals and over ten amino acids as well as its own natural enzymes (Wade 1973 p.62).

6 The first recorded example of using sunflower seeds as a source of oil was in Russia in 1779. Now sunflower is the fourth most important oil seed crop in the World, only ranking below soya, rapeseed and palm oil.

References:

Anonymous 1990 Lipids and multiple sclerosis. Lancet 336: 25–26.
Bartram T 1996 Encyclopedia of herbal medicine. Grace, Christchurch p.410
Bruneton J 1995 Pharmacognosy, phytochemistry, medicinal plants. Intercept, Andover pp 134–135
Chevallier A 1996 Encyclopedia of medicinal plants. Dorling Kindersley, London p.47
Earle L 1991 Vital oils. Ebury Press, London p.62
Mabey R 1988 The complete new herbal. Elm Tree Books, London
Millar J H D et al 1973 Double blind trial of linoleate supplementation of the diet in multiple sclerosis. British Medical Journal 1:765–768
Reynolds J E F (ed.) 1993 Martindale: the extra pharmacopoeia. Pharmaceutical Press, London p.1417
Stier B 1990 Secrets des huiles de première à froid. Self published, Quebec
Swank R L, Dugan B B 1990 Effect of low saturated fat diet in early and late cases of multiple sclerosis Lancet 336: 37–39
Winter R 1999 A consumer's dictionary of cosmetic ingredients. Three Rivers Press, New York

Tamanu oil

Scientific name

Calophyllum inophyllum
Family: Guttiferaceae

Etymology

Meaning 'with beautiful leaves', the tree is also known as beauty leaf. *Calo* means beautiful, *phyllum* is leaf (hence the name beauty leaf tree) and *ino* is fibre.

Ballnut is another common name, also Alexandrian laurel and dilo oil tree – and there are many others – ati or tamanu (Tahiti), kamani or tamanu (Hawaii – where the nuts are called punnai), ndamanu (Fiji), fetau (Samoa), nambagura (Vanuatu) and foraha or vintanina (Madagascar).

The plant and its environment

Tamanu is a large evergreen tree up to about 20m in height, native to East Africa and grows from southern coastal India to Australia and is cultivated in many tropical regions, including several Pacific Islands. It is an ornamental plant with a crackled, dark bark, having dark green glossy leaves (10–20cm (4–8in) long) and white, fragrant flowers (25mm (1in) diameter): the main flowering periods are January and July.

The fruit is a round, green drupe with a thick skin having a single thick shelled seed which is about the size of a walnut. When ripe, the fruit is wrinkled and its color varies from yellow to brownish–red; the seeds can be dispersed by bats and, because the trees flourish in coastal areas and the nuts drop into the water, they are also dispersed by sea tides to other shores.

The oil

The shells of the tamanu nuts are lightly cracked and then, as fresh nuts do not give any oil, they are dried in the sun for about 4–6 weeks,. During this process of oxidation the kernel becomes darker, brownish and develops a viscous oil with a sweet smell. The average yield per tree is about 200 pounds of tamanu fruits per year yielding about 4 or 5 litres of tamanu oil. This low yield per tree means that supply of the oil is limited and it is relatively expensive.

Method of extraction

The oil is cold pressed from the sun dried fruit and seed together to extract the thick, dark green–brown oil, initially containing resins which are separated out.

Principal constituents

Type	Based on	Content – %
Saturated fatty acid:		
C16:0	palmitic	12–15
C18:0	stearic	8–13
C20:0	arachidic	<1.0
Typical saturated fatty acid content		20
Monounsaturated fatty acid:		
C16:1	palmitoleic	<1.0
C18:1	oleic	35–49
C20:1	eicosenoic	<1.0
Typical monounsaturated fatty acid content		38
Polyunsaturated fatty acid:		
C18:2	linoleic	21–40
C18:3	α–linolenic	0.3–1.3
Typical polyunsaturated fatty acid content		38

Physical properties

Appearance	dark, cola colour
Aroma	nutty
Iodine value (wijs)	99–108
Flash point	283°C
Relative density	0.919

The oil contains:
- calophyllolide ($C_{25}H_{22}O_5$) an antiinflammatory coumarin (Bhalla *et al* 1980), the molecule of which contains a lactonic and amethoxyl group.
- balsam.
- about 7% wax.
- 3 basic classes of lipids; 92% neutral lipids, 6.4% glycolipids, and 1.6% phospholipids.
- xanthones of jacareubin which inhibit *Staphylococcus aureus, S. typhimurium, P. aeruginosa* and *Bacillus subtilis*.
- calanolide A and costatolide, coumarins useful against HIV.
- calophyllic acid (upon saponification).
- benzoic and oxybenzoic acids.

Folklore and traditional plant remedies

The oil, as well as decoctions and tinctures from the rest of the tree, have been used traditionally as medicines and wound healers. Tamanu oil has been used in Pacific islands for a wide range of skin disorders and conditions and with such a long history of folk use, there are a multitude of properties ascribed to this oil; it is used as analgesic, antibacterial, antiinflammatory, antiinfectious, cicatrizant, circulatory (anticoagulant) and immunostimulant (via the skin). It is said to be helpful for sciatica, shingles, eczema, psoriasis, neuritis, skin allergies, rheumatism, phlebitis, varicose veins, heavy legs, varicose ulcers, acne, herpes, vitiligo, bedsores, chilblains, cracked skin, stretch marks and sunburn. It is also used for nappy rash on babies and as a safeguard against mosquito stings.

This nut oil has been in use since the late 1920's to alleviate leprous neuritis (formerly tamanu was used to treat leprosy).

The pulverized seeds have been used to cure ulcers and wounds and the bark also has medicinal uses as an infusion and in other herbal remedies. The fruits are expressed to yield a pasty mass rich in triacylglycerols; the paste itself is used in several countries as a healing and analgesic agent in the treatment of burns (Bruneton 1995).

Therapeutic properties – external use
- can help with various problems of the hair and scalp
- acne, eczema, psoriasis, scars (Muller 1993)
- facial neuralgia
- a combination of tamanu vegetable oil and Ravensara aromatica essential oil has been used successfully as a treatment for shingles (Herpes zoster) (Pénoël 1981)
- effective for shingles (Cadwallader 1997, Keville & Green 1995)
- stimulates phagocytosis (Schnaubelt 1994)
- claimed to have antiinflammatory and pain relieving properties (Anon 1997) which make it useful in cases of sciatica and rheumatism; it is rubefacient (Quisumbing 1951)
- non irritant to mucous membranes and so can be used on anal fissures, for vaginitis and on cracked nipples

Cosmetic uses

Tamanu oil has been used for years as an ingredient in many European cosmetics. The oil is said to delay the onset of age freckles and is good for dry skin.

Cautions

There are no known contraindications when tamanu oil is to be used topically: it should not be taken internally.

Additional notes

1   Besides being a popular ornamental plant, its wood is hard and strong and has been used in construction and boatbuilding.

2   Several species of the tree grow wild in the tropical climes in the Pacific and the tree is regarded as sacred in some islands. Calophyllum inophyllum is the preferred variety, producing the best quality oil.

3   Tamanu oil saponifies on contact with sea water: (calophyllic acid $(C25H24O6)$ results from the saponification of calophyllolide).

4   It can be used at 10–20% dilution in a base carrier oil or used neat on small areas for such as acne and haemorrhoids.

5   The antiinflammatory activity of tamanu oil is due partly to the 4–phenyl coumarin calophyllolide (Bhalla *et al* 1980).

6   All the xanthones in tamanu oil show antiinflammatory activity, which makes it effective for rashes, sores, swellings and abrasions

7   The plant is cultivated as an ornamental tree due to its handsome leathery, glossy foliage and fragrant white flowers and is frequently found near the ocean because of its resistance to salt air (Britannica CD 1996)

8   This tree was once considered to be sacred in several tropical countries and the number of trees grown fell with the advent of Christianity.

9   In Java it is believed to have diuretic properties, whereas in Samoa every part of the plant is considered a virulent poison, with the milky juice causing blindness, the sap once introduced into the circulation causing death and so used as an arrow poison (Dweck & Meadows 2002).

References

Anon 1997 http://www.manglobe.com./tamanu/info.html

Bhalla T N *et al* 1980 Calophyllolide: a new non steroidal antiinflammatory agent. Indian Journal of Medical Research November 72: 762–5

Britannica CD 1996 Calophyllum inophyllum. Encyclopaedia Britannica.

Bruneton J 1995 Pharmacognosy, phytochemistry, medicinal plants. Intercept, Andover p.300

Cadwallader M 1997 Aromatherapy in Australia. Paper given at Aromatherapy Clinical Practitioner's Course, Melbourne

Dweck A C, Meadows T 2002 Tamanu (Calophyllum inophyllum) – the African, Asian, Polynesian and Pacific panacea.. International Journal of Cosmetic Science, 2002, 24: 1– 8

Franchomme P, Pénoël D 1981 Phytochemistry No 1 Aromatherapy. International Phytomedical Foundation, La Courtête

Keville K, Green M 1995 Aromatherapy: a complete guide to the healing art. Crossing Press, Fredom p.24

Muller A 1993 The Pacific Ocean oils. L'Ami, September no.5

Quisumbing E 1951 Medicinal Plants of the Philippines. Technical Bulletin 16. Manila, Philippine Islands, Manila Bureau of Printing.

Randriambola T 1984 Mémoire d'Ingéniorat. Université d'Antananarivo

Schnaubelt K 1994 Aromatherapy and chronic viral infections. In Aroma '93 Conference Proceedings, Aromatherapy Publications, Hove p.37

Sources

Adeniyi Adeyeye 1991 Studies on seed oils of Garcinia kola and Calophyllum inophyllum. Journal of the Science of Food and Agriculture 57(3):441–442

Walnut oil

Scientific name
Juglans regia
Family: Juglandaceae

Etymology
Walnut is also
known as the royal
walnut and the Persian
walnut. *Regia* conveys the
meaning of royal, and *Juglans* means
godlike (from jovis – of Jupiter). We speak
of Adam's apple, which is probably a
mistranslation from the Greek, where it is
referred to as Adam's walnut. The prefix *wal–*
is from the Anglo Saxon *wealh* meaning
foreign, and *knut* means nut. Alternatively, Iberg (2004 p.189) writes that
walnuss derives from middle high German *walhisch nuz* meaning romance
nut.

The plant and its environment
It has been established from fossil walnuts found in northern Europe that
the walnut tree is a pre–Ice Age plant. It is native to the Himalayas, China,
eastern Europe and places in between, but is now grown in all temperate
countries for its timber (the lightest wood to be grown in Europe) and its
edible nuts. America is the largest walnut producer but there is quite a large
nut and oil industry in France. Before the Great War France exported to the
USA double the quantity of walnuts (noix de Grenoble) that were grown in
California at that time, but today California produces two thirds of the world
production.

The deciduous trees have a greyish brown bark and can live for more
than 100 years. They grow to a height of 30m (97ft) although they tend to be
trimmed very occasionally to a more manageable height for nut collection.
The globe–like green fleshy fruits (drupes) containing the nut appear singly
or in small groups of two or three and are harvested in October. The chief
constituent present in the fresh plant is juglone which has antibacterial and
fungicidal qualities. It is interesting to note that the leaf contains a small
quantity of essential oil (Bruneton 1995).

The oil

A deep golden brown oil is obtained from the kernel which must be extricated from its hard shell before pressing; there are special machines for this purpose in large scale production. The oil containers should be stored in a cool place away from the light when the oil will keep for a maximum of twelve months. The refined oil, unlike the cold pressed oil, is light in colour, has a bland taste and a low odour: it has superior keeping qualities to that of the organic oil.

Method of extraction

On a small scale, the walnuts are cracked with a wooden mallet to remove the shell, then the kernel is ground and pressed to yield about 50% oil. The kernels are roasted first when producing the oil for culinary purposes, to increase the flavour.

Principal constituents

Type	Based on	Content – %
Saturated fatty acid:		
C16:0	palmitic acid	7–8
C18:0	stearic acid	2–3
Typical saturated fatty acid unit content		10
Monounsaturated fatty acid:		
C16:1	palmitoleic acid	0–0.2
C18:1	oleic acid	16–36
Typical monounsaturated fatty acid unit content		18
Polyunsaturated fatty acid:		
C18:2	linoleic acid	40–70
C18:3	linolenic acid	11–14
Typical polyunsaturated fatty acid unit content		73

Physical properties

Odour	Typical walnut aroma
Acid value	0.25 max
Specific gravity	0.919–0.925
Energy value Kcal/100ml	903
Mineral content	Ca, S, P, Cl, Na, K, Mg, Fe, Au, Cu, Mn, Zn
Vitamin E /100ml	12mg

The nuts contain folic acid magnesium and iron.

Folklore and traditional plant uses

The fleshy outer part of the fruit and also the leaves have been used for thousands of years to dye hair. Theophrastus (371–287 BC) and Pliny (AD 23–79) both described this application; a natural brown dye can also be extracted from the shells; the leaves of the walnut tree have astringent properties and have been used both for skin problems and digestive ailments. A decoction of the leaves repels ants (Mabey 1988) and a homoeopathic skin remedy may be prepared from the leaves. The leaves of the walnut tree are a well known household remedy for chronic eczema, scrofula and inflammation of the eyelids, and are suitable when combined with wild pansy for children's skin complaints (Weiss 1988).

Therapeutic properties – internal use

Alleged to give protection to nerve and brain cells, walnut oil also protects against hardening of the arteries and rickets, and is a mild laxative (Bartram 1996).

Walnut oil has been used for treating kidney stones, and nursing mothers have taken it in order to increase lactation. Antianaemic and tonic properties have also been mentioned as well as for the symptomatic treatment of mild diarrhoea.

Observation of some populations and a controlled study have shown that frequent consumption of walnuts appears to be associated with decreased risk of mortality due to ischemic heart disease and myocardial infarction. Subjects in the study on a walnut rich diet experienced a significant drop in total cholesterol compared with a control group (Sabaté *et al* 1993). A tea made from dried walnut has been used as a wash for skin disorders and shingles (Bartram 1996).

Therapeutic properties – external use

Indications and uses are:
• scalp itching, peeling and dandruff
• an emollient and itch–relieving treatment in skin disorders
• sunburn and superficial burns
• an antalgic for mouth and throat
• said to be effective in treating eczema (Bartram 1996)

Cosmetic use

The oil is used in hair and skin preparations and leaf extracts are used in cosmetology.' (Bruneton 1995)

Culinary use

Unrefined walnut oil is a high quality culinary oil with an excellent flavour when used in salad dressings and on potatoes. In France its delicate flavour is utilized in cakes, bread and some bean dishes. The nuts can be picked and pickled before the shell has formed, with delicious results. The unripe fruits and leaves are also used to flavour wine or to make an aperitif.

The nuts can be a rather dirty brown colour naturally and organically grown nuts are washed in water. Large commercial producers often soak them in a bleach to make them more 'attractive' to the purchaser. This imparts a slightly bitter taste and unbleached nuts are best for the health. Organically produced walnuts are not bleached and therefore make the best oil for use in both food and aromatherapy.

Cautions

Walnut oil has no known contraindications although the wood has been reported as an irritant (Schleicher 1974).

Additional notes

1 All nuts have been found to improve cholesterol. Walnuts are an excellent source of plant based omega 3 fatty acids. Dr Stephen Pratt, of Scripps Memorial Hospital, La Jolla, California, says studies show that the risk of cardiovascular disease can be lowered by 15–50% by eating about seven walnuts each week (Anon 2005).

2 Walnut leaves are used in hair products for 'split ends'.

3 The bark of the walnut tree is used to treat constipation

References

Anonymous 2005 Superfoods. Costa Life issue 8 p.57
Bartram T 1996 Encyclopedia of herbal medicine. Grace, Christchurch p.449
Bruneton J 1995 Pharmacognosy, phytochemistry, medicinal plants. Intercept, Andover p.348
Mabey R (ed.) 1988 The complete new herbal. Elm Tree Books, London p.161
Sabaté J, Fraser G E, Burke K, Knutsen S F, Bennett H, Lindsted K D 1993 Effects of walnuts on serum lipid levels and blood pressure in normal men. New England Journal of Medicine 328:603–607
Schleicher H 1974 Uber phytogene allergische Kontaktekzeme. Dermatologische Monatsschrift 160: 433
Weiss R F 1988 Herbal medicine. Beaconsfield Publishers, Beaconsfield p.332

Watermelon seed oil

Scientific name
Citrullus vulgaris
Family: Cucurbitaceae

Etymology
A middle English word from the Latin *melere* to make water; and water obviously refers to the high water content of the fruit. Common names in Europe are *pasteque* (France), *sandia* (Spain), *cocomera* (Italy), *melancia* (Portugal)

The plant and its environment
Grown around the Mediterranean for thousands of years, it is an annual climbing vine with yellow flowers which produce round to oval fruit weighing from 3–13kg (8–30lb). The skin is green, perhaps variegated, the colour of the flesh varies, red or yellow, with black or white seeds. There are also seedless varieties. Introduced into the USA with the slave trade, the US is now the fourth largest producer.

The oil
The seeds contain about 30% of a reddish brown fixed oil

Principal constituents
The constituents of water melon seeds and pumpkin seeds are quite similar.

Type	Based on	Content – %
Saturated fatty acid:		
C16:0	palmitic	8–13
C18:0	stearic	7–10
C20:0	arachidic	<1.0
C22:0	behenic	<1.0
C24:0	lignoceric	<1.0
Typical saturated fatty acid content		17
Monounsaturated fatty acid:		
C16:1	palmitoleic	<1.0
C18:1	oleic	14–18

C20:1	ecosenoic	<1.0
C22:1	erucic	<2.0
Typical monounsaturated fatty acid content		16
Polyunsaturated fatty acid:		
C18:2	linoleic	55–65
C18:3	α–linolenic	<1.0
Typical polyunsaturated fatty acid content		

Physical properties

Peroxide value (meq/kg oil)	3.0 max
Refractive index at 20EC	1.470–1.480
Iodine value (wijs)	120–128
Saponification value	185–195
Free fatty acid (% as oleic)	<5.0

Vitamin and mineral content

Trace amounts of vitamins B and C.

Therapeutic properties

The indications for use and the properties this oil are similar to those of pumpkin seed oil (qv).

Folklore and traditional plant remedies

Water melon seeds have been used in affections of the urinary passages and are regarded as having diuretic properties (Grieve 1984 p.528). The seeds are good vermicides

Culinary

Watermelon is sometimes used to make jam in France and elsewhere it is used in soups and sweet recipes: the skin can be used in pickles (Worldwide Gourmet).

References

Grieve M 1984 A modern herbal. Penguin, Harmondsworth
http\\:www.theworldwidegourmet.com

Wheatgerm oil

Scientific name
> *Triticum vulgare, T. turgidum (T. durum), T. aestivum*
> Family: Graminaceae

Etymology
> Wheat is derived from *whete*, the Middle English (1151–1500) word which means white.
> The generic and specific names come from Latin; *Triticum* was the word for wheat, *vulgar* means common, *durum* means hard, *aestivum* means summer, with *turgidum* meaning swollen.

The plant and its environment
> A cereal grass native to West Asia (reputed to have been cultivated in Kurdistan for more than 8000 years) is now widely cultivated in subtropical and temperate regions. The stems, up to 1m (3ft) high, each bear a cylindrical head of up to a hundred flower clusters grouped in vertical rows.

The oil
> The oil contains high levels of vitamin E, a natural antioxidant, so it can be added to other carrier oils to act as a preservative. Although it is fairly expensive, wheatgerm oil is the richest food source we have for vitamin E; soybean oil also has a high tocopherol content. The unrefined wheatgerm oil has a strong odour which some people find unattractive. The germ oil contains a major percentage of EFA.

Method of extraction
> Milling the grains of wheat for white flour separates out the wheat germ, which contains 25% protein, and a wide selection of vitamins and minerals.
> The oil is extracted from the germ but it should be noted that it is rarely possible to procure pure cold pressed oil. Wheatgerm, like grapeseed, contains only around 13% of oil, so cold expression produces only small amounts. When it is done, pressing takes place at 30–40°C so that the fatty acids and vitamins are not degraded; this is followed by a special process to stabilise the extracted oil which is not refined (Goëb 1998 p.42). It should be noted that eighteen tonnes of wheat gives 36 kg of wheatgerm and with this method only 1kg of oil is yielded.

Because of this low yield, the oil is mostly extracted by a process that is similar to maceration (Stier 1990) but solvent extraction and hot pressing are also used. For the maceration process, the wheatgerm is stirred with another good quality cold pressed oil, during which process the germ soaks up the base oil. This product is then cold pressed, yielding a form of macerated oil, which contains about 20–30% wheatgerm oil with the rest being the base oil (eg olive, sweet almond, sunflower etc). The constituents may vary because of the precise method of extraction.

Principal constituents

Type	Based on	Content – %
Saturated fatty acid:		
C14:0	myristic acid	<0.1
C16:0	palmitic acid	11–21
C18:0	stearic acid	1
C20:0	arachidic acid	<1
C24:0	lignoceric acid	<1
Typical saturated fatty acid unit content		21
Monounsaturated fatty acid:		
C16:1	palmitoleic acid	0.2
C18:1	oleic acid	15–26
Typical monounsaturated fatty acid unit content		18
Polyunsaturated fatty acid:		
C18:2	linoleic acid	49–60
C18:3	linolenic acid	6
Typical polyunsaturated fatty acid unit content		60

Physical properties

Specific gravity	0.920
Colour	orange–yellow

Vitamins

The oil contains vitamins A, B1, B2, B3, B6, E (levels of 3500 parts per million compared to 250–600ppm in other oils) and F.

Mineral content: A, Cl, Co, Cu, Fe, K, Mg, Mn, Na, S, Si, Zn.

Therapeutic properties – internal use

In growing children, the oil helps to maintain healthy spines, bones and muscles. It can also be taken to help prevent eczema, indigestion and the development of varicose veins and it is said to be anticoagulant. Wheatgerm oil has antioxidant properties due to the high tocopherol content and helps to remove cholesterol deposits from the arteries and is a useful food oil in the battle against low density lipoprotein.

Therapeutic properties – external use
- rich in lipid soluble vitamins therefore very good for revitalizing dry skin (Sanecki 1987)
- believed to help relieve symptoms of dermatitis
- beneficial for tired muscles, making a good base for after sport massage

Cosmetic use
It is useful on ageing skin (Sanecki 1987) where its natural antioxidants are an effective weapon in the war against free radicals, softening the skin and making it more supple because of its cell regenerative properties, especially for mature, damaged, impure skins (Lubinic 1997, Battaglia 1995). Recommended for dry, devitalised skin and for dry eczema and chapped skin blended with sweet almond oil (Goëb 1998 p.42). Wheatgerm oil is used in hair conditioners.

Culinary use
The high price of wheatgerm oil means it is little used in culinary applications.

On account of its richness in fatty acids and vitamin E, Goëb (1998 p.42) advises taking a teaspoonful each day during one month two or three times a year and Lubinic (1997) says that it is good for the health when eaten with morning cereals, fromage blanc, salads, crudities.

Cautions
1   Those allergic to wheat flour should be tested for possible skin reaction before use in aromatherapy or massage.
2   Regular use on the face may encourage hair growth in those susceptible to it.
3   It is non–irritant on the skin of babies (Stier 1990).
4   Most wheatgerm oil is either refined or cut with other vegetable oils (Goëb 1998 p.42).
5   The CIR Expert Panel concluded that wheatgerm oil is safe as presently used in cosmetic formulations (Winter 1999 p.455).

Additional notes

1 *T. turgidum* is used for the making of semolina and pasta, while *T. aestivum* is used for bread. The wheat grain consists of the husk (bran) 12%, the germ 3% (the 'living' part of the grain) containing vitamins, minerals and protein, with the endosperm, consisting mainly of starch, making up the rest.

2 The pharmaceutical industry uses the antioxidant properties of tocopherols, often in synergy with ascorbic acid (Bruneton 1995).

3 The use of vitamin E in cardiovascular disorders has been reviewed by Kleijnen *et al* (1989).

References

Battaglia S 1995 The complete guide to aromatherapy. Perfect Potion, Virginia p.228

Bruneton J 1995 Pharmacognosy, phytochemistry, medicinal plants. Intercept, Andover pp 141–142

Goëb Ph 1998 Connaître l'essentiel sur les huiles essentielles. IAPM, Tamil Nadu p.42

Kleijnen J *et al* 1989 Vitamin E and cardiovascular disease. Eur Journal of Clinical Pharmacology 37:541–544

Lubinic E 1997 Handbuch Aromatherapie: Ätherische Öle und ihre Anwendung. MVS Medizinverlage, Stuttgart

Stier B 1990 Secrets des huiles de première pression à froid. Self published, Quebec p.65

Sanecki K 1987 The domestic and cosmetic uses of herbs. In: Stuart M (ed.) 1987 The encyclopedia of herbs and herbalism. Black Cat, London pp 108–109

Winter R 1999 A consumer's dictionary of cosmetic ingredients. 5th edn: Three Rivers Press, New York

Section 2B –
Macerated oils

Aloe oil

Scientific name
Aloe vera, *Aloe barbadensis*
Family: Liliaceae

Etymology
Aloe is derived from the native name; *vera* means true or genuine.

The plant and its environment
The aloe plant originated in the island of Socotra off the horn of Africa (Mabey p.191) and was introduced to the Antilles in the 17th century. *Aloe vera* is a perennial with spikes of fleshy, grey–green leaves, spotted red when young; in summer the plant has yellow tubular flowers. It is now grown commercially in Florida, the Caribbean and Africa.

Method of extraction
Aloe vera is a macerated oil and extraction of the lipids contained in the leaves is achieved by infusing the plant material in a base oil (e.g. almond, apricot kernel, soya or olive oils).

Therapeutic properties
Although the indications and properties are not properly researched, the macerated oil is said to be astringent, antiinflammatory and emollient and is alleged to have antifungal, antibacterial, and antiviral properties.

Aloe vera (in soya oil) used therapeutically in massage has a long reputation as it is said to heal wounds and reducing scarring, ulcers, lesions (especially burns) and it is also of help for arthritic pain, improving blood circulation. For therapeutic use aloe vera oil is usually blended at 5–10% in a base carrier oil.

Cosmetic uses
Aloe oil is suited to care of the skin and is used in facial and whole body massage, being especially good for sensitive or irritated skin. It hydrates the skin and is recommended after sunbathing or a session of UV exposure on a tanning machine to lessen the redness (Lubinic 2003 p.210).

Because of its reputation of penetrating the skin four times faster than water, it is used in many cosmetic formulations, as antiageing, for acne and inflammatory conditions.

217

Folklore and traditional plant remedies

Aloe is regarded as a 'first aid' plant and a 'wonder plant' for healing the skin (Mabey 1988 p.81).

The gel obtained by breaking the leaves is a remarkable healing agent (Mabey 1988 p.81) being helpful for skin regeneration, cuts, wounds, burns. The plant yields a juice which is a powerful cathartic and long ago it was valued as a purgative by the ancient Greeks who tried to conquer the island of Socotra to gain specimens (Mabey 1988 p.191).

Cautions

1   There are no known contraindications to the use of aloe oil on the skin.
2   Commercially available gel is very often adulterated (Mabey 1988 p.81) and so may not achieve the beneficial results expected.

Additional notes

1   The saponification values are NAOH: 191 and KAOH: 267.88
2   The shelf life is up to two years.
3   The leaves are cut from 2 to 3 year old plants and left to drain: the yellow juice is then concentrated either by evaporation or boiling (Grieve 1984 p.26).
4   The gel contains barbaloin and isobarbaloin, aloe–emodin, resin and a volatile oil; the brownish crystalline solid achieved by drying the gel is used as a purgative (Stuart 1987 p.149).
5   Reversed phase HPLC has been used to separate and quantify the aloe leaf compounds aloenin, aloesin (aloeresin B), aloeresin D, barbaloin, nataloe–einodin–7–0–glucoside, and 2"-0–pcoumaroyl aloenin. The methanol extract of leaves from Aloe macrosiphon was similar to that of Aloe vera for barbaloin, aloesin, and aloeresin–D (Oketch–Rabah 1996).

References

Grieve M 1984 A modern herbal. Penguin, Harmondsworth
Lubinic E 2003 Manuel pratique d'aromathérapie. Vigot, Paris
Mabey R 1988 The complete new herbal. Elm Tree Books, London
Oketch–Rabah H A T 1996 Leaf compounds in potential plantation species of aloe in Kenya. Journal of Herbs, Spices & Medicinal Plants 4(3): 25–33
Stuart M 1987 The encyclopedia of herbs and herbalism. Black Cat, London

Arnica Oil

Scientific name

Arnica montana (Linn.)

Family: Asteraceae (Compositae)

Etymology

It is also known as Leopard's bane and Mountain tobacco. *Arnica* is from the Greek *arnakis* meaning lambskin, from the texture of the leaves; *montana* means growing in the mountains

The plant and its environment

Arnica montana is a perennial plant that grows to a height of 1 to 2 feet (30–60 cm) with golden–yellow daisy–like flowers 2–3in (5–7cm) across and bright green leaves. Native to the mountainous regions of Central Europe and Siberia, it is also cultivated in America.

The flowers are collected in autumn after the leaves have died down; they are then dried and any insect damaged parts are removed. The rhizome, which is used less often than the flowers, is dark brown and cylindrical, with brittle rootlets on the underside.

The oil and extraction

To achieve an oil suitable for use in massage the flowers are macerated in a fixed oil (often soya oil according to Lubinic (2003 p.211) with a proportion of ten parts oil to one part blossoms).

Principal constituents

The chemical and physical composition depends largely on the type and quality of the fixed oil employed in the maceration process. The chemical make up includes:

- an essential oil containing: thymol, thymol methyl ether, azulene
- linoleic acid (C18:2), oleic acid (C18:1), palmitic acid (C16:0), ·–stearic acid (C18:0), linolenic acid (C18:3), stearic acid (C18:0) (Lubinic 2003 p.211)

219

Therapeutic properties

Arnica macerated oil is used in topical preparations for various purposes:
- as a stimulant, hyperaemiant, (Lubinic 2003 p.211)
- in sports massage for muscles and joints (Lubinic 2003 p.211)
- for stress relieving massage of neck, shoulders and back
- to improve elasticity of various tissues
- for wounds, bruises and the pain associated with these
- to encourage irrigation of the skin
- strained muscles and swelling
- to treat bruises, contusions, strains, sprains and pain and swelling associated with rheumatism (empirical data from several centuries seem to show efficacy)
- inflammation, sunburn and nappy rash
- for bruised or aching muscles after sport or strenuous activity; deep acting

Folklore and traditional plant remedies

Arnica has been used for a long time by both Europeans and Native Americans to soothe muscle aches, reduce inflammation, and heal wounds. An effective remedy for the topical treatment of bruises, sprains, inflammation, reducing pain and swelling. The herb is used as a vulnerary i.e. for wound healing (vulnerary comes from the Latin word *vulnus* meaning wound).

Cautions

1   Use of arnica is subject to legal restriction in some countries and the essential oil, which is classified as toxic, must be used diluted in a carrier oil; the macerated oil is not classified in this way.
2   Arnica has become a rare plant, due partly to popular increasing use in complementary medicine and due partly to its mountain habitat, so closely related species also are used e.g. A. chamissonis, A. cordifolia, A. fulgens, A. latifolia, and A. sororia
3   Arnica flowers are sometimes adulterated with other composite flowers, especially *Calendula officinalis, Inula brittanica, Kragapogon pratensis,* and *Scorzonera humilis.*
4   Some people are particularly sensitive to the plant
5   For external use only
6   Not to be taken orally
7   Not to be used during pregnancy: the herb contains a compound that acts in the same way as oxytocin (used to induce labour) and for this reason pregnant mothers should not use arnica in any form or way.

8 Severe cases of poisoning have resulted from use of the herb taken internally.

9 Arnica may be taken as a tea

10 There are no known scientific reports of interactions between arnica and conventional medications

11 Can induce allergic reactions in a small population of individuals who develop contact dermatitis (perhaps due to helenin): use of arnica should be discontinued immediately.

12 Arnica should not be used on broken skin, such as leg ulcers.

Additional notes

1 The plant contains a bitter principle (arnicin), the antiinflammatory sesquiterpenoid lactone helenalin, flavones, flavonols, triterpenoids, phenolic acid, polysaccharides, tannin, phulin and a volatile oil; the flowers contain more arnicin than the rhizome, but no tannin.

2 Today, arnica, most commonly prepared as a tincture, is used topically in liniments , ointments, compresses and creams for many conditions including bruises, sprains, muscle aches, wound healing, acne, superficial phlebitis, rheumatic pain, inflammation from insect bites, chilblains, varicose ulcers, stress conditions and swelling due to fractures.

3 Used topically, arnica is generally safe. However, prolonged use may irritate the skin, causing eczema, peeling, blisters, or other skin conditions.

It is not taken internally as serious side effects may ensue although it may be used as a mouth wash and gargle against inflammation of the mucus membranes.

4 Homoeopathic doses are extremely dilute and generally considered safe for internal use.

5 Helenin reverses the effect of pain causing prostaglandins and thereby has a pain relieving effect, This is further enhanced by the sesquiterpene lactones helenalin and dihydrohelenalin and some esters of these compounds which have been shown to be active constituents of the Arnica species. Helenalin and its derivatives found in arnica have been shown to inhibit the migration of certain white blood cells known as polynuclear leukocytes, as well as inhibiting the rupture of lysosomal membranes. These compounds have also been reported to exhibit an inhibitory activity on platelet aggregation.

6 The saponification values for the macerated oil are NaOH value 189, KOH value 265 and the shelf life is one year.

References

Lubinic E 2003 *Manuel pratique d'aromathérapie.* Vigot, Paris p.211

Bibliography

Bisset N G ed. 1994 Herbal drugs and phytopharmaceuticals: a handbook for practice on a scientific basis. CRC Press, Boca Raton

Blumenthal M ed. 1998 The complete German Commission E monographs: therapeutic guide to herbal medicines. Integrative Medicine Communications, Boston Mass

Blumenthal M, Goldberg A, Brinckmann J eds 2000 Herbal Medicine: Expanded Commission E Monographs. Integrative Medicine Communications, Newton Mass

Gruenwald J, Brendler T, Jaenicke C, *et al* eds 1998 PDR for Herbal Medicine. Medical Economics Company, Montvale, NJ

Kowalchik C, Hylton W 1997 Rodale's illustrated encyclopedia of herbs. Rodale Press, Emmaus, Pa

Lyss G, Schmidt T J, Merfort I, Pahl H L 1997 Helenalin, an anti–inflammatory sesquiterpene lactone from Arnica, selectively inhibits transcription factor NF–kappa B. Biol Chem. 378(9): 951–961.

Mills S, Bone K 1999 Principles and practice of phytotherapy. Churchill Livingstone, Edinburgh

Robbers J, Tyler V 1999 Tyler's herbs of choice: the therapeutic use of phytomedicinals. Haworth Herbal Press, New York

Schmidt T J, Bomme U, Alfermann A W 1998 Sesquiterpene lactone content in leaves of in vitro and field cultivated Arnica montana. Planta Medica 64(3):268–270.

Schulz V, Hänsel R, Tyler V 1998 Rational phytotherapy: a physicians' guide to herbal medicine. 3rd edn: Springer Verlag, Berlin

Weiss R, Fintelmann V 2000 Herbal medicine. Thieme, Stuttgart

Wijnsma R, Woerdenbag H J, Busse W 1995 The importance of Arnica–species in phytomedicine. Z Phytother 16(1):48–62

Calendula oil

Scientific name
Calendula officinalis
Family: Asteraceae (Compositae)

Etymology
Also known as pot marigold or marybud. Calendula is the diminutive form of the Latin *calendae* (the first day of the month) and the plant is so called because of its habit of flowering all the year round in the wild. *Officinalis* is applied to all plants which have in the past been used as medicinal herbs. The common English name for this widespread pretty plant is made up of Mary (the Virgin Mary) and gold, referring to the glorious golden colour of the flower:

> And winking Marybuds begin
> To ope their golden eyes
> With everything that pretty bin
> My lady sweet arise
> **William Shakespeare: Cymbeline Act 2, Scene 3**

The plant and its environment
The plant originated in the Mediterranean area and the annual herb has been grown since the Middle Ages for its single or double, yellow or bright orange flowers. It is now to be found in gardens all over the world where it grows to a height of 50cm (20in) and seeds itself freely once established.

The oil
A fixed oil is not obtained from this plant but extracts (including the volatile elements) are produced which make the therapeutic properties of the plant available to therapists. Chiefly, the flowers are macerated in a fixed oil to produce calendula oil, also known as marigold oil: also a small quantity of concrete is occasionally produced by another process but in such small quantities that it can be ignored, especially as this product is not used in massage.

Method of extraction (Maceration)

Calendula oil is obtained by means of maceration in which the blossoms are steeped in a vegetable oil that has been stabilised against rancidity. Because of this process, calendula oil contains as active principles the lipid soluble constituents of the calendula flowers. The vegetable oil employed can vary, but organically produced sunflower oil is normally used, producing excellent results, although Lubinic (1997) mentions maceration taking place in a mixture of sweet almond, soya and peanut oils.

Principal constituents

The chemical and physical characteristics depend on the type and quality of the fixed oil used in the maceration process and the colour of the macerated oil takes on the orange colour of the calendula flowers. In commercial production, the orange variety is always used because the double orange flowers have the highest concentration of active ingredients. These active components include:

- an essential oil containing: menthone, isomenthone, caryophyllene and an epoxide and ketone derivative, pedunculatina, α–ionone, β–ionone, a α–ionone epoxide derivative and dihydroactinidiolide (Gracza 1987); the essential oil has oxygenated sesquiterpenoid derivatives (Bruneton 1995)
- pigments (carotenoids)
- bitter compounds
- saponins
- flavonoid glycosides
- mucilage
- resin

Folklore and traditional plant uses

Historically, calendula has held a reputation for being antispasmodic, mildly diaphoretic, antiinflammatory, antihaemorrhagic, emmenagogic, styptic and vulnerary.

Herbalists value calendula as a healer and it has been widely used as a remedy since ancient times. Internally it is used for gastric and duodenal ulcers, indigestion, gallbladder complaints, amenorrhea and dysmenorrhoea. Extracts, tinctures and infusions of its flowers have been employed topically in popular medicine for slow healing wounds, bed sores, bruises, cuts, scratches, varicose veins, gum inflammation, piles, persistent ulcers and burns (Duke 1985).

Calendula is recognised, along with witch hazel, as an effective astringent. The plants have a tightening affect on the skin by virtue of a reaction between the tannins they contain and skin proteins. The flowers are rubbed on to bee stings to soothe the irritation (Duke 1985). Calendula extract is indicated for enlarged or inflamed lymph nodes, sebaceous cysts and acute or chronic skin lesion. A mouthwash suitable for use after tooth extraction can also be produced from a calendula extract.

Therapeutic properties – internal use

Calendula has vulnerary, choleretic and antispasmodic properties.

Therapeutic properties – external use

Calendula oil has a favourable effect on the skin and can be used for
- broken veins
- varicose veins
- soothing tired, heavy legs with a tendency to vein problems (Lubinic 1997)
- bruises
- eczema
- cuts, etc. (Monograph 1986). The results are enhanced if two or three drops of appropriate essential oils are added to help with these and other conditions

Like all macerated oils it is more expensive than a basic carrier oil so it is common to mix 25% calendula oil with 75% of an appropriate fixed oil. In this event extra essential oils should certainly be added. Calendula is beneficial when used alone on small areas e.g. facial broken veins or an inflamed baby's bottom.

Calendula extracts are used to promote healing and to reduce inflammation (Fleischner 1985, ESCOP). A 20% calendula tincture has been reported to be useful in the treatment of chronic ear infections (Shaparenko 1979). A proprietary cream containing calendula and other plant extracts used on rats, has been shown to be effective against oedema due to burns and for acute lymphoedema (Casley–Smith 1983). However, the same researcher reported there was no significant difference in the production of oedema between control and trial groups of humans, although a reduction in the pain associated with post–mastectomy lymphoedema was observed.

Cosmetic use

The application of calendula blossom decoctions for beauty purposes is well known, e.g. for facial compresses. The oil has proved highly successful in preparations for chapped and cracked skin – especially hand and body products: useful for irritated or sensitive skin (Lubinic 1997). It is often incorporated (at levels of 3–10%) in oily and emulsified cosmetics for cleansing, softening and soothing.

Calendula extracts are used in creams etc where a gentle peeling and toning effect is required and are widely used in cosmetology as an emollient and hydrating agent (Bruneton 1995).

Culinary use

Calendula petals may be sprinkled on salads to add colour and flavour, used for a tea or added to omelettes. In the past the orange petals have been used in the production of butter and cheese as a way of adding natural colour and flavour (Grieve 1998). The flowers add a slightly salty flavour and colour; sometimes used as a substitute for saffron (Leung & Foster 1996).

Taken as a tea, perhaps with honey, it is beneficial to the heart and will ease menstrual problems and generally improve the complexion. The tea can be made by pouring 600ml (1pt) of boiling water over 5–10ml (1–2tsp) of chopped marigold petals, and allowing it to infuse thoroughly before use.

Cautions

1   A brief note to underscore the difference between two types of marigold, namely calendula and tagetes, hopefully to avoid unfortunate confusion. Tagetes is an essential oil from a completely different plant (*Tagetes patula*) although in the UK, among the uninitiated, this is also known as marigold oil. It is important to be mindful of this and always to specify by name either calendula or tagetes, rather than use the common name of marigold.

2   Calendula has no known contraindication and Rose (1972) says that it is a plant that causes no allergic reaction.

3   Bruneton (1995) states that marigold (calendula) preparations must be reserved for local use because of non–trivial toxicity of the ethanol and aqueous extracts (this does not of course apply to the maceration in oil).

Additional notes

1   The flowers are used by those of the Hindu faith to decorate their temples and holy places. Romans used it as an inexpensive food colorant, a substitute for saffron, and it was they who introduced it to other parts of Europe. During the Middle Ages it continued to be used as a food colorant, particularly for soups and sauces. It was also applied to old wounds and scars, just as later in 1886 in the American West a Dr Reynolds used calendula compresses to stop bleeding from bullet wounds.

2   For a relaxing home massage, fill a 300ml (2pt) jar with calendula flowers and top up with sweet almond oil; place on a sunny windowsill for about 3 weeks, shaking every other day, then pour into a pan and heat until the flowers are crisp. Strain and bottle.

3   Calendula tea, apart from being a soothing drink, can be applied cold to cuts and bruises: also it can be used to soothe swollen feet, chilblains and calm skin inflammation.

4   Calendula macerated oil (soya oil) has saponification values of NAOH 189, KOH 265 and the shelf life is one year.

References

Bruneton J 1995 Pharmacognosy, phytomedicine, medicinal plants. Intercept, Andover pp 562–563

Casley–Smith J R, Casley–Smith J R 1983 The effect of "Unguentum lymphaticum" on acute experimental lymphoedema and other high–protein edemas. Lymphology. 16: 150–156

Duke J A 1985 Handbook of Herbs. CRC Press, Boca Raton p.87

ESCOP Vol. 3. Proposals for European monographs on Calendulae flos / Flos cum herba

Fleischner A M 1985 Plant extracts: to accelerate healing and reduce inflammation. Cosmetics & Toiletries. 100: 45

Gracza L 1987 Oxygen–containing terpene derivatives from Calendula officinalis. Planta Medica 53: 227

Grieve M 1998 A modern herbal. Tiger Books, London p.517–518

Lubinic E 1997 Handbuch Aromatherapie – Ätherische Öle und ihne Anwendung. Haug Verlag, Heidelberg

Monograph 1986 Calendulae flos. Bundesanzeiger. 13 March, no. 50

Rose J 1972 Herbs and things. Grosset & Dunlap, New York p.323

Shaparenko B A 1979 On the use of medicinal plants for the treatment of patients with chronic suppurative otitis. Zh Ushn Gorl Bolezn. 39: 48–51

Carrot oil

Scientific name

Daucus carota L. ssp *sativus*, *D. carota* ssp *carota* L, *D. communis* Rouy and Camus

Family: Apiaceae

Etymology

The flower head of the wild carrot, known as Queen Anne's lace, is distinctive and is easily recognisable by a small black spot in the middle of the doyley–like flower. *Daucus* is the Latin for carrot and the Greek is *karoton*: *sativus* indicates a cultivated plant.

The plant and its environment

Flemish refugees introduced the carrot into Britain during the reign of Elizabeth l. The root crop we know so well was developed from the wild variety at that time. It is biennial and consists mainly of water (87%) along with red pigment, carotene ($C_{40}H_{56}$) in both the optically active alpha and inactive beta forms, sugars, pectins, lecithin, cellulose and other trace materials. *Daucus carota* ssp. *sativus* has an edible, fleshy, orange tap root, while the wild carrot, or Queen Anne's lace *D. carota* ssp. *carota* has an inedible tough whitish root (Leung & Foster 1996).

The oil

The macerated fixed oil is produced using the root of the plant. The fruit (seeds) are distilled for their essential oil content (0.5–1.6%).

Method of extraction (Maceration)

The production of macerated carrot oil requires expert attention. The root of the carrot is minced or chopped up into small pieces and left to steep in a vegetable oil with some agitation for about three weeks. The material is then filtered to produce a clear orange coloured liquid known as carrot oil. Organic sunflower oil is frequently used as the medium for maceration, although sometimes soya oil is used. The shelf life is about one year.

Folklore and traditional plant uses

Carrot juice is taken as a remedy for flatulence and stomach acidity. Carrot root oil has been approved for use as a food colour; it is used mainly as a yellow colouring due to its carotene content.

Therapeutic properties – internal use

True carrot oil is rich in beta–carotene, vitamins A, B, C, D, E and F. Good for the health of the skin, beta carotene can be transformed into vitamin A according to the needs of the body. It prepares the body for exposure to the sun, especially in people with a light skin, by promoting the production of melanin (Europhyto–Institut p.27)

Therapeutic properties – external use
- tonic to the skin
- helps the healing process by assisting in the formation of scar tissue
- soothes itching skin
- claimed to be helpful in cases of psoriasis and eczema

Cosmetic use

It is said to be particularly good for the (ageing) neck due to its claimed reputation for delaying the ageing process. Carrot root oil is used in some sun screen preparations and as a source of beta–carotene and vitamin A (Leung & Foster 1996).

Cautions

1   The macerated oil is sometimes confused with the essential oil, which is obtained by steam distillation of carrot seeds and is quite different. The essential oil is often used in cosmetics, in particular in suntan preparations. Carrot seeds and their essential oil promote the onset of menstruation (Franchomme & Pénoël 1990) and are to be avoided during pregnancy.

2   The ingestion of carrots and carrot juice in excess can be toxic due to hypervitaminosis, as can excessive intake of tablets designed to 'tan' the skin artificially. In such cases (which are not at all uncommon) the palms of the hands and soles of the feet turn an orange colour, the skin becomes progressively flaky, the whole system becomes toxic and in extreme cases death can result.

Imitation carrot oils

There are other ways of producing 'carrot oil' and the resulting products may well have properties in common with the genuine article. These techniques include:
- adding carotene alone to a base oil without the use of carrots
- the addition of some carrot based product obtained by solvent extraction
- adding material extracted from tagetes flowers
- adding beta–carotene obtained from tagetes

The bases used for these are usually sunflower oil or soya bean oil.

Additional notes

1 A study (Palan *et al* 1991) has shown that the antioxidants beta–carotene and Vitamin E function together in the prevention of cervical abnormalities and cervical cancer. The levels of beta–carotene and Vitamin E in the blood of 116 women were measured and it was shown that women with cervical dysplasia (precancerous cells) and cancer had low levels of both antioxidants.

2 Saponification values mentioned for carrot oil are NAOH value: 189; KOH value: 265.

References

Europhyto–Institut undated La phytothérapie: la santé par les plantes. Editions Alpen, Monaco p.27

Palan P *et al* 1991 Plasma levels of antioxidant β–carotene and α–tocopherol in uterine cervix dysplasia and cancer. Nutrition and Cancer 15: 13–20

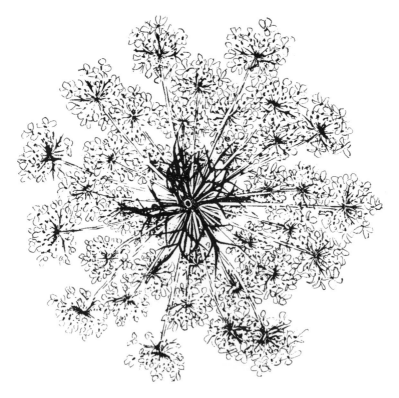

Centella, Hydrocotyle oil

Scientific name
Centella asiatica, *Hydrocotyle asiatica*
Family: Apiaceae

Etymology
Another common name for centella oil is hydrocotyle oil; the plant is also known as Indian pennywort, gotu kola, Asiatic pennywort, spadeleaf, tiger grass, thankuni and Peng Da.

The plant
One of about twenty species of low growing perennials, *Centella asiatica* is a perennial herb found in India and islands in the Indian ocean from Madagascar to Indonesia. The plant has a height of 15–20cm (6–8in), has small kidney shaped leaves up to 5cm (2in) across with indented margins on long running stems and has umbels having very small pink flowers borne beneath the foliage in summer. It is known to contain an essential oil but this is not extracted. Hydrocotyle resembles the related European marsh pennywort (*Hydrocotyle vulgaris*) in appearance.

The oil
A macerated oil is available for which sweet almond oil is normally used as a base.

Folklore and traditional plant uses
Used in India since antiquity to treat dermatitis, to aid the healing of superficial wounds (this healing property is now thought to be associated with asiaticoside, a triterpenoids saponin) and for care of the skin. Centella extracts are used topically in the treatment of surgical wounds and minor burns, and as a complementary treatment of leg ulcers of venous origin because it improves circulation of the lower limbs. Orally it is used to relieve symptoms of venous and lymphatic insufficiency (Bruneton 1995). It is thought that this oil stimulates regeneration of the skin and loss of elasticity. It has long been used to aid meditation in India and has been used both there and in Africa for leprosy (Bown 1995) and entered into the French pharmacopoeia via Madagascar. Centella oil has a reputation for longevity and for treating cellulite.

231

Cosmetic uses

Reduces the appearance of stretch marks and is thought to have a beneficial effect on varicose veins.

Cautions

No contraindications are known for use on the skin.

Additional notes

1   The seeds have been used as food in times of famine.
2   *Centella asiatica* herb is said to increase collagen production by inducing its precursor enzyme.
3   A double blind trial on 30 mentally retarded children indicated a significant improvement in both general ability and behavioural patterns when the plant was administered over a period of time (Appa Rao *et al* 1973).
4   The herb is used in India against senile decay and loss of memory (Patnaik 1994 p.47).

Reference

Appa Rao M V R, Srinivasan K, Koteswara Rao T 1973 Effect of Centella asiatica on the general mental ability of mentally retarded children.(six month's result). Indian Journal of Psychiatry XIX : 54–59
Bown D 1995 Encyclopedia of herbs and their uses. BCA, London pp 275–258
Bruneton J 1995 Pharmacognosy, Phytochemistry, Medicinal plants. Intercept, Andover pp 561–562
Patnaik N 1994 The garden of life. Aquarian, London

Chamomile oil

Scientific name

Matricaria recutita, *Matricaria chamomilla*
Family: Asteraceae

Etymology

The common names are German chamomile, wild chamomile.

Matricaria derives from its having once been found useful in treating infections of the uterus. (mater, mother, and caries, decay). *Recutita* from the Latin meaning skinned, apparently bare of epidermis. The derivation of *chamomilla* is uncertain

The plant and its environment

German chamomile is an annual plant, native to Europe and western Asia, but has become widely naturalised and can now be found growing not only all over Europe but also the temperate regions of Asia, North America and Australia. It often grows near roads, waste spaces and as a weed in farmed fields.

A scented annual growing to a height of about 60cm (2ft), the flowers are aromatic but have a very bitter taste because they contain a volatile oil, a bitter extract and tannins. It is not classed as a true chamomile and is quite different from Roman chamomile (*Chamaemelum nobile*).

Method of extraction

Extraction of the lipophilic molecules contained in chamomile flowers is achieved by maceration in a fixed oil, often soya oil

Principal constituents

The chemical and physical characteristics of the macerated oil achieved depend on the type and quality of the fixed oil used in the process. Unfortunately no analysis of the macerated oil is available.

Therapeutic properties

It may perhaps be assumed that some of the lipid soluble molecules may give the macerate some of the therapeutic properties attributed to the plant.

Cosmetic uses

For care of the face or body, also in massage, chamomile oil affords protection for sensitive or irritated skin because of the soothing and resolving properties. It is particularly recommended for babies and small children (Lubinic 2003).

Folklore and traditional plant remedies

German chamomile – the plant – has a long traditional use as compress or fomentation for a wide variety of ailments – sciatica, gout, lumbago, inflammation, rheumatism, skin problems. Infusion of the flowers or tincture has very many uses – colic, diarrhoea, indigestion, fever, insomnia and so on (Leung & Foster 1996, Duke 1985).

Cautions

There are no known contraindications to the use of German chamomile, save for an extremely rare contact allergy (ESCOP 1990).

Additional notes

1   The herb is used as a carminative, sedative and tonic.
2   An infusion of the flowers in water is given to children for childhood ailments.
3   The plant is included in the pharmacopoeia of 26 countries (Salamon 1992).

References

Duke J A 1985 CRC handbook of medicinal herbs. CRC Press, Boca Raton Fl.
ESCOP 1990 proposal for a European monograph on the medicinal use of Matricaria flos (chamomile flowers). October. European Scientific Cooperative for Phytotherapy, Brussels
Leung A Y, Foster S 1996 Encyclopedia of common natural ingredients used in food, drugs and cosmetics. 2nd edn Wiley, New York
Lubinic E 2003 Manuel pratique d'aromathérapie. Vigot, Paris p.212
Salamon I 1992 Chamomile: a medicinal plant. The Herb, Spice and Medicinal Plant Digest 10(1):1–4

Sources

Foster S 1996 Chamomile: *Matricaria recutita & Chamaemelum nobile*. Botanical series 307. American Botanical Council, Austin, Tx

Lime blossom oil

Scientific name
Tilia cordata Mill.
Synonyms *T. europaea*, *T. platiphyllos*
Family: Tiliaceae

Etymology
Also known as the linden tree, *cordata* is Latin for heart shaped and *platiphyllos* means broad leaved.

The plant and its environment
The lime is a tall graceful tree which grows up to 30m (100ft) high. It has bright green, heart–shaped leaves, and yellowy–white powerfully scented flowers borne in clusters. The odour of the flowers is linked to a small content of essential oil of variable composition according to their situation; that from the bracts is rich in aldehydes, whereas that from the flowers is mainly monoterpene hydrocarbons; both contain oxygenated mono– and sesquiterpenes (linalool, geraniol, farnesol, camphor, carvone, cineole), aromatic alcohols (phenyl ethanol, benzyl alcohol), phenols and aliphatic compounds (Bruneton 1995). It is native to Europe and the northern hemisphere.

The oil
An absolute is produced by solvent extraction of the dried flowers, but the macerated oil is of greater importance.

Method of extraction
The flowers are left to steep in good quality vegetable oil (usually organic sunflower oil) for several days with occasional agitation before the plant material is filtered off.

Folklore and traditional plant uses
Culpeper stated that lime flowers are a 'good cephalic and nervine, excellent for apoplexy, epilepsy, vertigo and palpitation of the heart'. Lime blossom has been used for migraine, hysteria, arteriosclerotic hypertension, feverish colds (British Herbal Pharmacopoeia 1983), and specifically for raised blood pressure associated with nervous tension (Wren 1988).

The flowers are used medicinally; they contain a volatile oil, sudorific glycosides and hesperidin (Weiss 1988) and lime blossom is a good diaphoretic (sudorific); still occasionally used as a diuretic, stomachic, antispasmodic and sedative (Bisset 1994). Traditionally used in the symptomatic treatment of nervous disorders in adults and children, especially in case of minor sleep disturbances (Bruneton 1995).

Therapeutic properties – internal use

Lime blossom has been reported as possessing a restricted range of antifungal activity (Guerin & Reveillere 1984). Antispasmodic (Schauenberg & Paris 1990), diuretic and sedative action has also been claimed (Sticher 1977).

Lime blossom tea has been used in cases of headaches due to high blood pressure, in hysteria, insomnia and to aid digestion (Bartram 1996) and to take the edge off anxiety (Landis 1998).

Therapeutic properties – external use

- wrinkles
- soothes rheumatic pain
- relaxing, aiding sleep (de Boek 1991)
- may be used as an emollient and itch relieving treatment of skin problems
- often used in baby massage as it is said to be calming and gentle on young skin

Culinary use

Linden blossom tea, known as tilleul (the French name for the plant) is drunk a great deal on the Continent as a general relaxant and to aid sleep.

Cautions

There are no known contraindications to the use of the macerated oil. It has been suggested that lime blossom should be avoided by individuals with an existing cardiac disorder (Duke 1985, Hamon & Blackburn 1985).

References

Bartram T 1996 Encyclopedia of herbal medicine. Grace, Christchurch p.270

Bisset N G (ed.) 1994 Herbal drugs and phytopharmaceuticals. (Wichtl M, ed German edition), Medpharm, Stuttgart pp 496–498

British Herbal Pharmacopoeia 1983 British Herbal Medicine Association.

Bruneton J 1995 Pharmacognosy, phytochemistry, medicinal plants. Intercept, Andover pp 103–105

De Boek W 1991 Personal communication.

Duke J A 1985 Handbook of medicinal herbs. CRC, Boca Raton.

Guerin J–C, Reveillere H–P 1984 Antifungal activity of plant extracts used in therapy. I. Study of 41 plant extracts against 9 fungal species. Ann Pharm Fr B: 553–559.

Hamon N W, Blackburn J L 1985 Herbal products – a factual appraisal for the health care professional. Cantext, Winnipeg.

Landis R 1998 Herbal defence against illness and ageing. Thorsons, London p.309

Schauenberg P, Paris F 1990 Guide to medicinal plants. Lutterworth Press, Cambridge p.257

Sticher O 1977 Plant mono–, di– and sesquiterpenoids with pharmacological and therapeutical activity. In: Wagner H, Wolff P (eds) New natural products with pharmacological, biological or therapeutical activity. Springer–Verlag, Berlin pp 137–176.

Weiss R F 1988 Herbal medicine. Beaconsfield Publishers, Beaconsfield p.227

Wren R C 1988 Potter's new cyclopedia of botanical drugs and preparations. Revised, Williamson E W, Evans F J. Daniel, Saffron Walden.

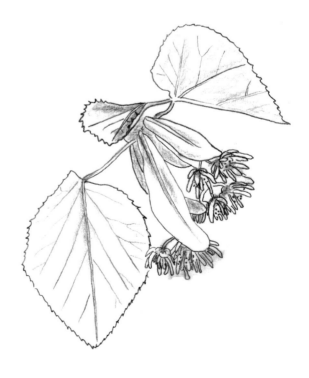

Monoi oil

Scientific name
Gardenia tahitensis.
Family: Palmaceae

Etymology
The name *Monoi* means "sweet scented oil" in Mahoi, the traditional language of the French Polynesians.
Gardenia is named after the Scot Dr. Garden (18th century), physician and botanist while *tahitensis* means of Tahiti,

Extraction
Monoi oil is the result of soaking Tahitian gardenia (tiare) flowers in pure coconut oil for 15 days: the flower is picked at the bud stage – they must be used fresh.

Principal constituents and properties
This oil is basically scented coconut oil (q.v.).

Cosmetic uses
The oil is used as a skin moisturizer – especially for dry, flaky skin. It has uses also as bath oil and a conditioner for dry hair. it is said that pure coconut oil is the best product available as a tanning oil, but monoi has no natural sunscreen so it is best to avoid excessive exposure to the sun; however, it can be used successfully as an after sun moisturizer

Folklore and traditional plant remedies
It has been used not only in traditional cosmetology, but also was used in traditional pharmacology in different curative preparations and, indeed, it is still in use today to alleviate migraines and mosquito bites.

Additional notes
1   Tahitian monoi oil has been used by Polynesian women for more than 2,000 years as a beauty remedy for hair and skin.
2   Tahitian monoi oil has been produced commercially since 1942 and there is French Government 'Appellation d'origine' (guarantee of origin).

Passion flower oil

Scientific name
Passiflora incarnata L.
Family: Passifloraceae

Etymology
Also known as apricot vine, granadilla, maypop and maracuja; also called passiflora or passion vine because the stigma, stamens and sepals are likened to the instruments associated with Christ's passion and crucifixion.

The plant and its environment
The passion flower is a native of Brazil, Australasia, Mexico and parts of Africa. It is a perennial, clinging vine, having alternate leaves with a woody stem up to 10m (33ft) in length, with pretty white and purple flowers, which give rise to the edible fruit.

The oil
It is the macerated oil which is of particular importance in aromatherapy.

A fixed oil is obtained from the seeds by expression, the seed hulls and kernels releasing the crude oil, which is then filtered to remove sediment and impurities: this oil (C16:0 9%, C18:1 13%, C18:2 76%) is used in the food and cosmetic industries.

Method of extraction (maceration)
For use as a massage oil base in aromatherapy, the flowers are macerated usually in organic sunflower oil.

The flowers contain, among other things, 0.1% essential oil, which has been shown to be sedative on inhalation (Buchbauer *et al* 1992).

Physical properties

Colour	pale yellow
Odour	odourless

239

Folklore and traditional plant uses

The Aztecs and Incas of South America valued the passion flower because of its pain relieving and soothing powers. It has been used as a remedy for neuralgia and irritative disorders.

Tradition attributes to the passion flower sedative, antispasmodic and tranquillizing properties (Bianchini & Corbetta 1985), partially confirmed by animal experiments, although the constituents responsible for the sedative activity are not known with certainty. There is an absence of clinical trials, but observation supports the usefulness of neurosedative preparations of this plant. Powders, infusions and extracts are traditionally used to treat cardiac rhythm abnormalities in adults, and nervousness and sleeplessness in children and adults; for this it is often used for this in combination with hawthorn, valerian and other sedative plants (Bruneton 1995). Herbal compresses containing the extract appear to reduce inflammation (Earle 1991). Passion flower extract has been used successfully to treat burns.

Therapeutic properties – internal use

Passion flower is stated to possess sedative, hypnotic and antispasmodic properties (Newall 1996), and extracts are used to combat sleeplessness, nervous excitability and tachycardia (Bartram 1996).

Therapeutic properties – external use
- in massage, the oil is said to be helpful against insomnia
- good relaxant
- soothing effect on skin
- believed to have antiinflammatory properties

Culinary use

The edible fruits are refreshing, and are sometimes used commercially in drinks, but not all species of passion flower are tasty.

Cautions

Passion flower macerated oil has no known contraindications. The herb is generally considered to be safe but should be used with caution in conjunction with CNS–depressants or stimulants.

Additional notes

1   With regard, not to the macerated oil, but to the herb, its many uses have been employed worldwide in many different countries from Brazil, Peru, to Turkey, England and the rest of Europe. Some examples are:

agitation, alcoholism, anxiety, arthritis, asthma, bronchitis, burns, colic, cough, constipation, convulsions, delirium, depression, diarrhoea, dysentery, epilepsy, eye problems, flu, gout, headache, heart tonic, haemorrhoids, hyperactivity, hypertension, hysteria, infantile convulsions, insomnia, intestinal worms, irritability, menopause, menstrual disorders, mood disorders, muscle problems, nervous disorders, nerve pain, neuralgia, palpitations, restlessness, rheumatism, seizures, shingles, skin problems, spasms, stress, tetanus, ulcers, urinary insufficiency, whooping cough, worms and as an antiinflammatory, antispasmodic, aphrodisiac, diuretic, pain–reliever, relaxant, tranquilizer and sedative.

2   It has been shown that an extract of the plant depresses the motor nerves of the spinal cord (Winter 1999 p.329)

References

Bartram T 1996 Encyclopedia of herbal medicine. Grace, Christchurch p.330

Bianchini F, Corbetta F 1985 The complete book of health plants. Crescent Books, New York p.106

Bruneton J 1995 Pharmacognosy, phytochemistry, medicinal plants. Intercept, Andover p.285

Buchbauer G, Jirovetz L, Jüger W 1992 Passiflora and lime blossoms: motility effects after inhalation of the essential oil and of some of the main constituents in animal experiment. Archiva Pharmaceutica (Weinheim) 325:247–248

Earle L 1991 Vital Oils. Ebury, London p.105

Newall C A, Anderson L A, Phillipson J D 1996 Herbal medicines. Pharmaceutical Press, London p.206

Winter R 1999 A consumers dictionary of cosmetic ingredients. 5th edn: Three Rivers Press, New York

Sea buckthorn

Scientific name
Hippophae rhamnoides
Family: Elaeagnaceae

Etymology
The spiny shrubs grow on seaside sand dunes, which may have given rise to the common name. Other common names are argousier (France), espino armarillo (Spain), finbar (Sweden), oblepikha (Russia), rokitnik (Poland), Sanddorn (i.e. sand thorn) (Germany), tindved (Denmark), and yashildoo chatsargana (Mongolia).

One legend has it that sea buckthorn leaves were the preferred food of Pegasus, the flying horse; this is perhaps why the ancient Greeks used sea buckthorn leaf in a diet for race horses, hence the botanical name Hippophae – shiny horsehorse (although another version gives it as being horse and poison).

The plant and its environment
The plant reaches 2–4m in height and grows from the Atlantic coasts of Europe to northwestern China. In western Europe, it favours the sea shores where salt spray deters other plants in competition, and in Asia it grows well in dry semi–desert sites where other plants cannot survive. The branches of sea buckthorn are rigid and very thorny. The narrow leaves are silver green 3–8cm (1.5–3in) long. There are male and female plants and it is the female plants which produce the orange berries 8mm (¹⁄₃in) diameter – they contain vitamin C (on average 120mg per 100g), vitamin A and minerals.

Sea buckthorn is not from the same family as buckthorn (Rhamnaceae) – they are quite different plants.

Extraction
The oil is extracted from the berries of sea buckthorn by maceration, usually in olive oil but almond, apricot and other oils are sometimes used. (See also Additional notes below).

Principal constituents
The EFA content in the sea buckthorn oil extract is 80 – 95%.

Monounsaturated fatty acids	
C15:1	pentadecenoic
C16:1	palmitoleic
C17:1	heptadecenoic
C18:1	oleic
C20:1	ecosenoic
C24:1	nervonic
Polyunsaturated fatty acids	
C18:2	linoleic
C18:3	α–linolenic

Physical properties

Colour	yellow to light brown
Odour	very little
Shelf life	2 years

Therapeutic properties and cosmetic uses

Cosmetics and skin care products made of sea buckthorn are valued for their rejuvenating, restorative and anti–ageing action.

Sea buckthorn oil is readily absorbed and has a high content of EFA, carotenes, tocopherols and phytosterols, which are all important for the maintenance of a healthy skin.

It is applied to help improve conditions affecting mucous membranes, including ulcers, lesions, erosions.

Aromatherapists have credited the oil with:

• reducing wrinkles
• regenerating skin cells
• helping dry skin
• promoting healing of skin injuries such as burns, sunburns, wounds and eczema

It is used to help rosaceae (www.rosacea–remedy.com May 2007).

Folklore and traditional plant remedies

Sea buckthorn extracts are traditionally utilized in the treatment of injuries of the skin and mucous conditions, including bed sores, burns, chronic wounds, erosions and ulcers.

Sea buckthorn has been used for centuries in central and south eastern Asia to prevent and treat various ailments.

243

Cautions

No known contraindications. Refrigeration after opening is recommended.

Additional notes

1   Information on this macerated oil is difficult to obtain because the literature is not always absolutely clear whether it is the macerated oil, the essential oil or plant extract that is being discussed. Oil can be extracted from either the seed or the pulp of the fruit. Sea buckthorn seed oil and pulp oil differ considerably in fatty acid composition. While linoleic acid and α–linolenic acid are the major fatty acids in the seed oil, sea buckthorn pulp oil contains a up to 50% of palmitoleic acid. Few other vegetable oils contain a similar quantity of this fatty acid. Both the seed and pulp oils are rich in tocopherols, tocotrienols and plant sterols. In addition, the pulp oil contains especially high level of carotenoids (Risto & Baoru 2003).

2   Sea buckthorn medicines are used in many countries to promote the recovery of various skin conditions, including burns, ulcers, bad healing wounds, skin damaging effects of sun, therapeutic radiation treatment and cosmetic laser surgery.

3   Preparations from sea buckthorn berries are used to prevent gum bleeding, to help recuperate mucous membranes of the stomach and other organs. It is used as a healing remedy for many ulcerative and inflammation–related disorders such as canker sores, oesophagitis, peptic ulcers, ulcerative colitis, and cervicitis. Carotenes in sea buckthorn are α– and β–carotenes, lycopene, cryptoxanthin, zeaxanthin, taraxanthin and phytofluin. Tocopherols are vitamin E and gamma–tocopherol. Phytosterols include beta–sitosterol, beta–amirol and erithrodiol. The berries have a high content of essential fatty acids and phytosterols.

4   Sea buckthorn was introduced to America by Russian immigrants at the beginning of 20th century.

5   The berries contain an essential oil and vitamins A, B1, B2, B6, C and E.

6   Oil from the juice is rich in palmitic and palmitoleic acids (C16:0 and C16:1) while the oil from the seed contains unsaturated fatty acids of C18 type oils (linolenic acids) (Bernáth & Földesi 1992).

7   The oil contains β–sitosterol, which has been used in therapeutic applications.

References

Bernáth J, Földesi 1992 Sea buckthorn (Hippophae rhamnoides L.): a promising new medicinal and food crop. Journal of Herbs, Spices & Medicinal Plants 1(1/2): 27–35

Risto E, Baoru Y 2003 Sea buckthorn oil: toward healthy mucous membranes. AgroFood Industry Hi-tech May/June: 53–57.

St. John's wort oil

Scientific name
Hypericum perforatum Linnaeus
Family: Hypericaceae, Clusiaceae

Etymology
St. John's wort oil is also known as hypericum. *Hypericon* is the ancient Greek name and one version of the root of this word is *erica*, meaning heather; another version is that *hypericum* is derived from *hyper* and *eikon* meaning over, and icon, alluding to use of the herb as a protection against evil spirits because it was believed to purify the air. In the same vein, a common name used to be *Fuga Demonum* (Fernie 1897). *Perforatum* is from the Latin for perforated and applies to the 'perforated' appearance of the leaves due to the translucent dots which can be seen when held up to the light.

When the buds of this plant are crushed between the fingers hypericin is released, staining the fingers blood red. This, coupled with the fact that the plant is in full flower on St John's day (24th June) and that St John was beheaded, is one explanation for the common name, because hypericum became known as *herba Sanctus Ioannis* or, in English, St John's wort. (Wort is from the Middle English *wyrt* meaning root, herb or plant.) An alternative explanation is that the translucent 'dots' in the leaves looked like wounds and the plant was used during the crusades by the Knights of St John to heal their wounds.

The plant and its environment
There are 160 species of hypericum, nine of them British, *H. perforatum* being known as common hypericum. A perennial plant, hypericum stands almost 1m (39in) tall, is native to Britain and France, and spreads easily by means of runners. From summer to autumn it is covered in flowers each with five slightly asymmetrical petals and many stamen. The edges of the yellow flowers have small black dots which contain, among other pigments, hypericin (Bruneton 1995). When held up to the light the leaves appear to be covered in tiny holes which are the translucent oil glands. An essential oil can be obtained from hypericum, but the quantity is so small that production is not

commercially viable. The wild plant may be propagated by division in autumn, and efforts are being made to cultivate it commercially.

The oil

The hypericin in the flower buds is responsible for the deep red colour of the macerated oil.

Method of extraction (Maceration)

In the south of France, hypericum buds and flowers are steeped in good quality vegetable oil (virgin olive oil is the preferred medium) for many days in full sun and with occasional agitation, after which the plant material is filtered off. Exposure to sunlight reportedly results in a four fold increase in flavonoid content (quercetin) (Maisenbacher & Kovar 1992). Smith *et al* (1996) recommend that the flowers be macerated in oil at 45°C for 10 days, while Hobbs (1989) recommends 70°C for 12–24 hours. The shelf life of the oil is one year.

Constituents

The plant contains 0.059–0.35% of an essential oil consisting mainly of monoterpenes and sesquiterpenes (Benigni *et al* 1971) including 2 methyl octane (16.4%) and α–pinene (10.6%). Apart from the volatile oil, called red oil, the plant contains a resin, a red pigmented glycoside, hypericin; a poly–phenolic flavonoid, hyperoside; tannin (8–9% in the whole herb and 16% in the flower); carotene; vitamin C.

As with some essential oils, the properties of hypericum may vary according to the season of harvest; the flavonoid and proanthocyanidins, useful in wound healing, are highest when flowers are in bud; for the antiviral activity, due to hypericin and pseudohypericin, the optimum time is when the flowers have just blossomed; whereas hyperforin and adhyperforin are at their highest in the fruit/seed capsules for best antidepressant action (Chevallier 1999).

Folklore and traditional plant uses.

At one time this plant was popularly regarded as being able to ward off witchcraft, and in the Middle Ages it was hung in doorways and windows to keep evil spirits and devils at bay.

Knights would put it on sword wounds to help the healing process and there is modern evidence of the plant's bactericidal power. Fresh flowers in tea, tincture or olive oil is reportedly a popular domestic medicine for external ulcers, wounds (especially with severed nerve tissue), sores, cuts and bruises

247

(Leung & Foster 1996). Samuel Gray (1818) recommends a tincture of the flower in 'maniacal and melancholic' illness. The plant is diuretic, expectorant and calming to the nervous system and infusions are used for rheumatism. Hobbs (1990) states that modern applications of hypericum (except antiviral) date back 2000 years.

Therapeutic properties – internal use

Hypericum has been used for anxiety, depression, gastric conditions (Krylov & Ibatov 1993) and unrest. Hypericum extracts are licensed in Germany and sold in profusion for the treatment of depression, anxiety and sleep disorders. A recent review concluded that more patients with depression responded to hypericum extracts than responded to either placebo or antidepressant medications (Linde *et al* 1996).

Hypericin, the red pigment present in hypericum, is being studied as an antiviral agent which may have use in the management of AIDS (Abrams 1990, Anon 1991). Hypericin has no antidepressant property, but in vitro tests have shown that it affects infected cells and prevents replication of the retrovirus (HIV) (Chevallier 1999). In Germany the oil is allowed internally for dyspeptic complaints and externally for treatment of injuries, myalgia and first degree burns (Monograph 1989).

Therapeutic properties – external use
- beneficial on wounds where there is nerve tissue damage
- inflamed nerve conditions, hence its use in cases of neuralgia, sciatica and fibrositis
- on burns and inflammation, including sunburn; the oil lowers the skin temperature
- it is said that hypericum oil can be massaged on to the lower back in cases of bed wetting
- has been suggested for haemorrhoids, gout, rheumatism, sores, ulcers and wounds, urticaria, herpes (Blumenthal *et al* 1997, Bruneton 1995, Shaparenko 1979, Bartram 1996)
- a 50/50 mix with calendula oil is effective on contusions and bruises
- also useful for stress, when blended in a 25% dilution with a base carrier oil and used in full body massage

In France drugs based on the flowering tops of St. John's wort may claim indications only for local treatment, as an emollient, itch–relieving, trophic protective (for chaps, bruises, frostbite or insect bites), for sunburn and other superficial burns, for pain linked to disorders of the oral cavity and the oropharynx (Bruneton 1995).

Cosmetic use

The oil is excellent for use on the skin, as it is soothing, antiseptic and analgesic. It has been recommended as a cosmetic skin tightener.

Culinary use

The leaves were once used in salads, but this is not to be recommended (see Cautions below).

Cautions

1   There are no known contraindications to the judicious use of the macerated oil. However, excessive use may cause skin allergy in some sensitive individuals, which is made worse by exposure to the sun.

2   Delayed hypersensitivity or photo dermatitis has been noted following ingestion of a herbal tea made from the leaves (Benner & Lee 1979). The volatile oil of St. John's wort is irritant (Capelletti *et al* 1982). Treatment with hypericum gel followed by exposure to sunlight has resulted in second degree burns (Upton 1997). The photosensitizing properties of St. John's wort in grazing animals is often misunderstood; it is a question of dosage. Animals which ingest too much of the herb in sunny weather may suffer swollen lips, so that they are unable to eat, but this is reversible if the animals are kept in dark barns for a few days. Similarly fair skinned people may experience sunburn like reactions with high levels of hypericin ingestion.

Additional notes

1   Uses of the fresh or dried flowering plant, fresh flower, fresh leaves are: vulnerary; weakly diuretic; sedative; antiinflammatory; antidiarrhoeic; cholagogic; antidepressant; antiviral; antibiotic; astringent.

2   Many virtues have been ascribed to this plant, ranging from the antipyretic and anthelmintic properties reported by the most ancient writers, to modern suggestions of antiviral activity.

3   Taken internally the herb is effective in irregular menstruation and stimulates both gastric and bile secretions. It has been shown to improve the blood circulation and to be of use in some conditions characterized by neurosis and disturbed sleep patterns. Note: in 1992 the FDA issued a notice that St. John's wort has not been shown to be safe and effective as claimed in OTC products (Winter 1999 p.379).

4   The plant is one of the most effective agents for assisting in the healing of wounds or burns when applied externally, especially where nervous tissue has been damaged; it is also applied to haemorrhoids and bruises.

5   The plant contains an antibiotic which has been patented as a possible food preservative.

6   Aqueous extracts of hypericum inhibit the growth of Myobacterium tuberculosis. Success has been reported (Newall *et al* 1996) in treating vitiligo by oral and topical administration of hypericum extracts.

7   Blossom, leaf, capsule and stalk are all said to be antibiotic.

8   The leaves were once used as a salad herb.

9   The oil glands when crushed release a balsamic odour similar to incense.

References

Abrams D I 1990 Alternative therapies in HIV infections. AIDS 4: 1179–1187

Anonymous 1991 Treating AIDS with worts. Science 254: 522

Bartram T 1996 Encyclopedia of herbal medicine. Grace, Christchurch p.239

Benigni R, Capra C, Cattorini P E 1971 Hypericum. Piante Medicinale: Chimica, Farmacologia e Terapia. Inverni & Della Beffa, Milano

Benner M H, Lee H J 1979 Medical Letters 21: 29–30

Blumenthal M, Grünwald J, Hall T, Riggins C W, Rister R S (eds) 1997 German Commission E Monographs: Therapeutic monographs of medicinal plants for human use. American Botanical Council, Austin

Bruneton J 1995 Pharmacognosy, phytochemistry, medicinal plants. Intercept, Andover p.367–368

Capelletti E M *et al* 1982 External antirheumatic and antineuralgic herbal remedies in the traditional medicine of north–eastern Italy. Journal of Ethnopharmacology 6: 161–190

Chevallier A 1999 Lecture report: St. John's Wort (Hypericum perforatum). Herbs 24(3):22

Fernie W T 1897 Herbal simples. John Wright & Co., Bristol

Hobbs C 1990 Pharm Hist 32(4):166

Hobbs C 1989 St. John's wort: Hypericum perforatum L. A review. Herbalgram 18/19:24–33

Krylov A A, Ibatov A N 1993 The use of an infusion of St. John's wort in the combined treatment of alcoholics with peptic ulcer and chronic gastritis. Vrach–Delo. Feb–Mar (2–3):146–148

Leung A Y, Foster S 1996 Encyclopedia of common natural ingredients. John Wiley & Sons, New York p.311

Linde K *et al* 1996 St John's Wort for depression – an overview and meta–analysis of randomised clinical trials. British Medical Journal Aug 3; 313: 253–258

Maisenbacher P, Kovar A K 1992 Analysis and stability of Hyperici oleum. Planta Medica 351–354

Monograph 1989 Hyperici herba. Bundesanzeiger no. 228 revised 2 March

Newall C A *et al* 1996 Herbal medicines. Pharmaceutical Press, London

Shaparenko B A *et al* 1979 On the use of medicinal plants for treatment of patients with chronic suppurative otitis. Zh Ushn Gorl Bolezn 39: 48–51

Upton R (ed.) 1997 St. John's wort; Hypericum perforatum monograph. American Herbal Pharmacopoeia p.27

Winter R 1999 A consumer's dictionary of cosmetic ingredients. 5th edn: Three Rivers Press, New York

Section 3 –

Appendices
Bibliography and sources
Glossary
Index

Appendix A
Properties and indications of principal fixed and macerated carrier oils

Fixed oils Almond – Rosehip

T = traditional use
X = external use
I = internal use

Common name	Scientific name	Analgesic	Antiinflammatory	Antifungal	Antiirritant, antipruritic	Antispasm	Antiviral	Anxiety, stress	Acne	Astringent	Bruises, contusions	Burns	Cicatrisant, (healing)	Circulatory	Dandruff	Diabetes	Diarrhoea	Diuretic	Eczema, dermattis	Emollient	Haemorrhoids	Hair conditioning	Hypertension
Almond sweet	Prunus amygdalis var. dulcis		X		X														X	X			
Apricot	Prunus armeniaca, P. americana				X														X	X			
Argan	Argania spinosa												T	T								X	
Avocado	Persea gratissima		X											X						X			
Babassu	Orbignya phalerata																			X		X	
Borage	Borago officinalis		T															T	X	X			
Camelina	Camelina sativa																		X	X			
Camellia	Camellia sinensis																		X	X			
Castor	Ricinus communis																I					T	
Cherry stone	Prunus avium, P. cerasus																		X	X			
Cocoa butter	Theobroma cacao																	T	X				
Coconut	Cocos nucifera											T		T						X		TX	
Cohune	Attalea cohune, Orbignya cohune											T		T						X		TX	
Corn	Zea mays																		I	X			
Cottonseed	Gossypium barbadense																						
Evening primrose	Oenethera biennis, O. lamarkania													X	I				IX				I
Grapeseed	Vitis vinifera																						I
Hazelnut	Corylus avellana									X				X	I							X	
Hemp seed	Cannabis sativa	T																	T				
Jojoba	Simmondsia chinensis, Buxus chinensis	T	X																X			T	
Kukui	Aleurites moluccans																		X		X		
Linseed	Linum usitatissimum											X	T						X				
Macadamia	Macadamia ternifolia, M. integrifolia																		X	X			
Mango seed	Mangifera indica																		X				
Meadowfoam	Limnanthes alba																		X				
Olive	Olea europaea				X		X		X	X		X						X	T	X			TI
Palm kernel	Elaeis guineensis											TX		T					X			TX	
Peach Kernel	Prunus persica				X														X				
Peanut	Arachis hypogea																			X			
Pecan	Carya illinoinensis																						
Perilla seed	Perilla frutescens var.		T																X			X	
Pistachio	Pistacio vera																						
Poppy seed	Papaver somniferum																				X		
Pumpkin seed	Curcurbita pepo						I											I		I			
Rapeseed	Brassica napus, B. campestris																						
Rice bran	Oryza sativa																						
Rosehip	Rosa mosquetta, R. rubiginosa, R. canina						T					X						TI	X				

Fixed oils Almond – Rosehip (continued)

T = traditional use
X = external use
I = internal use

Common name	Scientific name	Laxative, purgative	Lowers blood cholesterol	Muscular pain	Neuralgia	Psoriasis	Rheumatism, arthritis	Scars	Skin – chapped, cracked	Skin – dry, dry scalp	Skin – irritated	Skin – oily, acne	Skin – sensitive	Skin – toning	Skin – wrinkled, ageing	Skin – sun protection	Skin – sunburn	Skin – suntan aid	Sprains/bruises	Ulcers	Varicose, broken veins	Vermifuge	Wounds, sores
Almond sweet	Prunus amygdalis var. dulcis	I				X				X							X						
Apricot	Prunus armeniaca, P. americana	I	I							X			X		X								
Argan	Argania spinosa														X								
Avocado	Persea gratissima	I								X					X								
Babassu	Orbignya phalerata																						
Borage	Borago officinalis		I			X									X								
Camelina	Camelina sativa																						
Camellia	Camellia sinensis											T											
Castor	Ricinus communis	I					T																X
Cherry stone	Prunus avium, P. cerasus																						
Cocoa butter	Theobroma cacao														T								
Coconut	Cocos nucifera															X	X	X					
Cohune	Attalea cohune, Orbignya cohune															X	X	X					
Corn	Zea mays		I																				
Cottonseed	Gossypium barbadense																						
Evening primrose	Oenethera biennis, O. lamarkania					X	I			X					X								TX
Grapeseed	Vitis vinifera																						
Hazelnut	Corylus avellana											X			X	X							
Hemp seed	Cannabis sativa																						
Jojoba	Simmondsia chinensis, Buxus chinensis					X	X		X	TX		X					X						T
Kukui	Aleurites moluccans					X				X		X			X	X							
Linseed	Linum usitatissimum	TI																					
Macadamia	Macadamia ternifolia, M. integrifolia	I	I												X								
Mango seed	Mangifera indica									X							X						
Meadowfoam	Limnanthes alba																						
Olive	Olea europaea	I	XI							X					X						X		
Palm kernel	Elaeis guineensis															X	X	X					
Peach Kernel	Prunus persica	I	I							X			X		X								
Peanut	Arachis hypogea				X													X					
Pecan	Carya illinoinensis									X					X								
Perilla seed	Perilla frutescens var.					X																	
Pistachio	Pistacio vera																						
Poppy seed	Papaver somniferum																						
Pumpkin seed	Curcurbita pepo	I																			X	I	X
Rapeseed	Brassica napus, B. campestris																						
Rice bran	Oryza sativa																						
Rosehip	Rosa mosquetta, R. rubiginosa, R. canina	T						X							X								X

255

Fixed oils Soya – Wheatgerm

T = traditional use
X = external use
I = internal use

Common name	Scientific name	Analgesic	Antiinflammatory	Antifungal	Antiirritant, antipruritic	Antispasm	Antiviral	Anxiety, stress	Acne	Astringent	Bruises, contusions	Burns	Cicatrisant, (healing)	Circulatory	Dandruff	Diabetes	Diarrhoea	Diuretic	Eczema, dermatitis	Emollient	Haemorrhoids	Hair conditioning	Hypertension
Safflower	Carthamus tinctorius													I		I		I	X				
Sesame	Sesamum indicum																		X			T	X
Shea butter	Vitellaria paradoxa			X															X				
Sisymbrium	Sysimbrium irio																		T				
Soya	Glycine max																						
Sunflower	Helianthus annuus						X													I	X	X	X
Tamanu	Calophyllum inophyllum	TX	TX								T	T						T					
Walnut	Juglans regia				T										T				XT				
Watermelon seed	Citrullus vulgaris																	TI					
Wheatgerm	Triticum vulgare, T. durum, T. aestivum																		XI				

Macerated oils

T = traditional use
X = external use
I = internal use

Common name	Scientific name	Analgesic	Antiinflammatory	Antifungal	Antiirritant, antipruritic	Antispasm	Antiviral	Anxiety, stress	Acne	Astringent	Bruises, contusions	Burns	Cicatrisant, (healing)	Circulatory	Dandruff	Diabetes	Diarrhoea	Diuretic	Eczema, dermatitis	Emollient	Haemorrhoids	Hair conditioning	Hypertension
Aloe vera	Aloe vera	X	X				X			X			X							X			
Arnica	Arnica montana	T							X														
Calendula	Calendula officinalis	TX			TI					T		T	TIX						X				
Carrot	Daucus carota				X								X						X				
Centella	Centella asiatica, Hydrocotyle asiatica											T	T	T					T				
Chamomile	Matricaria recutita		T																				
Cumin	Cumin cyminum								X														
Lime blossom, linden	Tilia europaea, T. cordata	X			X	I					TIX								TI	X			T
Monoi	Gardenia tahitensis																					X	
Passionflower	Passiflora incarnat	T			T	T		TXI															
Sea buckthorn	Hippophae rhamnoides																		X				
St. John's wort	Hypericum perforatum		X				I	TI			X	T							T			X	

Fixed oils Soya – Wheatgerm (continued)

T = traditional use
X = external use
I = internal use

Common name	Scientific name	Laxative, purgative	Lowers blood cholesterol	Muscular pain	Neuralgia	Psoriasis	Rheumatism, arthritis	Scars	Skin – chapped, cracked	Skin – dry, dry scalp	Skin – irritated	Skin – oily, acne	Skin – sensitive	Skin – toning	Skin – wrinkled, ageing	Skin – sun protection	Skin – sunburn	Skin – suntan aid	Sprains/bruises	Ulcers	Varicose, broken veins	Vermifuge	Wounds, sores
Safflower	Carthamus tinctorius	TI	I				I		X														
Sesame	Sesamum indicum	TI				X	X										X	X					
Shea butter	Vitellaria paradoxa						X			X							X				X		X
Sisymbrium	Sysimbrium irio						T								X								
Soya	Glycine max		I												X								
Sunflower	Helianthus annuus		I			X	TX														X	X	
Tamanu	Calophyllum inophyllum				X	X			X														
Walnut	Juglans regia	I					T										T						T
Watermelon seed	Citrullus vulgaris																					TI	
Wheatgerm	Triticum vulgare, T. durum, T. aestivum		I						X							X					I		

Macerated oils (continued)

T = traditional use
X = external use
I = internal use

Common name	Scientific name	Laxative, purgative	Lowers blood cholesterol	Muscular pain	Neuralgia	Psoriasis	Rheumatism, arthritis	Scars	Skin – chapped, cracked	Skin – dry, dry scalp	Skin – irritated	Skin – oily, acne	Skin – sensitive	Skin – toning	Skin – wrinkled, ageing	Skin – sun protection	Skin – sunburn	Skin – suntan aid	Sprains/bruises	Ulcers	Varicose, broken veins	Vermifuge	Wounds, sores
Aloe vera	Aloe vera		I																				X
Arnica	Arnica montana			X							X						X						
Calendula	Calendula officinalis							X											TX	T	TX		TX
Carrot	Daucus carota				X	X										X	X						
Centella	Centella asiatica, Hydrocotyle asiatica																				T	X	T
Chamomile	Matricaria recutita												X										
Cumin	Cumin cyminum			X	X				X														
Lime blossom, linden	Tilia europaea, T. cordata						X								X								
Monoi	Gardenia tahitensis									X							X						
Passionflower	Passiflora incarnat			T																			
Sea buckthorn	Hippophae rhamnoides									X							X	X			T		
St. John's wort	Hypericum perforatum			X		X								X			X		TX	TX			TX

Appendix B
Table of iodine values

Oil/fat	Iodine value (IV)	Oil/fat	Iodine value (IV)
Almond	95–103	Mustard seed	95–120
Apricot kernel	95–115	Olive	80–90
Avocado	80–95	Passionflower	137–147
Babassu	10–18	Peach kernel	103
Blackcurrant	143	Peanut	80–106
Borage	140–170	Pecan	110–120
Butter fat	26–38	Perilla	185–208
Camelina	155–165	Pistachio	88
Castor	84	Pumpkin	119
Cherry kernel	103–117	Rapeseed	102
Cocoa butter	40	Rice bran	109
Coconut	9	Rosehip	183
Corn	124	Safflower refined	140–150
Dripping	35–45	Safflower high oleic	87 94
Evening primrose	140–170	Sesame	103–118
Grapeseed	125–145	Shea butter – off white	50
Hazelnut	90–100	Shea butter – semi–solid	70
Jojoba	80–85	Sisymbrium	96–103
Kukui	160–170	Soya	125–140
Lard	47–67	Sunflower refined	120–140
Linseed	185	Sunflower high oleic	80–90
Macadamia	70–80	Walnut	145–158
Mango	40–60	Watermelon seed	120–128
Meadowfoam	90–105	Wheatgerm	115–140

References and sources

Fox B A 1970 Food Science: a Chemical Approach. Unibooks, English University Press, London
Keville K, Green M 1995 Aromatherapy: a complete guide to the healing art. Crossing Press, Fredom
Product information sheets, undated, Anglia Specialty Oils, Kingston Upon Hull
Product Information leaflet, undated, Jan Dekker International, Wormerveer

Appendix C
Other oils which may be encountered

Allspice
Pimenta dioica
Oil is obtained from the leaves of the tree which grows in northern Guatemala. The oil is used for flavouring and is emollient.

Brazil nut oil
Bertholletia excelsa
Grown in Brazil, this oil is high in linoleic acid; it is emollient.

Burdock root
Arctium lappa Asteraceae
Oil extract, also called Bur oil. Traditional hair care and scalp care remedy.

Celandine
Chelidonum majus Papaveraceae
Oil extract is traditionally used to help combat eczema, skin inflammatory disease, to reduce skin pigmentation and to help get rid of warts.

Chickweed
Stellaria media Caryophyllaceae
Macerated in sunflower oil for 28 days (a full lunar cycle).

Custard apple seed oil
Annona sp. Annonaceae
Cold pressed from the seed kernels and filtered. It is a very stable liquid oil, contains oleic and linoleic acids and is used in cosmetics (body care creams, lotions, soaps, shampoos): amber coloured, almond oil flavour with unsaturated fatty acids 85-88%, palmitic 7.4%, stearic 1.9% (Arun Kumar *et al* 2002).

Kiwi seed

Actinidithia chinensis Actinidiaceae

Contains linoleic acid; also alpha linolenic acid which is good for promoting cellular growth of the skin; multiple sclerosis sufferers have been found to have low levels of this fatty acid.

Mullein

Verbascum thapsis Scrophulariaceae

Oil is used for treating earache (not when ear drum is perforated).

Plantain

Plantago major Plantaginaceae

Oil extract was made in vegetable oil as well as in butter, used to promote healing of skin injuries, reduce inflammation.

Shorea stenoptera butter

Shorea stenoptera Dipterocarpaceae

Derived from the nuts of an exotic tree this oil is similar to cocoa butter.

Yarrow flower

Achillea millefolium Asteraceae

Oil extract traditionally used to help reduce skin inflammation, promote healing of cuts and wounds.

Appendix D
Essential fatty acids and health

Essential fatty acids (EFA) are required in the human diet but must be obtained from food as the body has no way of producing them internally. Fat brings into the body the three valuable essential fatty acids (arachidonic acid, linoleic acid, linolenic acid). These three essential fatty acids – called essential because our bodies cannot make them – promote internal growth and regrowth of body cells, tissues and organs, as well as aiding in other vital functions. As the body cannot synthesize these essential fatty acids it must obtain them solely from fat foods (Wade 1973 p.16). Originally designated vitamin F, as essential nutrients, when first discovered in 1923, EFA were a few years later classed with fats rather than as vitamins.

There are two closely related families of EFA: ω–3 (or omega–3 or n–3) fatty acid and ω–6 (omega–6 or n–6) fatty acid. Only one substance in each of these families is really needed, as the body is able to convert one type of omega–3 to another, but cannot create an omega–3 from scratch. Fish oils and flaxseed oil contain omega–3 alpha–linolenic fatty acids while borage and evening primrose oils contain omega–6 linoleic fatty acid and its derivative gamma–linolenic acid.

Linoleic acid is necessary for growth and reproduction and it helps protect against excessive loss of water. It may act as a protective agent against radiation and help in building a better skin. It has other metabolic functions that help promote better health: body fat contains about 10% linoleic acid (Wade 1973 p.50) and boosting this may help control cholesterol accumulation.

Linolenic acid helps stimulate the manufacture of intestinal bacteria, needed to produce B–complex vitamins which help promote better skin health and helps control cholesterol. It works in conjunction with linoleic and arachidonic fatty acids for bodily health (Wade 1973 p.50) and may provide protection against cardiac arrhythmias. It has been suggested that it may have an antiinflammatory influence that could benefit asthma and arthritis sufferers. (Soya oil has approximately 7% linolenic acid)

Arachidonic acid is made up of linoleic and linolenic fatty acids (Wade 1973 p.50) and both helps to control cholesterol and reduce accumulated deposits from arterial walls throughout the body.

Eicosapentaenoic acid (EPA) is an omega–3 fatty acid which is found in fish oils of cod liver, herring family, mackerel, salmon and sardine: also present in human breast milk, EPA acts as a precursor for prostaglandin–3 (which inhibits platelet aggregation), thromboxane–3 and leukotriene–5 groups.

Summary of the effects of essential fatty acids on bodily health and function

- EFA are components of cell membranes which keep the cellular contents intact, maintain shape and flexibility of cells and regulate passage of compounds in and out of each cell.
- omega–6 fatty acids help regulate cholesterol metabolism and blood clotting, fight immune infections and prevent development of allergies.
- transport and help absorption of fat soluble vitamins (A, D, E and K).
- are involved in the manufacture of prostaglandins which play a part in reproduction, hormone synthesis, immune function, inflammation, heart and lung functions.
- are used for energy, fat delivering 9cal/g whereas protein and carbohydrate provide only 4 cal/g.
- circulate constantly in the blood although a proportion is stored in adipose tissue as a reserve to protect the body from the cold, cushions vital organs and is a source of energy.
- are found in high concentrations in the brain and are essential for normal nerve impulse transmission and brain function: two thirds of the brain consists of fat and half of this is ω–3 type, and pregnant women are advised to eat fish because at birth more than three quarters of the brain cells are formed.
- docosahexaenoic acid (DHA), which is produced from omega–3 fatty acid, is essential for normal development of eye function and vision in the growing foetus: it can also prevent premature birth.
- omega–6 fatty acid may improve calcium absorption and reduce calcium excretion: beneficial in treating and reducing the risk of osteoporosis.
- EPA, alone or in conjunction with other ω–3 materials, is thought to be effective in reducing inflammation (NIH Medline Plus)
- Epidemiologic and animal studies have suggested that dietary fish or fish oil rich in ω–3 fatty acids, for example, docosahexaenoic acid (DHA) and eicosapentaenoic acid (EPA $C_{20}H_{30}O_2$) may be of use in caring for Alzheimer's disease (Freund–Levi *et al* 2006). It was concluded that administration of ω–3 fatty acid in patients with mild to moderate Alzheimer disease did not delay the rate of cognitive decline but positive effects were observed in a small group of patients with very mild Alzheimer's disease.

Summary of the effects of essential fatty acids on the health and function of the skin

- gamma linolenic acid (GLA) is well established as an important treatment in the control of skin problems: EFA are important for healthy skin; *in vivo* linoleic acid and linolenic acid are converted to long chain polyunsaturated acids and act as signalling molecules and cell membrane components both of which have an effect on the health and proper functioning of cells and organs (Sardesai 1992).
- epidermal barrier function, prevent trans epidermal water loss (Pieper & Caliri 2003, Prottey *et al* 1976)
- abnormal level of EFA may be implicated in some skin conditions e.g. eczema (Horobin 2000)
- regulate cell division (Pieper & Caliri 2003, Prottey *et al* 1976)
- shown to have beneficial effects in the treatment of psoriasis and other skin disorders.

Summary of the effects of essential fatty acids on cancer

- EFA may be beneficial in the treatment of pancreatic cancer.
- Fatty fish affords some protection against prostate cancer according to Hedelin *et al* (2006), who surveyed 1,500 Swedish men with diagnosed prostate cancer about their eating habits and then compared the answers with a healthy control group. The results strongly support the hypothesis of the healthiness of omega–3 fatty acids. Men who eat salmon more than once a week run a 43% less chance of developing prostate cancer than men who never eat salmon. There is also a hereditary factor; the men who carried a variant of the COX–2 gene and who often ate salmon had a 72% lower chance than men who never ate fatty fish.
- The role of omega–3 and omega–6 essential fatty acids in cancer prevention and treatment has been much researched, as shown in the Nutrition and Cancer Database 1993, a comprehensive publication of 3000 published scientific researches with abstracts.

Essential fatty acid deficiency

The ideal balance of omega–3 and omega–6 is 1:2 (where this occurs in an oil it gives a long shelf life). According to Kellow (2006) most children have the wrong balance of EFA, with insufficient omega–3 and too many omega–6. Low omega–3 intake may be linked to hyperactivity, learning difficulties, temper tantrums; fatty acid deficiency predicts the severity of reading and related difficulties in dyslexic children (Richardson *et al* 2000). Australian research found 8–11 year old children who ate fish were 4 times less likely to

263

develop asthma than those who never ate it. Simpson (1991) writes that deficiency of essential fatty acids is liable to arise in patients who receive prolonged parenteral alimentation without supplementation. Cutaneous changes by this deficiency have been reported in infants (Caldwell *et al* 1972) and adults (Riella *et al* 1975; Skolnik *et al* 1977). After 2–4 months of deficient alimentation the patient develops redness and scaling in the scalp and eyebrows, hair is shed, and what remains is dry and lighter in colour. The suspected diagnosis can be confirmed by demonstrating a high serum level of the fatty acid eicosatrianoic acid and a low concentration of arachidonic acid. The cutaneous changes are reversed by the topical application of safflower oil which contains 60–70% linoleic acid (Skolnik *et al* 1977).

Deficiencies of EFA may be involved not only in skin problems, but also PMS, hyperactivity, immune function, inflammation. Ageing brings about a decline in the cellular levels of PUFA, arachidonic (C20:4) and docosohexaenoic (C22:6) acids being the most important of these. Protection of these two PUFA could delay the onset of the degenerative disease conditions associated with old age.

Sources of EFA

Linoleic acid (omega–6 family)
Good sources (Livernais–Saettel 2000)
• Oils from sunflower, safflower, corn, sesame, poppy, wheatgerm, soybean and walnut
• Wheat germ
• Vegetables
• Seeds and nuts – sunflower, sesame, poppy, pumpkin seeds and walnuts
• Grains

Alpha–Linolenic Acid (Omega–3 family)
Good sources (Livernais–Saettel 2000)
• Oils from walnut, rapeseed, wheat germ, flax seed and soybean
• Cold water fish
• Seeds – linseed (flax)
• Mustard and pumpkin seeds
• Dark green vegetables
• Soybeans
• Walnuts
• Wheatgerm
• Some sea foods
• Oils which contain high level of α–linolenic acid are best used only for salad dressings and sauces; because when cooked the EFA is destroyed

List of omega–3 fatty acids

Common name	Lipid name	Chemical name
α–Linolenic acid (ALA)	18:3 (n–3)	octadeca–9,12,15–trienoic acid
Stearidonic acid	18:4 (n–3)	octadeca–6,9,12,15–tetraenoic acid
Eicosatetraenoic acid	20:4 (n–3)	eicosa–8,11,14,17–tetraenoic acid
Eicosapentaenoic acid (EPA)	20:5 (n–3)	eicosa–5,8,11,14,17–pentaenoic acid
Docosapentaenoic acid	22:5 (n–3)	docosa–7,10,13,16,19–pentaenoic acid
Docosahexaenoic acid (DHA)	22:6 (n–3)	docosa–4,7,10,13,16,19–hexaenoic acid

References

Caldwell M D, Jonnson H T, Otherson H B 1972 Essential fatty acid deficiency in an infant receiving prolonged parenteral alimentation. Journal of Pediatrics 8 p.894

Freund–Levi Y et al 2006 ω–3 Fatty acid treatment in 174 patients with mild to moderate Alzheimer disease: OmegAD study. Archives of Neurology 63:1402–1408

Hedelin M, Chang E T, Wiklund F, Bellocco R, Klint Å, Adolfsson J, Shahedi K, Jianfeng Xu, Adami H–O, Grönberg H, Bälter K A 2006 The association of frequent consumption of fatty fish with prostate cancer risk is modified by OX–2 polymorphism. International Journal of Cancer Online October 25 2006, DOI 10.1002/ijc.22319

Horrobin D F 2000 Essential fatty acid metabolism and its modification in atopic eczema. American Journal of Clinical Nutrition 71: 367S–372S

Kellow J, Vijayakar S 2006 Miracle foods for kids. Hamlyn, UK

Livernais–Saettel 2000 website

Namias N 2003 Honey in the management of infections. Surg Infect (Larchmt) 4(2):219–226

Pieper B, Caliri M H 2003 Non traditional wound care: evidence for the use of sugar, papaya and fatty acids. Journal of Wound, Ostomy and Continence Nursing 30(4): 165–166

Prottey C, Hartop P J, Black J G, McCormack J I 1976 The repair of epidermal barrier function in rats by the cutaneous application of linoleic acid. British journal of Dermatology 94: 13–21

Richardson et al 2000– Fatty acid deficiency signs in dyslexic children. Prostaglandins Leukotrienes and Essential Fatty Acids 63: 69–74

Riella M C, Broviac J W, Wells M, Scribner B H 1975 Essential fatty acid deficiency in human adults during parenteral nutrition. Annals of Medicine 83 p.786

Sardesai V M 1992 The essential fatty acids. Nutrition in Clinical Practice 7: 179–186

Simpson N B 1991 Diffuse alopecia: endocrine, metabolic and chemical influences on the follicular cycle. In: Rook A, Dawber R eds 1991 Diseases of the hair and scalp. 2nd edn Blackwell Scientific, London p.149

Skolnik P, Eaglstein W H, Zibouh V A 1977 Human essential fatty acid deficiency. Archives of Dermatology 113 p.939

Wade C 1973 Fats, oils and cholesterol. Keats Publishing, USA

Appendix E
Trans fatty acids and health

Plant oils are vulnerable to oxidation, heat and light and which leads to rancidity. To overcome this problem, methods of processing were developed so that oils could have a longer shelf life and greater temperature stability. Today most oils are processed in a manner that destroys some of the essential fats or changes them to another chemical form, known as trans fat, which is not only not useful to the body but which may be harmful. Foods containing trans fatty acids include margarines, biscuits, crackers, pastries, fried foods, dairy products and meats.

Hydrogenation

Trans fatty acids are created in the food supply by a process called hydrogenation, which dates back to the 1900s. Hydrogenation is the heating of liquid oils in the presence of metal catalysts, e.g. nickel, aluminium, and hydrogen which hardens the oils into margarine and shortening (Ascherio & Willett 1997) The resultant hydrogenated fat has become widely used in foods over the past quarter of a century, mostly because it was viewed (erroneously) as a healthier alternative to animal fats, which contain saturated fat and cholesterol.

The problem is that during the process, essential fatty acids (EFA) are destroyed and the cis– position they used to have is changed into a trans– position. The trans fatty acids act in our body as if they were saturated fats, so in the case of margarines, food manufacturers change the double bonds in the oil from cis– to trans–, which gives the oil a higher melting point, producing a cheaper product with a longer life, but which contains trans fatty acids.

Trans fatty acids in the diet

It is now thought that there is no safe level of trans fatty acids and it is recommended to minimise their consumption (National Academies of Science 2002). Trans fatty acid intake is associated with a raised total of 'bad' low density lipoprotein (LDL) cholesterol, therefore an increased risk of coronary heart disease. Since low levels of trans fatty acids are found naturally in some nutrient–rich animal products, it is recommended that consumption of trans fatty acids in fried and processed foods be minimized.

Studies conducted over the last two decades confirm that a $2\frac{1}{2}$% increase in consumption of trans fatty acids doubles the risk of developing heart disease. These trans fatty acids are used to increase food appeal, add a crunchy texture, reduce costs and prolong shelf life and appreciable amounts are to be found in all processed and refined foods, deep–fat fried foods, commercial bakeries, crackers, tinned soups and foods such as baby rusks, biscuits, chips, croissants, fish sticks, etc. The FDA (Federal Drug Administration) estimates that almost 43,000 products found on grocery store shelves may contain trans fatty acids; affording about 2'⬜²% of the total energy in the American diet (Allison *et al* 1999); saturated fat and trans fat combined make up an average of 15% of total calories in the American diet.

There is cause for concern about the negative health effects of trans fatty acids because, as is the case with saturated fat, trans fatty acids raise total and 'bad' LDL cholesterol levels (Mensink & Katan 1990, Judd *et al* 1994, Lichtenstein *et al* 1999). In addition, trans fats lower the 'good' high density lipoprotein (HDL) cholesterol, whereas saturated fats may not (National Academies of Science 2002, Lichtenstein *et al* 2001). The effects of trans fatty acids on blood lipids and lipoprotein concentrations are viewed as strong risk factors for the development of cardiovascular disease (Willett & Ascherio 1994). Therefore, there is good reason to be concerned about the negative health effects of trans fatty acids; there is a clear need for proper labelling of trans fats on foods, as this will help consumers lower the intake of these harmful fats and switch to 'good fats' in their diet.

References

Allison *et al* 1999 Estimated intakes of trans fatty and other fatty acids in the US population. Journal of American Diet Association Feb;99(2): 166–74.

Ascherio A, Willett W C 1997 Health effects of trans fatty acids. American Journal of Clinical Nutrition. 66:10065–10105.

Judd J T, Clevidence B A *et al* 1994 Dietary trans–fatty acids: effects on plasma lipids and lipoproteins of healthy men and women. American Journal Clinical Nutrition 59:861–868.

Lichtenstein A H, Ausman L A *et al* 1999 Comparison of different forms of hydrogenated fats on serum lipid levels in moderately hypercholesterolemic female and male subjects. New England Journal of Medicine 340:1933–1940.

Lichtenstein AH, Jauhiainen M *et al* 2001 Impact of hydrogenated fat on high density lipoprotein sub fractions and metabolism. Journal of Lipid Research. 42:597–604.

Mensink R P, Katan M B 1990 Effect of dietary trans–fatty acids on high density and low density lipoprotein cholesterol levels in healthy subjects. New England Journal of Medicine 323:439–445.

National Academies of Science/Institute of Medicine Report on Dietary Reference Intakes for Energy, Carbohydrate, Fiber, Fat, Fatty Acids, Cholesterol, Protein and Amino Acids. Food and Nutrition Board/Institute of Medicine. September 5. 2002. www.nationalacademies.org

Willett W C, Ascherlo A 1994 Trans fatty acids: are the effects only marginal? American Journal of Public Health. 84:722–4.

Appendix F
Vitamin E

This is a generic term that covers a range of molecules which have been widely studied for health benefits and which are antioxidant.

Vitamin E is a fat soluble vitamin that exists in eight different forms and each form has its own biological activity: vitamin E comprises both
- tocopherols: alpha–tocopherol, beta–tocopherol, gamma–tocopherol and delta–tocopherol
- tocotrienols: alpha–tocotrienol, beta–tocotrienol, gamma–tocotrienol and delta–tocotrienol
- and because they all possess individual unique shapes their effect on the body varies

Vitamin E is antioxidant, protecting body cells against the effects of free radicals, which can damage cells, possibly leading to the development of cardiovascular disease and cancer. It has been shown to play a role in immune function, in DNA repair, and other metabolic processes (Traber 1999, Farrell & Roberts 1994).

Alpha–tocopherol can be found in unprocessed vegetable oils, nuts, rice bran oil and leafy green vegetables (Packer & Colman 1999 p.55); much research has focused on the tocopherols derived from corn, wheat and soybean. Alpha–tocopherol is probably the best known for its ability to protect membranes from lipid peroxidation.

The tocotrienols appear to have great antioxidant properties also and are to be found in rice bran, oat bran, wheat bran, barley, palm and cranberry seed oil. Studies show that tocotrienols are strong antioxidants (Theriault *et al* 1999, Packer, Weber & Rimbach 2001); in some cases the antioxidant activity is up to 40 times stronger than alpha–tocopherol (Packer, Weber & Rimbach 2001). Easily absorbed on topical application, tocotrienols afford some protection against oxidation due to UV rays Weber *et al* 1997). Tocotrienols have also been reported to lower cholesterol and have antitumour properties (Thierault *et al* 1999). Their properties inhibit the activity of the compound HMG–CoA reductase, an enzyme involved in cholesterol biosynthesis.

The recommended dietary allowance (RDA) sufficient to meet the nutrient requirements of nearly all (97–98%) healthy adults is 22.5 IU daily (e.g. about one tablespoonful of wheatgerm oil, or three ounces dry roasted almonds). Taking vitamin E in any form for a long time can be harmful; the upper tolerable intake of vitamin E for adults is 1500 IU. [IU = international units: 1mg alpha–tocopherol vitamin E = 1.49 IU].

References

Farrell P, Roberts R 1994 Vitamin E. In: Shils M, Olson J A, and Shike M, ed. Modern nutrition in health and disease. 8th edn Lea and Febiger, Philadelphia p.326–41.

Packer L, Colman C 1999 The antioxidant miracle. Wiley & Sons, New York

Packer L, Weber S U, Rimbach G 2001 Molecular aspects of alpha–tocotrienol antioxidant action and cell signalling. Journal of Nutrition 131: 369S–373S

Theriault A, Chao J, Wang Q, Gapor A, Adeli K 1999 Tocotrienol: a review of its therapeutic potential. Clinical Biochemistry 32: 309–319

Traber M G. 1999 Vitamin E. In: Shils M E, Olson J A, Shike M, Ross AC, ed. Modern nutrition in health and disease. 10th edn Williams & Wilkins, Baltimore p.347–62.

Weber C, Podda M, Rallis M, Thiele J J, Traber M G, Packer L 1997 Efficacy of topically applied tocopherols and tocotrienols in protection of murine skin from oxidative damage induced by UV irradiation. Free Radical Biology and Medicine 22: 761–769

Appendix G
Recipes

ARGAN

Goat's cheese salad with fruit
4 rounds of goat cheese
50g (1½oz) finely chopped nuts
12 cherry tomatoes
100g (3oz) raspberries
150g (5oz) strawberries
4 branches of red currants
4 tablespoons argan oil
Two tablespoons raspberry vinegar
Salt and pepper to taste

Cut the tomatoes in half and the strawberries in slices
Mix all fruit together – add all other ingredients except cheese and nuts
Divide mixture into 4 serving dishes
Roll each goat's cheese in chopped nuts and serve on top of fruit
Serves four people

AVOCADO

Avocado salad
2 hardboiled eggs
2 avocados
55g (2oz) Leicester cheese
125g (4½ oz) chestnut mushrooms
1 dessertspoon sunflower oil
Knob butter
2 tablespoons avocado oil
2–3 stems coriander or parsley
Salt

Slice mushrooms and cook in sunflower oil and butter – allow to cool
Cut avocados into chunks and cheese into small cubes
Toss all the above in avocado oil
Serve on a bed of rocket or lamb's lettuce
Slice eggs into quarters
Arrange eggs in centre (narrow ends inwards) to form flower

Basil and avocado dressing
3 tablespoons avocado oil
Juice of 1 lime
½ teaspoon Dijon mustard
½ teaspoon sugar
1 teaspoon vermouth
1 tablespoon finely chopped basil
Salt and pepper

Mix mustard and sugar into lime juice
Add this slowly a little at a time to avocado oil
Add water if needed to give right consistency
Mix in seasoning
Stir in chopped basil leaves
Serve with mixed leaf salad accompanied by smoked salmon and sliced avocado

Cucumber soup
1 cucumber
3 tablespoons fromage blanc (or plain yoghurt)
Large pinch sugar (mustard spoonful)
6 large prawns (or 2 slices smoked salmon)
4–6 radishes
Small bunch chives – or 1 spring onion
1 teaspoon very finely chopped rosemary
½ small avocado
1 tablespoon avocado oil
Salt and pepper
Rosemary flowers or calendula petals for decoration

Cut cucumber into small pieces
Place in mixer with fromage blanc or yogurt, chopped rosemary, sugar
and seasoning
Mix till smooth – adjust seasoning if necessary and place in fridge
Cut prawns or salmon into small pieces 1cm (½")
Cut radishes and avocado into small dice
Cut chives (or spring onion) finely
Add avocado oil and mix together
Season if necessary
Divide mixture into four and mould into small mounds
Place each in the centre of a soup plate
Spoon cold cucumber blend around mounds
Decorate with rosemary flowers or calendula petals
Serve with wholegrain bread

Trout tartare with avocado
200g (7oz) fresh trout
110g (4oz) smoked trout
½ mango
½ avocado
1 lime
1 large shallot
Handful chives
4 tablespoons avocado oil
1 tablespoon mayonnaise
Seasoning

Cut fresh and smoked trout into small ½cm (¼") dice
Chop onion very finely and add to the above
Slice half the mango for decoration and chop rest into small dice
Slice avocado, saving half for decoration and cut rest into small dice
Cut chives into ½cm (¼") lengths and add to mix
Add avocado oil and mayonnaise and season to taste
Mix together gently and put into fridge for 15 min
Place trout mix in centre of serving dish
Arrange mango and avocado slices alternately around it
Serve with rocket salad and freshly toasted triangles of bread

GRAPESEED OIL

Anchovy and grapeseed dressing
4 tablespoons grapeseed oil
2 tablespoons vinegar
1 teaspoon anchovy paste
½ teaspoon grain mustard
1 level teaspoon sugar

Mix together oil, mustard, sugar and anchovy paste
Gradually add vinegar to obtain a smooth dressing
Serve with iceberg lettuce and smoked mackerel

Lentil and lemon pâté
110g (4oz) split lentils (red)
110g (4oz) grated carrot
1 large shallot – finely chopped
1 clove garlic – finely chopped
1 cm square root ginger
1 tablespoon grapeseed oil
½ teaspoon turmeric powder
2 tablespoons fromage frais
1 lemon
Seasoning
1 sprig fresh tarragon (parsley if unavailable)
Rocket leaves

Put lentils in a pan and cover well above their level with cold water
Bring to the boil and boil for 20–25 min
Heat oil and gently cook onion, garlic, ginger and grated carrot, stirring frequently
Cook till carrots are tender and onions are soft, but not browned
Add turmeric and lemon rind and cook a further 2 min
Place all in blender with cooked lentils, lemon juice and season to taste
Fold in fromage frais and chopped tarragon (or parsley)
Place mixture into ramekin dishes and cover with cling film
Place in fridge for several hours, garnishing each with a sprig of parsley before serving
Serve with triangles of fresh toast and a few rocket leaves

Stir fried tofu with grapes

    1 block firm tofu – cut into dice
    2 carrots
    1 Spanish onion or 2 small onions
    110g (4oz) mushrooms
    55g (2oz) cheddar cheese
    8–10 seedless grapes
    85g (3oz) brown rice
    1 vegetable stock cube (or home made stock)
    2 teaspoons chopped fresh parsley
    1 tablespoon grapeseed oil
    ½ teaspoon salt

    Bring 100ml (3½floz) water – or stock – to the boil
    Add rice, salt and – if not using stock, a vegetable cube
    Simmer for 20–25 min, until all water absorbed; do not allow to go dry!
    Meanwhile, heat oil in large frying pan
    Add carrots, mushrooms and onion – all thinly sliced
    Stir fry till all vegetables are soft
    (Keep an eye on rice! Add a little boiling water if needed)
    Add diced tofu – and cook further few minutes till heated through
    Add grapes, cut in half or three – and mix in grated cheese
    Stir in rice and parsley – and serve.

Pork in cider

    4 pieces of pork loin (or fillet)
    1 Spanish onion
    Marinade:
    2 tablespoons grapeseed oil
    100ml (3½floz) cider
    4–5 sprigs marjoram
    2–3 stems of coriander
    6 juniper berries (or coriander seeds)
    Mix for sauce:
    110g (4oz) mushrooms – sliced or chopped
    2 spring onions
    1 tablespoon grapeseed oil
    1 teaspoon brown sugar
    2 teaspoons grain mustard
    2 tablespoons crème fraîche

Marinade:
Place pork slices in dish – not overlapping
Slice onion, leaving in whole rounds – place on top of pork
Mix all marinade ingredients together – pour over pork and onion
Leave overnight
Drain off marinade, keeping liquid
Cooking:
Heat grapeseed oil and fry meat and onion circles till meat is well sealed
and browned
Add mushrooms, sugar, mustard and reserved marinade
Cook around 15–20 min, till pork cooked
Lift out pork and stir in crème fraîche
Place sauce in serving dish and place pork slices on top
Decorate with sprigs of marjoram or coriander

Rich chocolate cake

175g (6oz) self raising flour
1 rounded teaspoon bicarbonate of soda
110g (4oz) bar of dark chocolate
55g (2oz) cocoa powder
75g (just under 3oz) sugar
2 tablespoons treacle
2 eggs
150ml (5floz) milk
150ml (5floz) grapeseed oil
Filling
175g (6oz) chocolate
2 tablespoons whipping cream
30g (1oz) butter

Pre–heat oven to 170°C (gas 3)
Line bases of two 8" sandwich cake tins with greaseproof paper
Sieve flour into large bowl
Add bicarbonate of soda, cocoa and sugar
Cut up dark chocolate bar coarsely and add to above
Add beaten eggs, treacle and grapeseed oil – mix gently till smooth
Divide mixture between tins and bake on middle shelf for 20–25 min
Allow to cool slightly before turning onto cooling tray
Melt chocolate for filling in a basin over a pan of boiling water
Whip cream till thick but not too solid and fold into mix
Spread half between the cakes and half on the top cake and decorate

HAZELNUT OIL

Gaspacho

6 ripe tomatoes – de-seeded and diced
2 green peppers – diced
1 cucumber – diced
2 garlic cloves – chopped
1-2 cups water
A few fresh mint leaves
4 tablespoons hazelnut oil
2 tablespoons cider vinegar
Salt and pepper to taste

Fill 2 ramekin dishes with diced tomato and cucumber
Cover and set aside for garnishing – or serving separately
Put rest of chopped vegetables, oil, vinegar and 1 cup of water into mixer
Blend until well puréed and season to taste – add more water if needed
Place in bowl and stir in chopped mint
Chill for at least an hour before serving

Hazelnut mayonnaise

4 tablespoons hazelnut oil
55g (2oz) hazelnuts
1 teaspoon mustard
1 lemon
Salt and pepper

Put hazelnuts and oil into blender and whiz still smooth
Add mustard and seasoning
Juice lemon and add a few drops at a time, mixing well in between
NB This dressing can be made with almonds and almond oil or walnuts and walnut oil, depending on desired taste – and availability.

Hazelnut salad

Half a cup of chopped hazelnuts
300g (10oz) watercress
150g (5oz) tofu – cut into small pieces
12 stoned black olives
1 teacup (or small mug) grated carrot
2 tomatoes, cut into eighths – or 8 cherry tomatoes cut into halves

Juice of half a lemon or lime
Thyme or marjoram leaves to taste
4 dessertspoons hazelnut oil
Salt and pepper to taste

Mix together all ingredients except tomatoes and place in a salad bowl
Decorate with tomato pieces

Raspberry and hazelnut dressing

110g (4oz) raspberries
2 tablespoons raspberry vinegar
4 tablespoons hazelnut oil
2 tablespoons ground hazelnuts (or almonds)
Approximately 200ml (7floz) cranberry juice
Mash raspberries – if wished, put through sieve to remove seeds
Add ground hazelnuts and oil and mix well, adding vinegar gradually
Add just enough cranberry juice to make mixture creamy.
Serve with an avocado and salad using rocket leaves and Roquefort cheese cut into small squares

Salmon and hazelnut pie

Approximately 450g (1 lb) salmon – cut from middle for uniform shape and filleted to give two pieces (remove skin if preferred)
56g (2oz) hazelnuts
3 pieces stem ginger
1 packet puff or flaky pastry
2 tablespoons hazelnut oil
½ lemon
A few sprigs lemon thyme
1 stem tarragon
2 tablespoons dry white wine
Seasoning

Pre–heat oven at 200° C (gas 6–7)
Marinate salmon 3 hours or overnight in hazelnut oil, lemon juice, herbs, wine and seasoning.
Divide pastry in two
Roll each piece 2½cm (1") bigger all round than width of one fillet
Drain salmon (reserve juice)
Place one fillet (skin side down) on one half of pastry

Chop hazelnuts and stem ginger – make into paste using some marinade juice
Spread over salmon
Place second fillet on top
Brush pastry round edges – place second piece of pastry over fish
Seal edges and knock up with side of knife.
Brush with milk and place in hot oven for 30–40 min
Serve with green vegetables

MACADAMIA OIL

Feta cheese salad
150g (5oz) feta cheese, cut into small squares
1 red pepper cit into small pieces
8–10 macadamia nuts – cut into quarters or small pieces
1 leek (small diameter) – cut white into thin slices
½ cucumber
Red cabbage – same volume as red pepper – cut very very finely
Juice of ½ orange
Chopped basil leaves – or calendula petals
3 dessertspoons macadamia oil

Marinate cheese squares in orange juice for several hours
Mix together all other ingredients except basil leaves/calendula petals
Add macadamia oil and turn gently till well mixed. Serve in salad bowl

Macadamia nut bread
450g (1lb) wholemeal flour
½ teaspoon salt
1 teaspoon grated nutmeg
150ml (¼pt) water – or sunflower milk (see page 289)
1 level tablespoon dried yeast (1 sachet if using bread machine)
1 teaspoon sugar
55g (2oz) macadamia nuts – roughly chopped
2 tablespoons macadamia oil

Pre–heat oven to 250°C (6–7 gas) – grease and flour a 1lb loaf tin
Place sugar and two thirds of warmed water (or sunflower milk) into a jug
Boil remaining third and add to above
Sprinkle yeast on top and whisk thoroughly
Leave in warm place (10 min or so) till about 2cm (¾") froth covers surface
Meanwhile, place flour, salt, nutmeg and chopped nuts into a large bowl
Whisk frothed yeast mixture – add it with macadamia oil to flour mix
Knead dough well and return to bowl
Cover and leave in warm place for 1hr – till double its size
Knead dough again and place in greased bread tin – smooth side up
Leave dough in warm place to rise again (around 20 min) – then cook for 30–40 min
Turn out and 'knock' bottom. If cooked, sound will be hollow.
If not, return to oven – upside down – for further 5–10 min until cooked

OLIVE OIL

Beef with beetroot
2 pieces rump steak 2½cm (1") thick
2 anchovy fillets
2 shallots
2 cloves garlic
2 small beetroot – cooked
1 handful rocket leaves or lamb's lettuce
2 tablespoons olive oil (plus a little for frying)
1 tablespoon balsamic vinegar
Salt and pepper

Heat 1 tablespoon olive oil and colour beef on both sides
Cook further on each side till only middle remains rare
Place on rack and season both sides
When cold, slice and place along centre of serving dish
Chop shallots, garlic and anchovies finely
Mix vinegar and chopped ingredients with rest of olive oil – add a little pepper
(put in mixer if smooth sauce desired)
Cut beetroot into slices – arrange on either side of meat
Drizzle anchovy sauce over and around beetroot
Decorate meat slices with rocket leaves or parsley

Olive cake
250g (9oz) self–raising flour
3 eggs
100ml (3½floz) dry white wine
1 tablespoon olive oil
110g (4oz) cheddar cheese
150g (5oz) green and/or black olives
55g (2oz) walnuts
150g (5oz) lardoons
100ml (3½floz) cream
Handful chives – cut finely
Thyme, rosemary, sage or hyssop flowers (or tarragon or parsley leaves chopped finely)
Salt and pepper

Pre–heat oven to 200°C (gas 6)
Cut olives in half; grate cheese and cut walnuts in quarters
Mix flour and baking powder together
Add beaten eggs, oil, wine, cream and seasoning
Add rest of ingredients, plus flowers and chives – mix together
Put into greased and floured bread tin (one large or two small)
Test after 45 minutes and allow to cool when ready

Spinach and olive lasagne

350g (12oz) lasagne – green and/or yellow
Vegetable sauce:
3 tablespoons olive oil
1 large onion – finely chopped
2 cloves garlic – finely chopped
12–16 stoned olives – green or black (or/and 2oz chopped walnuts)
1 tin whole or chopped tomatoes
2 teaspoons brown sugar
3 or 4 sprigs marjoram, oregano and rosemary
1 small glass ruby port
Cheese sauce:
55g (2oz) flour
55g (2oz butter
1 tablespoon olive oil
2 teaspoons French mustard
1.2 litres (2 pints) milk
175g (5½oz) gorgonzola cheese
55g (2oz) cheddar cheese
450g (1lb) frozen spinach – thawed
Grated nutmeg
Seasoning

Pre–heat oven to 180°C (gas 4)
Vegetable sauce:
Puree tomatoes in blender with herbs
Place in bowl – do not wash blender
Add olives – cut into quarters
Chop garlic and onion very small
Heat olive oil and add the above, stirring continuously until soft and clear
Add to tomato mixture together with sugar – season to taste

Add port and mix well
Cheese sauce:
Puree spinach in blender
Melt butter – add olive oil and flour off heat
Add milk a little at a time till thin smooth paste
Pour in rest of milk and bring to boil, stirring continuously
Add spinach, mustard, salt and pepper and gorgonzola cheese
Place layer of lasagne in an ovenproof dish
Add layer of cheese and spinach sauce, then layer of vegetable sauce
Cover with another layer of lasagne
Repeat layers, finishing with a layer of sauce
Sprinkle grated cheddar cheese on top
Place in centre of oven for 40–45 min (top should be golden brown)

Stuffed ham slices

8 slices ham
2 red peppers
3 shallots
4 slices pineapple
39g (1oz) breadcrumbs
2–3 stems Parsley
6–8 mint leaves
6–7 rosemary leaves – chopped very small
100ml (⅕pt) olive oil

Dice peppers and shallots and finely chop herbs
Add breadcrumbs and olive oil – season to taste
Put in blender for few seconds (not too smooth)
Divide mix onto 4 slices of ham and cover with other 4 slices
Grill sandwich for around 5 min on each side
Warm 4 slices pineapple and serve on top of each sandwich

Tapenade

4 tablespoons olive oil
150g (5oz) olives – without stones if possible
Bunch of fresh mixed herbs, i.e. thyme, marjoram, parsley, etc.
1 garlic clove

Mix in blender till smooth, olives, olive oil, herbs and garlic
Put into small containers
NB If not many herbs are in season, use 1 drop each of marjoram and
sweet thyme (or basil) essential oils, together with fresh parsley for bulk.

SESAME OIL

Carrots and courgettes with sesame seed oil
1 courgette – cut in half inch thick slices
2 carrots – cut in fine slices
Salt
1 dessertspoon grated root ginger
1 piece stem ginger – chopped into small pieces
30g (1oz) dark brown sugar
1 tablespoons sesame seed oil
Knob of butter (walnut size) – approximately 30g (1oz)

Place slices of courgette in a bowl and sprinkle with salt
Leave for at least an hour
Meanwhile fry carrots gently with melted butter and sesame oil – without browning
Keep turning until tender – drain on kitchen towel
Rinse courgettes well – drain on kitchen towel
Fry courgettes in same pan as that used for carrots till golden brown
(add more oil and butter if necessary)
Add ginger and sugar – fry for further minute or two
Add carrots – mixing well together before serving

Citrus and sesame oil dressing
2 oranges
2 lemons
1 tablespoon pine nuts
6 tablespoons sesame seed oil
Salt and pepper

Peel fruit and separate segments from surrounding skin
Put in blender with all other ingredients
Blend until smooth and creamy
Serve with chicken salad

Pine and sesame salad
55g (2oz) pine nuts
30g (1oz) sesame seeds
1 red pepper – cut into small pieces
1 cup bulgar wheat – cooked and cooled

1 stick celery – cut into fine slices
1 grated carrot
1 shallot – finely chopped
1 small beetroot – diced
Several leaves fresh young mint
1 packet lamb's lettuce – or rocket
Fresh parsley
Juice of half a lemon
4 dessertspoons sesame oil

Roughly chop parsley and mint
Mix together all ingredients – place in salad bowl

Sautéed beef and rice

450g (1 lb) rump steak
200g (7oz) basmati rice
1 red pepper
1 yellow pepper
½ cucumber
6 chive stems
2 cloves of garlic
1 teaspoon grated ginger root
5cm lemongrass
2 tablespoons sesame oil
Salt and pepper
Sauce:
1 tablespoons sesame oil
1 tablespoon sesame seeds
1 teaspoon sugar
1 clove finely chopped garlic
Salt and pepper

Sauce:
Mix together all sauce ingredients – keep on one side
Rice mixture:
Cook rice in large pan with plenty of boiling water – strain
Meanwhile, cut peppers and cucumber in half, removing seeds and pith
from peppers
Cut both vegetables into small dice
Chop garlic and lemongrass finely – mix with grated ginger root

Heat sesame oil and add all above ingredients
Cook for 5 minutes, stirring continuously
Cut chives in small pieces
Add to vegetables and cook for further 5 minutes till vegetables are tender
Stir into rice, adding seasoning to taste
Place mix in a ring round large serving dish – keep hot
Meat:
Fry rump steak for 1–2 min (or own choice) on both sides
Cut in fine slices and place in middle of rice
Heat sauce in meat juices – pour over meat

Vegetable bake with feta cheese

2 red onions
2 courgettes
1 aubergine
2 red peppers
2 garlic cloves
3 tomatoes
2 field mushrooms
4 teaspoons chopped parsley
4 tablespoons sesame oil
300ml (½pt/10floz) vegetable stock
2 tablespoons balsamic vinegar
200g (7oz) feta cheese

Pre–heat oven to 200°C (gas 6)
Chop vegetables roughly – large pieces
Put all but tomatoes and mushrooms on baking tin – drizzle with oil
Season, stir around – bake for 30 min
Add tomatoes and mushrooms stir around again
Roast for further 30 min
Sprinkle with cubes of feta cheese – and serve

SUNFLOWER OIL

Beetroot and leek salad

4 small beetroots, cut into small dice
1 leek, including tender green part – cut into fine lengths, then 2½cm (1") strips across
1 clove garlic (or shallot if preferred), finely chopped
2 tablespoons fresh tarragon or coriander leaves
2 tablespoons sunflower oil
Salt and pepper
Juice of half a lemon or lime
1 teaspoon mixed herbs

Cook garlic (or shallot) and leek strips lightly in half of sunflower oil
Add beetroot and tarragon or coriander
Add rest of sunflower oil, citron juice and seasoning
Serve in salad bowl

Ginger and sunflower oil dressing

3 tablespoons sunflower oil
2 tablespoons tarragon vinegar
1 large piece stem ginger, chopped very small
1 small banana – thoroughly mashed

Add oil to mashed banana
Gradually add vinegar, then ginger and then mix well
NB Goes well with a chicken or ham salad

Sunflower milk

55g (2oz) sunflower seeds
Approximately 400ml (³/₄pt/ 15floz) water
½ teaspoon salt – optional
1 small teaspoon honey – optional

Put sunflower seeds in food liquidiser with 200ml (7floz) of water
Blend for full two minutes – make sure all seeds are puréed
Add rest of water, salt and honey and blend again
Bottle – keeps three–four days in fridge
Always shake before use, as tends to separate
If a less creamy milk is preferred, add more water to taste

WALNUT OIL

Walnut dressing 1
2 tablespoons mayonnaise
5 tablespoons sour cream
4 tablespoons walnut oil
4 tablespoons cider vinegar
2 tablespoons apple juice
1 teaspoon apple sauce
About 30g (1oz) walnuts, chopped small
Salt and pepper to taste

Mix first 6 ingredients together
Stir in walnuts and seasoning
Serve with cheese and apple salad

Walnut dressing 2
4 tablespoons walnut oil
Juice from one lemon
1 desertspoon sherry
1 teaspoon of finely chopped mixed herbs
About 30g (1oz) walnuts
Pepper and salt

Blend walnuts, oil, lemon juice and vinegar in food processor
Add herbs and seasoning to taste
Mix a little into a rocket salad just before serving – rest can be served in
sauce boat or bottled
Serve with cold meat or fish

Carrot and walnut sauce
30g (1oz) butter
1 shallot – finely chopped
Half a pound of carrots
30g (1oz) walnuts – broken into large pieces
Juice of an orange

Melt butter – cook carrots and shallot gently till tender – do not brown
Add orange juice and walnut pieces
Liquidise, adding a little water to obtain consistency required for sauce

Add salt and pepper to taste
Reheat before serving
Serve with chicken, turkey or pork

Walnut salad

1 packet of lamb's lettuce
55g (2oz) walnuts coarsely chopped – ie in quarters
55g (2oz) blue Stilton or Roquefort cheese – cut into small squares
Half bunch of chives
1 avocado – cut into chunks
3 dessertspoons walnut oil
1 tablespoon rosemary flowers

Mix together all ingredients except rosemary flowers – serve in a salad bowl
Sprinkle rosemary flowers on top

Walnut stuffing

1 tablespoon walnut oil
1 onion, peeled and chopped
1 garlic clove, peeled and crushed
55g (2oz) chopped walnuts
1 tomato, skinned, deseeded and chopped
Seasoning

Sauté onion and garlic until soft, but not brown.
Add walnuts and seasoning – mix well
Add tomato to onion and garlic half way through cooking
Use to stuff vegetables, fish or meat
NB Delicious on flat mushrooms or as filling for courgettes, peppers, aubergines or tomatoes.
(For courgette or tomatoes, remove centres – roughly chop; for peppers, remove seeds and pith – add to onion and garlic half way through cooking)

Spring salad with walnuts

Handful young dandelion and plantain leaves (plus any other edible leaves)
Handful each of rocket, baby spinach and watercress
2 eggs

1kg (2lb) floury potatoes
30g (1oz) butter
200g (7oz) lardons (small bacon strips)
1 clove garlic
60g (1–2oz) walnuts
1 tablespoon walnut oil
1 tablespoon sherry or other sweet vinegar
Aromat seasoning (or herb salt and pepper)

Boil potatoes – mash roughly with butter and keep warm
Boil eggs (10 min) – put in cold water till cool enough to shell
Fry lardons and finely chopped garlic clove without oil
Meanwhile, break up salad leaves fairly small and put into big bowl
Add herb seasoning
Chop eggs and add to salad leaves
Add lardons, garlic and roughly chopped walnuts
Add walnut oil and vinegar
Lastly add warm mashed potato – mix everything gently together before serving
NB This makes a superb meal!

Carrot, ginger and walnut cake

250g (8½oz) wholemeal flour
1 teaspoon baking powder
150g (5oz) brown sugar
2 large eggs
1 teaspoon powdered ginger
30g (1oz) preserved ginger
175g (6oz) finely grated carrot
175g (6oz) finely chopped walnuts
2 oranges
100ml (3½floz) walnut oil

Pre–heat oven at 180°C (gas 4–5) and grease 2lb loaf tin
Sift flour, baking powder and ginger into bowl
Add sugar, walnuts, carrot and grated orange rind – mix well
Whisk eggs – add orange juice and walnut oil
Add to flour mixture gently till evenly mixed
Place in prepared tin – bake for 45–60 min (skewer should come out dry)

Appendix H
Selection of useful massage blends

Very dry or ageing skin

50ml blend of any three or more of the following carrier oils:
apricot, argan, carrot, evening primrose, kukui, lime blossom, macadamia, rosehip (strongest acting in italics) e.g. 10ml carrot, 20ml macadamia, 20ml rosehip
4 drops each frankincense, geranium and lemon essential oils
1 drop each rose absolute, rose otto and sandalwood essential oils
Frankincense and lemon help rejuvenate skin cells.

Oily or acne type skin

50ml blend of one or more of the following carrier oils:
hazelnut, jojoba and kukui
5 drops each cedarwood and myrtle essential oils
3 drops each juniper wood and petitgrain essential oils
Petitigrain is particularly effective on infected acne.

Calming massage oil

50ml blend of one or more of the following carrier oils:
arnica, lime blossom and passion flower
5 drops each lavender and marjoram
3 drops each neroli and ylang ylang
Will help induce deep relaxation of the tissues, muscles and joints and re–establish energy.

Circulation

50ml blend of argan and hazelnut (or either one)
3 drops each cypress, lemon, passion flower, tamanu
4 drops rosemary
Strengthens the circulatory system (lymphatic system, capillaries and veins).

Eczema, dermatitis, psoriasis

50ml blend of any three of the following carrier oils:

almond, borage, carrot, evening primrose, jojoba, kukui, perilla seed, sesame, sunflower

4 drops each bergamot, immortelle, juniper, lavender,

2 drops each Moroccan chamomile, thyme (sweet)

Both carrier and essential oils have been selected which will benefit all three problems.

Neuralgia and sciatica

Carrier oil blend as in pain relief below

4 drops each of basil, cornmint, nutmeg and peppermint

Nerve pain is difficult to relieve and regular application is necessary.

Pain relief

50ml blend of one or more of the following carrier oils:

jojoba, lime blossom, tamanu

5 drops each of any four of the following essential oils:

basil, *Eucalyptus smithii*, cardamom, cinnamon bark, coriander, clove bud, cumin, geranium, ginger, juniper berry, lavender, marjoram (sweet), niaouli, pepper (black), peppermint, pine, rosemary, sage, silver fir

Useful for rheumatic crises, muscular aches and open sores.

Bibliography and sources

Alander J, Wennermark B 1992 Vegetable fats for cosmetic applications. in Fridd P (ed.) Natural Ingredients in cosmetics – II. Micelle, Weymouth

Arun Kumar H S, Kalakumar B, Reddy K S, 2002 Acute toxicity studies on custard apple seed oil in mice. Indian Veterinary Journal (79)2 p. 118–121

Bailey L H 1963 How plants get their names. Dover, New York

Bartram T H 1995 Encyclopedia of herbal medicine. Grace Publishers, Christchurch

Bruneton J 1995 Pharmacognosy, Phytochemistry, medicinal plants. Intercept, Andover

Coombes A J 1994 A–Z of plant names. Chancellor, London

Collings A J 1992 How safe is 'natural'? in Fridd P (ed.) Natural Ingredients in cosmetics II. Micelle, Weymouth p 24

Drury N, Drury S D 1988 Healing oils and essences. Robert Hale, London

Duke J A 1985 Handbook of medicinal herbs. CRC Press, Boca Raton Fl

Edwards G (ed) 1953 Vegetable oils and fats. Unilever Educational

Erasmus U 1986 Fats and oils. Alive Books, Burnaby

Goldstein R, Augustin A, Purucker E et al 1990 Effect of vitamin E and allopurinol on lipid peroxide and glutathione levels in acute skin grafts. Journal of Investigative Dermatology 95:470

Grant & Joice 1985 Food combining for health. Thorsons, London

Hölzl J, Demish L, Gollnik B 1989 Investigations about antidepressive and mood changing effects of Hypericum perforatum. Planta Medica 55:643

Houghton C 1995 Essential facts about specialty oils. Cosmetics & Toiletries Manufacturers & Suppliers Dec95/Jan96 9(8):20– 21

Hudson J B, Lopez–Bazzochi I, Towers G H N 1991 Antiviral activities of hypericin. Antiviral Research 15:101–112

Iburg A 2004 Dumont's lexicon of oil & vinegar. Rebo, Lisse

Jeans H 1978 Natural oils from nuts & seeds. Thorsons, London

Jojoba: a botanical with proven functionality. Cosmetics & Toiletries June 98:81–82

Journal of herbs, spices and medicinal plants 1(1/2); Food Products Press, Binghamton NY

Leung A Y, Foster S 1996 Encyclopedia of common natural ingredients used in food, drugs and cosmetics. Wiley–Interscience, New York

Mabey R 1988 New Herbal. Elm Tree Books, London

McCance and Widdowson's The composition of foods, 5th ed. Royal Society of Chemistry and Ministry of Agriculture, Fisheries and Food. Cambridge 1991

Miller D G, Williams S K, Palombo J D, Griffin R E, Bistrian B R, Blackburn G L 1987 Cutaneous application of safflower oil in preventing essential fatty acid deficiency in patients on home parenteral nutrition. American Journal of Clinical Nutrition September 46(3): 419–423

Mills S Y 1991 The essential book of herbal medicine. Penguin, London

Mindell E 1991 Evening primrose oil: what is it? The Vitamin Connection July/August pp 37–38

Palan P, Mikhail M, Basu J et al 1991 Plasma levels of antioxidant beta–carotene and alpha–tocopherol in uterine cervix dysplasia and cancer. Nutrition and Cancer 15:13–20

Patnaik N 1993 The garden of life. Aquarian, London

Pénoël D 1981 Phytoguide no. 1. International Phytomedical Foundation, La Courtête

Press M, Hartop P J, Prottey C 1974 Correction of essential fatty–acid deficiency in man by the cutaneous application of sunflower–seed oil. The Lancet, I 597

Product Data Sheets. Roche, Welwyn Garden City

Product Data Sheets. VSP, Papendrecht

Product Data Sheets. Slater & Frith, Wroxham

Product Data Sheets. Guinness Chemical, Reading

Product Data Sheets. Anglia Oils, Hull

Prottey C 1977 Investigation of functions of essential fatty acids in the skin. British Journal of Dermatology 97:29

Reuter H D 1993 Hypericum als pflanzliches antidepressivum. Zeitung für Phytotherapie 14:239–254

Rice R 1991 A fatty problem. The Vitamin Connection, July/August 12–13

Shreeve C 1991 Rheumatoid arthritis: nature's remedies. The Vitamin Connection July/August p.9

Stearn W T Botanical Latin. David & Charles, Newton Abbot

Stodola J, Volak J 1985 Herbs. Octopus, London

Stearn W T 1983 Botanical Latin. David & Charles, Newton Abbot

Trease G E, Evans W C 1983 Pharmacognosy. Baillière Tindall, Eastbourne

Vetvicka V 1985 Trees and shrubs. Octopus, London

Wade C 1973 Fats, oils and cholesterol. Keats, New Canaan

Weiss R F 1988 Herbal medicine. Beaconsfield publishers, Beaconsfield

Glossary

Abortifacient	inducing an abortion; causing expulsion of the foetus.
Acid value	a measure of the free acid content of vegetable oils, resins, etc. indicated by the amount of potassium. hydroxide (KOH) expressed in mg required to neutralise 1 g of the substance. The acid value of an oil may be used as a measure of quality. If the acid value of the oil is too high then this denotes an excessively high content of free fatty acids which causes the oil to turn sour and discoloration may occur.
Amino acid	building block for proteins; there exist more than 20 natural amino acids.
Analgesic	agent capable of relieving pain (by altering the perception of it) without producing anaesthesia.
Anaphylaxis	a severe allergic reaction during which there may be a rapid lowering of blood pressure, constriction of the airways in the lungs, pain in the abdomen and swelling of the tongue or throat.
Antalgic	analgesic; decreased pain perception.
Anthelmintic	destructive of intestinal worms; vermifuge.
Antioxidant	a natural or synthetic substance which minimises the destructive effects of free radicals e.g. vitamins C and E. Beta–carotene is also an antioxidant. Antioxidants slow down the deterioration due to oxygen of fatty acids.
Antipruritic	an agent that relieves itching
Aperient	mildly laxative.
Astringent	an agent causing contraction of tissues, control of bleeding; styptic.
Beta–carotene	two vitamin A molecules attached end to end; an orange vegetable pigment.
Cathartic	strongly laxative.
Cicatrizant	an agent promoting the formation of scar tissue and aiding healing.
CIR	Cosmetic Ingredient Review
CIR Expert Panel	established in 1976 this panel reviews the safety of ingredients used in cosmetics; their reports are published in the International Journal of Toxicology.

Cis–	where the single hydrogens joined to the carbons being part of a double bond are both positioned on the same side of the fatty acid molecule.
Cold pressed	an advertising term used to imply quality in edible oils (Erasmus 1986)
Density	all fats and oils have a density of approximately $0.9g/cm^3$. As temperature rises the density decreases and the volume increases. This thermal expansion is governed by the coefficient of cubic expansion (g = approx. $0.000727°C^{-1}$). Oils may increase in volume by 1% for each 14°C temperature increase; the ullage space (i.e. headspace in the container) must be calculated accordingly.
Desaturation	two hydrogens are removed by means of enzymes from neighbouring carbons and an extra bond is created in a fatty acid chain.
Diaphoretic	an agent that increases perspiration; sudorific.
Drupe	a fleshy fruit with one or more seeds each surrounded by a stony layer (endocarp) e.g. plum.
Drying oil	most vegetable oils will combine with oxygen to a more or less greater degree to give a sticky and ultimately a dry hard film. This property is made use of in varnishes, wood preservatives and many other products.
Elongation	a fatty acid chain lengthened by two carbon atoms by means of enzymes.
Enzyme	a protein produced in the body to enable certain particular chemical reactions.
Erucic acid	an irritant, toxic compound occurring in a few varieties of rapeseed oil. This has been bred out of the plants by genetic selection.
Essential fatty acids	named essential because they are necessary to good health, these lipid molecules with two or more double bonds in the carbon chain cannot be manufactured by humans. Omega–6 fatty acids (most common is linoleic acid found in nuts and seeds) and omega–3 fatty acids (most common is alpha–linolenic acid found principally in fish, but also in grass – and therefore cows' milk – and certain nuts and seeds) are fragile in that their properties can be destroyed by free radicals, heat and oxidation. (See Fig. 2.4 and Fig. 2.5)

FDA	the American Food and Drug Administration.
Fixed oil	non volatile oil; plant oils consist of esters of fatty acids, usually triglycerides.
Free radicals	groups of atoms in particular combinations capable of free existence under certain conditions for very short periods of time. They contain unpaired electrons and thus can latch onto and damage other molecules.
Galactogogue	see lactogenic.
Hypervitaminosis	a condition resulting from the ingestion of an excessive amount of a vitamin preparation; serious effects may be caused by over dose of fat–soluble vitamins such as vitamin A.
Hypoglycaemic	an agent which tends to reduce the concentration in the circulating blood.
Iodine value	(IV) is a measure of the degree of unsaturation of the fatty acids incorporated into oils. When iodine (in the form of iodine monochloride) is added to a triacylglycerol formed from unsaturated fatty acids it reacts with the carbon–carbon double bonds present, and one molecule of iodine is used to saturate each one. The IV is the number of grams of iodine needed to saturate one hundred grams of oil (Fox 1970). Thus, the greater the IV the greater the degree of unsaturation present in the oil. See appendix B.
Iodine value	is a measure of unsaturation (number of double bonds). Jojoba is almost exclusively composed of dienes making its Iodine Value similar to that of oleic acid. Iodine values are typically in the range between 78 and 90.
Lactogenic	promoting the secretion of milk; galactogogue.
Laetrile	trade mark name for a compound derived from amygdalin which occurs naturally in the stones of apricots, peaches and bitter almonds: used in the treatment of cancer.
Laxative	loosening the bowel contents, promoting evacuation.
Leukotrienes	stimulate chemotaxis of white blood cells and mediate inflammation.
Lipid	generic name for all fats, oils and fatty substances; a fat or fat–like substance insoluble in water and soluble in fat solvents
Lipolytic	breaking down fat.

299

Lipophilic	having strong affinity for lipids.
Lipoprotein	an association of protein and fatty materials; transport vehicle for fats and cholesterol in the circulatory system (blood and lymph).
Nephrosis	kidney disease, degeneration of renal tissue.
OTC	products which are sold without prescription 'over the counter'.
Parenteral	by some means other than through the gastrointestinal tract; referring particularly to the introduction of substances into an organism by intravenous, subcutaneous, intramuscular or intra medullary injection (Hensyl 1990).
Prophylactic	preventing disease.
Prostaglandins	partially oxidised fatty acids; they are involved in a broad range of biological activities, including smooth muscle contraction, secretion, blood flow, reproduction, platelet function, respiration, nerve impulse transmission, fat metabolism, immune responses; they also have roles in inflammation, neoplasia (cancer), promoting fever, intensifying pain (Goodman 1994). Thromboxane, a modified PG, constricts blood vessels and promotes platelet aggregation. There are about 30 different prostaglandins.
Purgative	strongly laxative.
Rancidity	fats and oils exposed to heat, light and oxygen develop an unpleasant smell and taste because of an oxidative process. Oxygen combines with the unsaturated fatty acids to produce this effect. Oils should be stored in a cool dark place with oxygen excluded.
Raynaud's disease	a disorder of the blood vessels in which exposure to cold causes the small arteries which supply the fingers and toes to contract.
Refined oil	a plant oil which has been treated to remove colour, flavour or sediment.
Saponification No.	measures the amount of KOH in mg required to saponify 1g of sample.
Smoke point	the temperature at which the molecules in a cooking oil begin to break down and smoke forms. Saturated fats have high smoke points and the smoke point lowers as the mono– and polyunsaturated content of the oil increases.

Styptic	an agent having an astringent effect, stopping bleeding; astringent.
Sudorific	an agent that produces sweat; diaphoretic.
Tonic	producing or restoring normal vigour or tension (tone).
Trans–	where the single hydrogens joined to the carbons which are part of a double bond are positioned on opposite sides of the fatty acid molecule.
Urticaria	an allergic skin condition, also known as hives, characterised by the development of itchy weals.
Vermifuge	expels intestinal worms; anthelmintic
Vulnerary	agent promoting healing of wounds.

References

Emerson M, Ewin J 1996 A feast of oils. Thorsons, London pp 125–134

Erasmus U 1986 Fats and oils. Alive, Vancouver p. 340

Goodman S 1994 The role of essential fatty acids in cancer. International Journal of Alternative and Complementary Medicine May

Hensyl W R 1990 Stedman's Medical Dictionary. 25th Edition. Williams and Wilkins, London: 1139–1140.

Index

This has two parts. The first lists diseases, symptoms and other key words. The second lists the oils, plants and botanical names.

1 Diseases, symptoms and other key words

avocado oil 57
borage oil 64
carrot oil 229
cocoa butter 80
essential fatty acids 264
macadamia oil 126
meadowfoam oil 133
rose hip oil 178
shea butter 187
table of oils used for 255, 257
tamanu oil 201
Antibacterial 26
carrier oils 26
perilla 160
St. John's wort 249, 250
tamanu oil 200
see also Antiinfectious; Antiviral
Anticancer
essential fatty acids 263
olive oil 143
primrose oil 100
rice bran oil 175
sweet almond 45
see also Antimitotic; Antitumour
Anticoagulant
evening primrose oil 101
wheatgerm oil 211
Antidepressant
borage 63
evening primrose oil 100
St. John's wort 248, 249
Antidote, perilla as 160
Antifungal, table of oils used 254, 256
Antihaemorrhagic
calendula 224
rose hip oil 177
Antiinfectious
rice bran oil 175
see also Antibacterial; Antiviral
Antiinflammatory
borage 63
calendula 224
jojoba oil 113
olive oil 143
passion flower oil 240
St. John's wort 249
shea butter 187
table of oils used for 254, 256
tamanu oil 201, 202

Antiirritant, table of oils used 254, 256
Antimicrobial, perilla 160
Antimitotic, pumpkin seeds 169
Antioxidant activity
argan oil 53
definition 297
mango seed oil 129
olive oil 143
Vitamin E 268
Antipruritic 297
table of oils used 254, 256
Antipyretic
perilla 160
St. John's wort 249
Antirritant, *see also* Skin, irritated
Antiscorbutic, rose hip oil 177
Antiseptic
olive oil 142
perilla 160
St. John's wort oil 249
Antispasmodic
calendula 224
evening primrose oil 101
lime blossom 236
passion flower 240
perilla 160
Antitumour, apricot kernel 49
Antitussive
apricot kernel 49
perilla 160
see also Coughs
Antiviral
cumin seed oil 97
St. John's wort 248, 249
Antiwrinkle
avocado oil 57
evening primrose oil 101
jojoba wax 114
meadowfoam oil 133
olive oil face mask 142
rose hip oil 178
Anxiety
evening primrose oil 100
St. John's wort 248
table of oils used 254, 256
Aperient
definition 297
see also Laxative

2 Oils, plants and botanical names

NOTES